FOURIER ANALYSIS

A SIMON AND SCHUSTER TECH OUTLINE

RAJ MEHRA, EDITOR

FOURIER ANALYSIS

HWEI P. HSU
Wayne State University

REVISED EDITION

**SIMON and SCHUSTER
TECH OUTLINES**

SIMON AND SCHUSTER, NEW YORK

Published by
Simon and Schuster
Reference, Technical and Review Book Division
1 West 39th Street
New York, N.Y. 10018

Printed in the United States of America

PREFACE

Jean-Baptiste-Joseph Fourier's *Theorie analytique de la chaleur* (The Mathematical Theory of Heat) inaugurated simple methods for the solution of boundary-value problems occurring in the conduction of heat. But, this "great mathematical poem," as Fourier analysis was called by Lord Kelvin, has extended far beyond the physical applications for which it was originally intended. In fact, it has become "an indispensable instrument in the treatment of nearly every recondite question in modern physics," communication theory, linear systems, etc.

The intention of the author, in writing this book, is to fully develop classical Fourier analysis and show the link between it and its modern applications.

This book is designed for students in mathematics, physics, and the various disciplines of engineering to be used in a formal course in Fourier analysis and throughout the numerous related courses which introduce and employ Fourier techniques. It combines the advantages of both the textbook and the so-called review book. As a textbook it can stand alone because it is complete and detailed enough so as not to require additional references. And in the direct way characteristic of the review book, it gives hundreds of completely solved problems that use essential theory and techniques.

New concepts, definitions, and the important fundamental theorems (or results) are tinted in grey throughout the text. The graded sets of completely solved problems constitute the integral part of the text, illustrating and amplifying the fundamental concepts and developing the techniques of Fourier analysis. The supplementary problems are designed not only for exercise but also to strengthen the skill and insight necessary for the practical use of Fourier techniques.

The first three chapters deal with Fourier series and the concept of frequency spectra. They are followed by a chapter on the Fourier integral and the Fourier transform, and a chapter on Fourier transforms of special functions. The second half of the text discusses the applications of Fourier analysis to linear systems, communication theory, and boundary-value problems. The final chapter deals with miscellaneous applications of the Fourier transform.

The only formal prerequisite is the knowledge of an eight-semester hour course in elementary calculus; however, the second half of the book assumes a basic familiarity with advanced calculus and applied mathematics.

The author wishes to thank Raj Mehra and Rhea Nichols of Simon & Schuster, Inc., for their editorial efforts towards the revision of the first edition. The author also wishes to acknowledge the encouragement received from Professor Forest E. Brammer, and Mr. Edward F. Weller, Jr., as well as the assistance given by Mr. Dennis F. Wilkie and Mr. Eugene A. Hanysz.

Hwei P. Hsu

Southfield, Michigan

TABLE OF CONTENTS

CHAPTER 1

FOURIER SERIES

1.1 Periodic Functions

A *periodic function* can be defined as any function for which

$$f(t) = f(t + T) \tag{1.1}$$

for all t. The smallest constant T which satisfies (1.1) is called the *period* of the function. By iteration of (1.1),

$$f(t) = f(t + nT), \quad n = 0, \pm 1, \pm 2, \cdots . \tag{1.2}$$

An example of a periodic function is shown in Fig. 1.1.

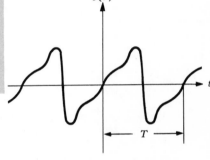

Fig. 1.1 A periodic function.

PROBLEM 1.1   Find the period of the function $f(t) = \cos \dfrac{t}{3} + \cos \dfrac{t}{4}$.

Solution: If the function $f(t)$ is periodic with a period T, then, from (1.1),

$$\cos \frac{1}{3}(t + T) + \cos \frac{1}{4}(t + T) = \cos \frac{t}{3} + \cos \frac{t}{4}.$$

Since $\cos(\theta + 2\pi m) = \cos \theta$ for any integer m,

$$\frac{1}{3}T = 2\pi m, \qquad \frac{1}{4}T = 2\pi n,$$

where m and n are integers.   Therefore $T = 6\pi m = 8\pi n$. When $m = 4$ and $n = 3$, we obtain the smallest value of T. (This can be seen by a trial and error procedure.) Hence, $T = 24\pi$.

In general, if the function

$$f(t) = \cos \omega_1 t + \cos \omega_2 t$$

is periodic with a period T, then it must be possible to find two integers m and n such that

$$\omega_1 T = 2\pi m, \tag{1.3}$$

$$\omega_2 T = 2\pi n. \tag{1.4}$$

The quotient of (1.3) and (1.4) is

$$\frac{\omega_1}{\omega_2} = \frac{m}{n}; \tag{1.5}$$

i.e., the ratio ω_1/ω_2 must be a rational number.

PROBLEM 1.2   Is the function $f(t) = \cos 10t + \cos (10 + \pi)t$ periodic?

Solution: Here $\omega_1 = 10$ and $\omega_2 = 10 + \pi$. Since

$$\frac{\omega_1}{\omega_2} = \frac{10}{10 + \pi}$$

is not a rational number, it is impossible to find a value T for which (1.1) is satisfied. Hence $f(t)$ is not periodic.

PROBLEM 1.3   Find the period of the function $f(t) = (10 \cos t)^2$.

Solution: Using the trigonometric identity $\cos^2\theta = \frac{1}{2}(1 + \cos 2\theta)$,

$$f(t) = (10 \cos t)^2 = 100 \cos^2 t = 100\,\frac{1}{2}(1 + \cos 2t) = 50 + 50 \cos 2t.$$

Since a constant is a periodic function of period T for any value of T and the period of $\cos 2t$ is π, we conclude that the period of $f(t)$ is π.

PROBLEM 1.4   Show that if $f(t + T) = f(t)$, then

$$\int_{a-T/2}^{a+T/2} f(t)\,dt = \int_{-T/2}^{T/2} f(t)\,dt, \tag{1.6}$$

$$\int_{T}^{T+t} f(t)\,dt = \int_{0}^{t} f(t)\,dt. \tag{1.7}$$

Solution: If $f(t + T) = f(t)$, then letting $t = \tau - T$,

$$f(\tau - T + T) = f(\tau) = f(\tau - T). \tag{1.8}$$

Now consider

$$\int_{\alpha}^{\beta} f(t)\,dt.$$

Making the substitution $t = \tau - T$, then using (1.8),

$$\int_{\alpha}^{\beta} f(t)\,dt = \int_{\alpha+T}^{\beta+T} f(\tau - T)\,d\tau = \int_{\alpha+T}^{\beta+T} f(\tau)\,d\tau.$$

Since any symbol can represent the dummy variable,

$$\int_{\alpha}^{\beta} f(t)\,dt = \int_{\alpha+T}^{\beta+T} f(t)\,dt. \tag{1.9}$$

Now, the left-hand side of (1.6) can be written as

$$\int_{a-T/2}^{a+T/2} f(t)\,dt = \int_{a-T/2}^{-T/2} f(t)\,dt + \int_{-T/2}^{a+T/2} f(t)\,dt.$$

Applying the result of (1.9) to the first integral of the right-hand side of the above equation,

$$\int_{a-T/2}^{a+T/2} f(t)\,dt = \int_{a+T/2}^{T/2} f(t)\,dt + \int_{-T/2}^{a+T/2} f(t)\,dt = \int_{-T/2}^{a+T/2} f(t)\,dt + \int_{a+T/2}^{T/2} f(t)\,dt$$

$$= \int_{-T/2}^{T/2} f(t)\,dt.$$

In (1.9), if $\alpha = 0$ and $\beta = t$, then (1.9) becomes

$$\int_0^t f(t)\,dt = \int_T^{T+t} f(t)\,dt.$$

In (1.6), if $a = T/2$, then (1.6) becomes

$$\int_0^T f(t)\,dt = \int_{-T/2}^{T/2} f(t)\,dt. \tag{1.10}$$

PROBLEM 1.5 Let $f(t + T) = f(t)$ and

$$g(t) = \int_0^t f(\tau)\,d\tau.$$

Show that $g(t + T) = g(t)$ if and only if

$$\int_{-T/2}^{T/2} f(t)\,dt = 0.$$

Solution: Since $g(t) = \int_0^t f(\tau)\,d\tau$,

$$g(t + T) = \int_0^{t+T} f(\tau)\,d\tau = \int_0^T f(\tau)\,d\tau + \int_T^{T+t} f(\tau)\,d\tau.$$

From (1.10) and (1.7),

$$\int_0^T f(\tau)\,d\tau = \int_{-T/2}^{T/2} f(\tau)\,d\tau = \int_{-T/2}^{T/2} f(t)\,dt, \qquad \int_T^{T+t} f(t)\,dt = \int_0^t f(t)\,dt.$$

Hence,

$$g(t + T) = \int_{-T/2}^{T/2} f(t)\,dt + \int_0^t f(t)\,dt$$

and $g(t + T) = g(t)$ if and only if $\displaystyle\int_{-T/2}^{T/2} f(t)\,dt = 0$.

PROBLEM 1.6 Let $f(t + T) = f(t)$, and

$$F(t) = \int_0^t f(\tau)\,d\tau - \frac{1}{2}a_o t,$$

where $a_o = \dfrac{2}{T}\displaystyle\int_{-T/2}^{T/2} f(t)\,dt$. Show that $F(t + T) = F(t)$.

Solution: Since $F(t) = \int_0^t f(\tau)\,d\tau - \frac{1}{2}a_o t$,

$$F(t + T) = \int_0^{t+T} f(\tau)\,d\tau - \frac{1}{2}a_o \cdot (t + T)$$

$$= \int_0^T f(\tau)\,d\tau + \int_T^{T+t} f(\tau)\,d\tau - \frac{1}{2}a_o t - \frac{1}{2}a_o T.$$

From (1.10) and (1.7),

$$\int_0^T f(\tau)\, d\tau = \int_{-T/2}^{T/2} f(\tau)\, d\tau = \frac{1}{2} a_o T,$$

$$\int_T^{T+t} f(\tau)\, d\tau = \int_0^t f(\tau)\, d\tau.$$

Hence,

$$F(t + T) = \frac{1}{2} a_o T + \int_0^t f(\tau)\, d\tau - \frac{1}{2} a_o t - \frac{1}{2} a_o T = \int_0^t f(\tau)\, d\tau - \frac{1}{2} a_o t = F(t).$$

1.2 Fourier Series

Let the function $f(t)$ be periodic with period T. Then this function can be represented by the trigonometric series

$$f(t) = \frac{1}{2} a_o + a_1 \cos \omega_o t + a_2 \cos 2\omega_o t + \cdots + b_1 \sin \omega_o t + b_2 \sin 2\omega_o t + \cdots$$

$$= \frac{1}{2} a_o + \sum_{n=1}^{\infty} (a_n \cos n\omega_o t + b_n \sin n\omega_o t), \qquad (1.11)$$

where $\omega_o = 2\pi/T$.

A series such as (1.11) is called a *trigonometric Fourier series*. It can be re-written as

$$f(t) = C_o + \sum_{n=1}^{\infty} C_n \cos (n\omega_o t - \theta_n). \qquad (1.12)$$

PROBLEM 1.7 Derive (1.12) from (1.11) and express C_n and θ_n in terms of a_n and b_n.

Solution: We can write

$$a_n \cos n\omega_o t + b_n \sin n\omega_o t = \sqrt{a_n^2 + b_n^2} \left(\frac{a_n}{\sqrt{a_n^2 + b_n^2}} \cos n\omega_o t + \frac{b_n}{\sqrt{a_n^2 + b_n^2}} \sin n\omega_o t \right)$$

Applying a trigonometric identity,

$$a_n \cos n\omega_o t + b_n \sin n\omega_o t = C_n (\cos \theta_n \cos n\omega_o t + \sin \theta_n \sin n\omega_o t)$$

$$= C_n \cos (n\omega_o t - \theta_n), \qquad (1.13)$$

where

$$C_n = \sqrt{a_n^2 + b_n^2}, \qquad (1.14)$$

$$\cos \theta_n = \frac{a_n}{\sqrt{a_n^2 + b_n^2}}, \qquad \sin \theta_n = \frac{b_n}{\sqrt{a_n^2 + b_n^2}};$$

hence,

$$\tan \theta_n = \frac{b_n}{a_n}, \qquad \text{or} \qquad \theta_n = \tan^{-1} \left(\frac{b_n}{a_n} \right). \qquad (1.15)$$

Also letting

$$C_o = \frac{1}{2} a_o, \qquad (1.16)$$

we obtain

$$f(t) = \frac{1}{2} a_o + \sum_{n=1}^{\infty} (a_n \cos n\omega_o t + b_n \sin n\omega_o t) = C_o + \sum_{n=1}^{\infty} C_n \cos (n\omega_o t - \theta_n). \qquad (1.17)$$

It is obvious from (1.12) that the Fourier series representation of a periodic function represents a periodic function as a sum of sinusoidal components having different frequencies. The sinusoidal component of frequency $\omega_n = n\omega_o$ is called the *n-th harmonic* of the periodic function. The first harmonic is commonly called the *fundamental component*, because it has the same period as the function, and $\omega_o = 2\pi f_o = 2\pi/T$ is called the *fundamental angular frequency*. The coefficients C_n and the angles θ_n are known as the *harmonic amplitudes* and *phase angles*, respectively.

1.3 Properties of Sine and Cosine: Orthogonal Functions

We call a set of functions $\{\phi_k(t)\}$ orthogonal on an interval $a < t < b$ if for any two functions $\phi_m(t)$ and $\phi_n(t)$ in the set $\{\phi_k(t)\}$,

$$\int_a^b \phi_m(t) \phi_n(t) \, dt = \begin{cases} 0 & \text{for } m \neq n \\ r_n & \text{for } m = n \end{cases} \qquad (1.18)$$

holds.

Let us consider a set of sinusoidal functions, for example. By use of elementary calculus, we can show that

$$\int_{-T/2}^{T/2} \cos (m\omega_o t) \, dt = 0 \qquad \text{for } m \neq 0, \qquad (1.19a)$$

$$\int_{-T/2}^{T/2} \sin (m\omega_o t) \, dt = 0 \qquad \text{for all } m, \qquad (1.19b)$$

$$\int_{-T/2}^{T/2} \cos (m\omega_o t) \cos (n\omega_o t) \, dt = \begin{cases} 0, & m \neq n \\ T/2, & m = n \neq 0, \end{cases} \qquad (1.19c)$$

$$\int_{-T/2}^{T/2} \sin (m\omega_o t) \sin (n\omega_o t) \, dt = \begin{cases} 0, & m \neq n \\ T/2, & m = n \neq 0, \end{cases} \qquad (1.19d)$$

$$\int_{-T/2}^{T/2} \sin (m\omega_o t) \cos (n\omega_o t) \, dt = 0 \quad \text{for all } m \text{ and } n, \qquad (1.19e)$$

where $\omega_o = 2\pi/T$.

These relations show that the functions $\{1, \cos \omega_o t, \cos 2\omega_o t, \cdots, \cos n\omega_o t, \cdots, \sin \omega_o t, \sin 2\omega_o t, \cdots, \sin n\omega_o t, \cdots\}$ form an orthogonal set of functions on an interval $-T/2 < t < T/2$.

PROBLEM 1.8 Verify (1.19c).

Solution: In view of the trigonometric identity

$$\cos A \cos B = \frac{1}{2}[\cos (A + B) + \cos (A - B)],$$

and

$$\omega_o t \bigg|_{t=\pm T/2} = \frac{2\pi}{T}\left(\pm \frac{T}{2}\right) = \pm \pi,$$

we have

$$\int_{-T/2}^{T/2} \cos (m\omega_o t) \cos (n\omega_o t)\, dt$$

$$= \frac{1}{2} \int_{-T/2}^{T/2} \{\cos [(m + n)\, \omega_o t] + \cos [(m - n)\, \omega_o t]\}\, dt$$

$$= \frac{1}{2}\, \frac{1}{(m + n)\, \omega_o}\, \sin [(m + n)\omega_o t]\, \bigg|_{-T/2}^{T/2}$$

$$+ \frac{1}{2}\, \frac{1}{(m - n)\omega_o}\, \sin [(m - n)\, \omega_o t]\, \bigg|_{-T/2}^{T/2}$$

$$= \frac{1}{2}\, \frac{1}{(m + n)\, \omega_o}\, \{\sin [(m + n)\pi] + \sin [(m + n)\pi]\}$$

$$+ \frac{1}{2}\, \frac{1}{(m - n)\, \omega_o}\, \{\sin [(m - n)\pi] + \sin [(m - n)\pi]\}$$

$$= 0 \quad \text{if } m \neq n.$$

If $m = n \neq 0$, by using the trigonometric identity $\cos^2\theta = \frac{1}{2}(1 + \cos 2\theta)$,

$$\int_{-T/2}^{T/2} \cos (m\omega_o t) \cos (n\omega_o t)\, dt = \int_{-T/2}^{T/2} \cos^2 (m\omega_o t)\, dt$$

$$= \frac{1}{2} \int_{-T/2}^{T/2} [1 + \cos 2m\omega_o t]\, dt$$

$$= \frac{1}{2} t \bigg|_{-T/2}^{T/2} + \frac{1}{4m\omega_o}\, \sin 2m\omega_o t \bigg|_{-T/2}^{T/2}$$

$$= \frac{T}{2}.$$

PROBLEM 1.9 Verify (1.19e).

Solution: With the trigonometric identity

$$\sin A \cos B = \frac{1}{2}[\sin (A + B) + \sin (A - B)],$$

we have

$$\int_{-T/2}^{T/2} \sin(m\omega_o t) \cos(n\omega_o t)\, dt$$

$$= \frac{1}{2} \int_{-T/2}^{T/2} \{\sin[(m+n)\omega_o t] + \sin[(m-n)\omega_o t]\}\, dt$$

$$= \frac{1}{2} \frac{-1}{(m+n)\omega_o} \cos[(m+n)\omega_o t]\Big|_{-T/2}^{T/2} + \frac{1}{2} \frac{-1}{(m-n)\omega_o} \cos[(m-n)\omega_o t]\Big|_{-T/2}^{T/2}$$

$$= 0 \quad \text{if } m \neq n.$$

If $m = n \neq 0$, by using the trigonometric identity $\sin 2\theta = 2 \sin\theta \cos\theta$,

$$\int_{-T/2}^{T/2} \sin(m\omega_o t) \cos(n\omega_o t)\, dt = \int_{-T/2}^{T/2} \sin(m\omega_o t) \cos(m\omega_o t)\, dt$$

$$= \frac{1}{2} \int_{-T/2}^{T/2} \sin(2m\omega_o t)\, dt$$

$$= -\frac{1}{4m\omega_o} \cos(2m\omega_o t)\Big|_{-T/2}^{T/2}$$

$$= 0.$$

Certainly for $m = n = 0$, the integral equals zero.

1.4 Evaluation of Fourier Coefficients

Using the orthogonality relations (1.19a-e), we can now evaluate the coefficients a_n and b_n of the Fourier series

$$f(t) = \frac{1}{2} a_o + \sum_{n=1}^{\infty} (a_n \cos n\omega_o t + b_n \sin n\omega_o t). \qquad [1.11]$$

Multiplying both sides by $\cos m\omega_o t$ and integrating over $[-T/2, T/2]$,

$$\int_{-T/2}^{T/2} f(t) \cos(m\omega_o t)\, dt = \frac{1}{2} a_o \int_{-T/2}^{T/2} \cos(m\omega_o t)\, dt$$

$$+ \int_{-T/2}^{T/2} \left[\sum_{n=1}^{\infty} a_n \cos(n\omega_o t) \right] \cos(m\omega_o t)\, dt$$

$$+ \int_{-T/2}^{T/2} \left[\sum_{n=1}^{\infty} b_n \sin(n\omega_o t) \right] \cos(m\omega_o t)\, dt.$$

Interchanging the order of integration and summation,

$$\int_{-T/2}^{T/2} f(t) \cos(m\omega_o t)\, dt = \frac{1}{2} a_o \int_{-T/2}^{T/2} \cos(m\omega_o t)\, dt$$

$$+ \sum_{n=1}^{\infty} a_n \int_{-T/2}^{T/2} \cos(n\omega_o t) \cos(m\omega_o t)\, dt$$

$$+ \sum_{n=1}^{\infty} b_n \int_{-T/2}^{T/2} \sin(n\omega_o t) \cos(m\omega_o t)\, dt.$$

In view of the orthogonality relations (1.19),

$$\int_{-T/2}^{T/2} f(t) \cos (m\omega_o t)\, dt = \frac{T}{2}\, a_m. \tag{1.20}$$

Hence,

$$a_m = \frac{2}{T} \int_{-T/2}^{T/2} f(t) \cos (m\omega_o t)\, dt. \tag{1.21}$$

If we integrate (1.11) over $[-T/2, T/2]$ and use (1.19),

$$\int_{-T/2}^{T/2} f(t)\, dt = \frac{1}{2} a_o \int_{-T/2}^{T/2} dt + \int_{-T/2}^{T/2} \left[\sum_{n=1}^{\infty} (a_n \cos n\omega_o t + b_n \sin n\omega_o t) \right] dt$$

$$= \frac{1}{2} a_o T + \sum_{n=1}^{\infty} a_n \int_{-T/2}^{T/2} \cos (n\omega_o t)\, dt + \sum_{n=1}^{\infty} b_n \int_{-T/2}^{T/2} \sin (n\omega_o t)\, dt$$

$$= \frac{1}{2} a_o T. \tag{1.22}$$

Hence,

$$\frac{1}{2} a_o = \frac{1}{T} \int_{-T/2}^{T/2} f(t)\, dt, \tag{1.23}$$

or

$$a_o = \frac{2}{T} \int_{-T/2}^{T/2} f(t)\, dt. \tag{1.24}$$

Note that $a_o/2$ is the average value of $f(t)$ over a period.

Equation (1.24) indicates that (1.21) which evaluates the coefficients of the cosine series also gives the coefficient a_o correctly since $\cos m\omega_o t \big|_{m=0} = 1$.

Similarly, if (1.11) is multiplied by $\sin m\omega_o t$ and integrated term by term over $[-T/2, T/2]$,

$$\int_{-T/2}^{T/2} f(t) \sin (m\omega_o t)\, dt = \frac{1}{2} a_o \int_{-T/2}^{T/2} \sin (m\omega_o t)\, dt$$

$$+ \sum_{n=1}^{\infty} a_n \int_{-T/2}^{T/2} \cos (n\omega_o t) \sin (m\omega_o t)\, dt$$

$$+ \sum_{n=1}^{\infty} b_n \int_{-T/2}^{T/2} \sin (n\omega_o t) \sin (m\omega_o t)\, dt.$$

Here the use of the orthogonality relations (1.19) yields

$$\int_{-T/2}^{T/2} f(t) \sin (m\omega_o t)\, dt = \frac{T}{2}\, b_m. \tag{1.25}$$

Hence,

$$b_m = \frac{2}{T} \int_{-T/2}^{T/2} f(t) \sin (m\omega_o t)\, dt. \tag{1.26}$$

Replacing m by n, we can rewrite (1.21) and (1.26) as

$$a_n = \frac{2}{T} \int_{-T/2}^{T/2} f(t) \cos (n\omega_o t)\, dt, \quad n = 0,1,2,\cdots, \tag{1.27}$$

$$b_n = \frac{2}{T} \int_{-T/2}^{T/2} f(t) \sin (n\omega_o t) \, dt, \quad n = 1, 2, \cdots. \tag{1.28}$$

In general, there is no necessity for the interval of integration of (1.27) and (1.28) to be symmetrical about the origin. In view of (1.6), the only requirement is that the integral shall be taken over a complete period.

PROBLEM 1.10 Find the Fourier series for the function $f(t)$ defined by

$$f(t) = \begin{cases} -1, & -\dfrac{T}{2} < t < 0 \\ \\ 1, & 0 < t < \dfrac{T}{2} \end{cases} \tag{1.29}$$

and $f(t + T) = f(t)$. (See Fig. 1.2.)

Solution: From (1.27) and $\omega_o t \Big|_{t = \pm T/2} = \dfrac{2\pi}{T} \left(\pm \dfrac{T}{2} \right) = \pm \pi$,

$$a_n = \frac{2}{T} \int_{-T/2}^{T/2} f(t) \cos (n\omega_o t) \, dt$$

$$= \frac{2}{T} \left[\int_{-T/2}^{0} -\cos (n\omega_o t) \, dt + \int_{0}^{T/2} \cos (n\omega_o t) \, dt \right]$$

$$= \frac{2}{T} \left(\frac{-1}{n\omega_o} \sin n\omega_o t \Big|_{-T/2}^{0} + \frac{1}{n\omega_o} \sin n\omega_o t \Big|_{0}^{T/2} \right)$$

$$= \frac{2}{T} \left\{ \frac{-1}{n\omega_o} [\sin 0 - \sin (-n\pi)] + \frac{1}{n\omega_o} [\sin (n\pi) - \sin 0] \right\}$$

$$= 0 \text{ for } n \neq 0 \tag{1.30}$$

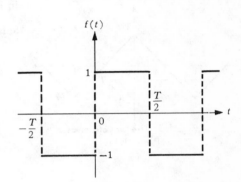

Fig. 1.2 The waveform of Prob. 1.10.

since $\sin 0 = \sin (n\pi) = 0$.

For $n = 0$,

$$\frac{1}{2} a_o = \frac{1}{T} \int_{-T/2}^{T/2} f(t) \, dt = 0 \tag{1.31}$$

since the average value of $f(t)$ over a period is zero.

From (1.28) and $\omega_o T = (2\pi/T) T = 2\pi$,

$$b_n = \frac{2}{T} \int_{-T/2}^{T/2} f(t) \sin (n\omega_o t) \, dt$$

$$= \frac{2}{T} \left[\int_{-T/2}^{0} - \sin (n\omega_o t) \, dt + \int_{0}^{T/2} \sin (n\omega_o t) \, dt \right]$$

$$= \frac{2}{T} \left[\frac{1}{n\omega_o} \cos (n\omega_o t) \Big|_{-T/2}^{0} + \frac{-1}{n\omega_o} \cos (n\omega_o t) \Big|_{0}^{T/2} \right]$$

$$= \frac{2}{n\omega_o T} \left\{ [1 - \cos (-n\pi)] - [\cos (n\pi) - 1] \right\}$$

$$= \frac{2}{n\pi} (1 - \cos n\pi). \tag{1.32}$$

Since $\cos n\pi = (-1)^n$,

$$b_n = \begin{cases} 0, & n \text{ even} \\[2mm] \dfrac{4}{n\pi}, & n \text{ odd.} \end{cases} \qquad (1.33)$$

Hence,

$$f(t) = \frac{4}{\pi} \sum_{n=\text{odd}}^{\infty} \frac{1}{n} \sin n\omega_o t$$

$$= \frac{4}{\pi} \left(\sin \omega_o t + \frac{1}{3} \sin 3\omega_o t + \frac{1}{5} \sin 5\omega_o t + \cdots \right). \qquad (1.34)$$

PROBLEM 1.11   Find the Fourier series for the function whose waveform is shown in Fig. 1.3.

Solution: The function $f(t)$ can be expressed analytically as

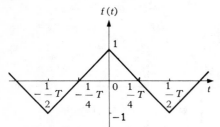

$$f(t) = \begin{cases} 1 + \dfrac{4t}{T}, & -\dfrac{T}{2} < t \le 0 \\[4mm] 1 - \dfrac{4t}{T}, & 0 \le t < \dfrac{T}{2}. \end{cases} \qquad (1.35)$$

Fig. 1.3 The waveform of Prob. 1.11.

Since the average value of $f(t)$ over a period is zero,

$$\frac{1}{2} a_o = \frac{1}{T} \int_{-T/2}^{T/2} f(t)\, dt = 0. \qquad (1.36)$$

From (1.27) and (1.35),

$$a_n = \frac{2}{T} \int_{-T/2}^{T/2} f(t) \cos (n\omega_o t)\, dt$$

$$= \frac{2}{T} \int_{-T/2}^{T/2} \cos (n\omega_o t)\, dt + \frac{2}{T} \int_{-T/2}^{0} \frac{4}{T} t \cos (n\omega_o t)\, dt$$

$$+ \frac{2}{T} \int_{0}^{T/2} -\frac{4}{T} t \cos (n\omega_o t)\, dt.$$

The first integral on the right-hand side equals zero. Letting $t = -\tau$ in the second integral,

$$a_n = \frac{8}{T^2} \int_{T/2}^{0} (-\tau) \cos [n\omega_o (-\tau)](-d\tau) - \frac{8}{T^2} \int_{0}^{T/2} t \cos (n\omega_o t)\, dt$$

$$= \frac{8}{T^2} \int_{T/2}^{0} \tau \cos (n\omega_o \tau)\, d\tau - \frac{8}{T^2} \int_{0}^{T/2} t \cos (n\omega_o t)\, dt$$

$$= -\frac{8}{T^2} \int_{0}^{T/2} \tau \cos (n\omega_o \tau)\, d\tau - \frac{8}{T^2} \int_{0}^{T/2} t \cos (n\omega_o t)\, dt$$

$$= -\frac{16}{T^2} \int_{0}^{T/2} t \cos (n\omega_o t)\, dt.$$

Now integrating by parts,

$$\int_0^{T/2} t \cos(n\omega_o t)\, dt = \frac{1}{n\omega_o} t \sin(n\omega_o t) \Big|_0^{T/2} - \frac{1}{n\omega_o} \int_0^{T/2} \sin(n\omega_o t)\, dt$$

$$= \frac{1}{(n\omega_o)^2} \cos(n\omega_o t) \Big|_0^{T/2}$$

$$= \frac{1}{(n2\pi/T)^2} (\cos n\pi - 1).$$

Hence,

$$a_n = -\frac{16}{T^2} \frac{1}{(n2\pi/T)^2} (\cos n\pi - 1)$$

$$= \frac{4}{n^2\pi^2} (1 - \cos n\pi). \tag{1.37}$$

Since $\cos n\pi = (-1)^n$,

$$a_n = \begin{cases} 0, & n \text{ even} \\ \dfrac{8}{n^2\pi^2}, & n \text{ odd}. \end{cases} \tag{1.38}$$

Similarly from (1.28) and (1.35),

$$b_n = \frac{2}{T} \int_{-T/2}^{T/2} f(t) \sin(n\omega_o t)\, dt$$

$$= \frac{2}{T} \int_{-T/2}^{T/2} \sin(n\omega_o t)\, dt + \frac{2}{T} \int_{-T/2}^{0} \frac{4}{T} t \sin(n\omega_o t)\, dt$$

$$+ \frac{2}{T} \int_{0}^{T/2} -\frac{4}{T} t \sin(n\omega_o t)\, dt$$

$$= \frac{8}{T^2} \int_{T/2}^{0} (-\tau) \sin[n\omega_o(-\tau)] (-d\tau) - \frac{8}{T^2} \int_{0}^{T/2} t \sin(n\omega_o t)\, dt$$

$$= \frac{8}{T^2} \int_{0}^{T/2} t \sin(n\omega_o t)\, dt - \frac{8}{T^2} \int_{0}^{T/2} t \sin(n\omega_o t)\, dt$$

$$= 0. \tag{1.39}$$

Hence,

$$f(t) = \frac{8}{\pi^2} \left(\cos \omega_o t + \frac{1}{3^2} \cos 3\omega_o t + \frac{1}{5^2} \cos 5\omega_o t + \cdots \right). \tag{1.40}$$

PROBLEM 1.12   Find the Fourier series for the function $f(t)$ defined by

$$f(t) = \begin{cases} 0, & -\dfrac{T}{2} < t < 0 \\[2mm] A \sin \omega_o t, & 0 < t < \dfrac{T}{2}, \end{cases} \tag{1.41}$$

and $f(t + T) = f(t)$, $\omega_o = 2\pi/T$. (See Fig. 1.4.)

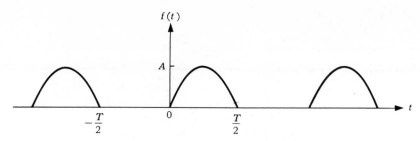

Fig. 1.4 The waveform of Prob. 1.12.

Solution: Since $f(t) = 0$ when $-T/2 < t < 0$, from (1.27) and (1.28),

$$a_o = \frac{2}{T} \int_0^{T/2} A \sin (\omega_o t)\, dt = \frac{2A}{T\omega_o} (-\cos \omega_o t)\Big|_0^{T/2}$$

$$= \frac{A}{\pi} (1 - \cos \pi)$$

$$= \frac{2A}{\pi}, \tag{1.42}$$

$$a_n = \frac{2}{T} \int_0^{T/2} A \sin (\omega_o t) \cos (n\omega_o t)\, dt$$

$$= \frac{A}{T} \int_0^{T/2} \{\sin [(1 + n)\, \omega_o t] + \sin [(1 - n)\, \omega_o t]\}\, dt. \tag{1.43}$$

When $n = 1$,

$$a_1 = \frac{A}{T} \int_0^{T/2} \sin (2\omega_o t)\, dt = \frac{A}{T} \left(-\frac{1}{2\omega_o} \cos 2\omega_o t\right)\Big|_0^{T/2} = \frac{A}{4\pi}[1 - \cos (2\pi)]$$

$$= \frac{A}{4\pi} (1 - 1)$$

$$= 0. \tag{1.44}$$

When $n = 2, 3, \ldots$,

$$a_n = \frac{A}{T} \left\{ -\frac{\cos [(1 + n)\, \omega_o t]}{(1 + n)\, \omega_o} - \frac{\cos [(1 - n)\, \omega_o t]}{(1 - n)\, \omega_o} \right\}\Big|_0^{T/2}$$

$$= \frac{A}{2\pi} \left\{ \frac{1 - [\cos (1 + n)\, \pi]}{1 + n} + \frac{1 - \cos [(1 - n)\, \pi]}{1 - n} \right\}$$

$$= \begin{cases} 0, & n \text{ odd} \\ \dfrac{A}{2\pi} \left(\dfrac{2}{1 + n} + \dfrac{2}{1 - n}\right) = -\dfrac{2A}{(n - 1)(n + 1)\pi}, & n \text{ even.} \end{cases} \tag{1.45}$$

Similarly,

$$b_n = \frac{2}{T} \int_0^{T/2} A \sin (\omega_o t) \sin (n\omega_o t)\, dt$$

$$= \frac{A}{T} \int_0^{T/2} \{\cos [(1 - n)\, \omega_o t] - \cos [(1 + n)\, \omega_o t]\}\, dt. \tag{1.46}$$

When $n = 1$,

$$b_1 = \frac{A}{T} \int_0^{T/2} dt - \frac{A}{T} \int_0^{T/2} \cos(2\omega_o t)\, dt = \frac{A}{2} - \frac{A}{T} \frac{\sin 2\omega_o t}{2\omega_o} \bigg|_0^{T/2} = \frac{A}{2}. \qquad (1.47)$$

When $n = 2, 3, \cdots$,

$$b_n = \frac{A}{T} \left\{ \frac{\sin[(1-n)\omega_o t]}{(1-n)\omega_o} - \frac{\sin[(1+n)\omega_o t]}{(1+n)\omega_o} \right\} \bigg|_0^{T/2}$$

$$= \frac{A}{2\pi} \left\{ \frac{\sin[(1-n)\pi] - \sin 0}{1-n} - \frac{\sin[(1+n)\pi] - \sin 0}{1+n} \right\}$$

$$= 0. \qquad (1.48)$$

Hence,

$$f(t) = \frac{A}{\pi} + \frac{A}{2} \sin \omega_o t - \frac{2A}{\pi} \left(\frac{1}{1 \cdot 3} \cos 2\omega_o t + \frac{1}{3 \cdot 5} \cos 4\omega_o t + \cdots \right). \qquad (1.49)$$

PROBLEM 1.13   Expand $f(t) = \sin^5 t$ in Fourier series.

Solution: Rather than proceed as in Prob. 1.12, we shall make use of the identities

$$e^{\pm jn\theta} = \cos n\theta \pm j \sin n\theta, \qquad (1.50)$$

$$\cos n\theta = \frac{e^{jn\theta} + e^{-jn\theta}}{2}, \qquad (1.51)$$

$$\sin n\theta = \frac{e^{jn\theta} - e^{-jn\theta}}{2j}. \qquad (1.52)$$

We write

$$\sin^5 t = \left(\frac{e^{jt} - e^{-jt}}{2j} \right)^5 = \frac{1}{32j} (e^{j5t} - 5e^{j3t} + 10e^{jt} - 10e^{-jt} + 5e^{-j3t} - e^{-j5t})$$

$$= \frac{5}{8} \sin t - \frac{5}{16} \sin 3t + \frac{1}{16} \sin 5t. \qquad (1.53)$$

Here the Fourier series has only three terms.

1.5 Approximation by Finite Fourier Series

Let

$$S_k(t) = \frac{a_o}{2} + \sum_{n=1}^{k} (a_n \cos n\omega_o t + b_n \sin n\omega_o t) \qquad (1.54)$$

be the sum of the first $(2k+1)$ terms of a Fourier series that is to represent $f(t)$ on $-T/2 < t < T/2$.

When $f(t)$ is approximated by $S_k(t)$, i.e.,

$$f(t) = \frac{a_o}{2} + \sum_{n=1}^{k} (a_n \cos n\omega_o t + b_n \sin n\omega_o t) + \varepsilon_k(t), \qquad (1.55)$$

$$\varepsilon_k(t) = f(t) - S_k(t), \qquad (1.56)$$

and $\varepsilon_k(t)$ is the difference or *error* between $f(t)$ and its approximation, then the *mean-square error* E_k is defined by

$$E_k = \frac{1}{T} \int_{-T/2}^{T/2} [\varepsilon_k(t)]^2 \, dt = \frac{1}{T} \int_{-T/2}^{T/2} [f(t) - S_k(t)]^2 \, dt. \quad (1.57)$$

PROBLEM 1.14 Show that if we approximate a function $f(t)$ by the finite Fourier series $S_k(t)$, then this approximation has the least mean-square error property.

Solution: Substituting (1.54) into (1.57),

$$E_k = \frac{1}{T} \int_{-T/2}^{T/2} \left[f(t) - \frac{a_o}{2} - \sum_{n=1}^{k} (a_n \cos n\omega_o t + b_n \sin n\omega_o t) \right]^2 \, dt. \quad (1.58)$$

Consider E_k as a function of a_o, a_n, and b_n. Then in order to have a minimum for the mean-square error E_k, its partial derivatives with respect to a_o, a_n, and b_n must be zero, i.e.,

$$\frac{\partial E_k}{\partial a_o} = 0, \quad \frac{\partial E_k}{\partial a_n} = 0, \quad \frac{\partial E_k}{\partial b_n} = 0 \quad (n = 1, 2, \cdots).$$

Interchanging the order of differentiation and integration,

$$\frac{\partial E_k}{\partial a_o} = -\frac{1}{T} \int_{-T/2}^{T/2} \left[f(t) - \frac{a_o}{2} - \sum_{n=1}^{k} (a_n \cos n\omega_o t + b_n \sin n\omega_o t) \right] dt, \quad (1.59)$$

$$\frac{\partial E_k}{\partial a_n} = -\frac{2}{T} \int_{-T/2}^{T/2} \left[f(t) - \frac{a_o}{2} - \sum_{n=1}^{k} (a_n \cos n\omega_o t + b_n \sin n\omega_o t) \right] \cos (n\omega_o t) \, dt, \quad (1.60)$$

$$\frac{\partial E_k}{\partial b_n} = -\frac{2}{T} \int_{-T/2}^{T/2} \left[f(t) - \frac{a_o}{2} - \sum_{n=1}^{k} (a_n \cos n\omega_o t + b_n \sin n\omega_o t) \right] \sin (n\omega_o t) \, dt. \quad (1.61)$$

Using the orthogonality properties (1.19), (1.27), and (1.28) of sine and cosine, the integrals (1.59), (1.60), and (1.61) reduce to

$$\frac{\partial E_k}{\partial a_o} = \frac{a_o}{2} - \frac{1}{T} \int_{-T/2}^{T/2} f(t) \, dt = 0, \quad (1.62)$$

$$\frac{\partial E_k}{\partial a_n} = a_n - \frac{2}{T} \int_{-T/2}^{T/2} f(t) \cos (n\omega_o t) \, dt = 0, \quad (1.63)$$

$$\frac{\partial E_k}{\partial b_n} = b_n - \frac{2}{T} \int_{-T/2}^{T/2} f(t) \sin (n\omega_o t) \, dt = 0. \quad (1.64)$$

PROBLEM 1.15 Show that the mean-square error E_k in an approximation to $f(t)$ by $S_k(t)$, defined by (1.57), reduces to

$$E_k = \frac{1}{T} \int_{-T/2}^{T/2} [f(t)]^2 \, dt - \frac{a_o^2}{4} - \frac{1}{2} \sum_{n=1}^{k} (a_n^2 + b_n^2). \quad (1.65)$$

Solution: From (1.57),

$$E_k = \frac{1}{T} \int_{-T/2}^{T/2} [f(t) - S_k(t)]^2 \, dt$$

$$= \frac{1}{T} \int_{-T/2}^{T/2} \{[f(t)]^2 - 2 f(t) \, S_k(t) + [S_k(t)]^2\} \, dt$$

$$= \frac{1}{T} \int_{-T/2}^{T/2} [f(t)]^2 \, dt - \frac{2}{T} \int_{-T/2}^{T/2} f(t) \, S_k(t) \, dt + \frac{1}{T} \int_{-T/2}^{T/2} [S_k(t)]^2 \, dt. \quad (1.66)$$

Now

$$\frac{2}{T} \int_{-T/2}^{T/2} f(t) \, S_k(t) \, dt = \frac{2}{T} \frac{a_o}{2} \int_{-T/2}^{T/2} f(t) \, dt + \frac{2}{T} \sum_{n=1}^{k} a_n \int_{-T/2}^{T/2} f(t) \cos(n\omega_o t) \, dt$$

$$+ \frac{2}{T} \sum_{n=1}^{k} b_n \int_{-T/2}^{T/2} f(t) \sin(n\omega_o t) \, dt.$$

In view of (1.27) and (1.28),

$$\frac{2}{T} \int_{-T/2}^{T/2} f(t) \, S_k(t) \, dt = \frac{a_o^2}{2} + \sum_{n=1}^{k} (a_n^2 + b_n^2). \quad (1.67)$$

Using the orthogonality relations (1.19),

$$\frac{1}{T} \int_{-T/2}^{T/2} [S_k(t)]^2 \, dt = \frac{1}{T} \int_{-T/2}^{T/2} \left[\frac{a_o}{2} + \sum_{n=1}^{k} (a_n \cos n\omega_o t + b_n \sin n\omega_o t) \right]^2 \, dt$$

$$= \frac{a_o^2}{4} + \frac{1}{2} \sum_{n=1}^{k} (a_n^2 + b_n^2). \quad (1.68)$$

Substituting (1.67) and (1.68) into (1.66),

$$E_k = \frac{1}{T} \int_{-T/2}^{T/2} [f(t)]^2 \, dt - \frac{a_o^2}{2} - \sum_{n=1}^{k} (a_n^2 + b_n^2) + \frac{a_o^2}{4} + \frac{1}{2} \sum_{n=1}^{k} (a_n^2 + b_n^2)$$

$$= \frac{1}{T} \int_{-T/2}^{T/2} [f(t)]^2 \, dt - \frac{a_o^2}{4} - \frac{1}{2} \sum_{n=1}^{k} (a_n^2 + b_n^2).$$

PROBLEM 1.16 Establish the following inequality:

$$\frac{2}{T} \int_{-T/2}^{T/2} [f(t)]^2 \, dt \geq \frac{a_o^2}{2} + \sum_{n=1}^{k} (a_n^2 + b_n^2). \quad (1.69)$$

Solution: From (1.57),

$$E_k = \frac{1}{T} \int_{-T/2}^{T/2} [f(t) - S_k(t)]^2 \, dt \geq 0. \quad (1.70)$$

And also from (1.65) we deduce that

$$\frac{2}{T} \int_{-T/2}^{T/2} [f(t)]^2 \, dt \geq \frac{a_o^2}{2} + \sum_{n=1}^{k} (a_n^2 + b_n^2). \quad (1.71)$$

Parseval's theorem states that if a_o, a_n, and b_n for $n = 1, 2, \cdots$ are the coefficients in the Fourier expansion of a periodic function $f(t)$ with period T, then

$$\frac{1}{T} \int_{-T/2}^{T/2} [f(t)]^2 \, dt = \frac{a_o^2}{4} + \frac{1}{2} \sum_{n=1}^{\infty} (a_n^2 + b_n^2). \tag{1.72}$$

PROBLEM 1.17   Prove Parseval's theorem.

Solution: From (1.65),

$$E_{k+1} = E_k - \frac{1}{2}(a_{k+1}^2 + b_{k+1}^2). \tag{1.73}$$

By (1.70) and (1.73), the sequence $\{E_k\}$ contains only nonnegative terms and it is nonincreasing. The sequence therefore converges. Also from (1.56),

$$\lim_{k \to \infty} \varepsilon_k(t) = f(t) - \lim_{k \to \infty} S_k(t) = 0. \tag{1.74}$$

Hence,

$$\lim_{k \to \infty} E_k = 0. \tag{1.75}$$

Consequently, from (1.65) we conclude that

$$\frac{1}{T} \int_{-T/2}^{T/2} [f(t)]^2 \, dt = \frac{a_o^2}{4} + \frac{1}{2} \sum_{n=1}^{\infty} (a_n^2 + b_n^2)$$

1.6   The Dirichlet Conditions

Previously we were concerned with the determination of the Fourier series of given functions, and we assumed that the given function can be represented by the Fourier series. Now we shall investigate the convergence of the Fourier series to $f(t)$.

The study of convergence is a rather elegant subject in Fourier theory. Here we shall simply state the conditions, known as the *Dirichlet conditions*, under which a Fourier series representation for a given function $f(t)$ is possible.

The Dirichlet conditions are as follows:

(1) The function $f(t)$ has a finite number of discontinuities in one period.

(2) The function $f(t)$ has a finite number of maxima and minima in one period.

(3) The function $f(t)$ is absolutely integrable over a period; i.e.,

$$\int_{-T/2}^{T/2} |f(t)| \, dt = \text{finite} < \infty. \tag{1.76}$$

We shall say that a function $f(t)$ is *piecewise continuous* in the finite interval $[-T/2, T/2]$ if it satisfies conditions (1) and (2).

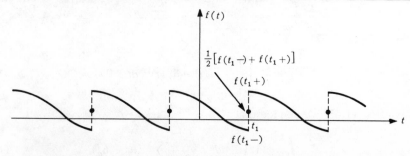

Fig. 1.5 Piecewise continuous function and left- and right-hand limits.

At a point of discontinuity, as shown in Fig. 1.5, which may be denoted by $t = t_1$, the Fourier series converges to

$$\frac{1}{2}[f(t_1-) + f(t_1+)], \tag{1.77}$$

where $f(t_1-)$ is the limit of $f(t)$ as t approaches t_1 from the left, and $f(t_1+)$ is the limit of $f(t)$ as t approaches t_1 from the right. The reason for this property of the Fourier series is discussed in Appendix A.

PROBLEM 1.18 If $\{a_n\}$ and $\{b_n\}$ are the sequences of the Fourier coefficients of $f(t)$, then show that

$$\lim_{n\to\infty} a_n = \lim_{n\to\infty} b_n = 0. \tag{1.78}$$

Solution: From (1.69),

$$\frac{1}{2}a_o^2 + \sum_{n=1}^{\infty}(a_n^2 + b_n^2) \le \frac{2}{T}\int_{-T/2}^{T/2}[f(t)]^2\, dt.$$

Since the series on the left-hand side is convergent, it is necessary that

$$\lim_{n\to\infty}(a_n^2 + b_n^2) = 0,$$

which implies $\lim\limits_{n\to\infty} a_n = \lim\limits_{n\to\infty} b_n = 0.$

PROBLEM 1.19 Show that if $f(t)$ is piecewise continuous and absolutely integrable over $-T/2 < t < T/2$, then

$$\lim_{n\to\infty}\int_{-T/2}^{T/2} f(t)\cos(n\omega_o t)\, dt = \lim_{n\to\infty}\int_{-T/2}^{T/2} f(t)\sin(n\omega_o t)\, dt = 0. \tag{1.79}$$

Solution: Since $f(t)$ is absolutely integrable over $[-T/2, T/2]$, its Fourier coefficients a_n and b_n exist. In view of (1.78), (1.79) follows from the definition of the Fourier coefficients; i.e.,

$$\lim_{n\to\infty} \begin{cases} a_n \\ b_n \end{cases} = \lim_{n\to\infty}\frac{2}{T}\int_{-T/2}^{T/2} f(t) \begin{cases} \cos(n\omega_o t) \\ \sin(n\omega_o t) \end{cases} dt = 0.$$

Hence,

$$\lim_{n\to\infty}\int_{-T/2}^{T/2} f(t) \begin{cases} \cos(n\omega_o t) \\ \sin(n\omega_o t) \end{cases} dt = 0.$$

1.7 Differentiation and Integration of Fourier Series

We next consider the differentiation and integration of the Fourier series of a function. We note that differentiation term-by-term of a trigonometric series

$$\frac{a_o}{2} + \sum_{n=1}^{\infty}(a_n\cos n\omega_o t + b_n\sin n\omega_o t)$$

multiplies the coefficients a_n and b_n by $\pm n\omega_o$. Hence differentiation tends to slow down convergence and may result in *divergence*. On the other hand, in term-by-term integration, the coefficients a_n and b_n are divided by $\pm n\omega_o$, and the result is a series whose convergence is enhanced.

PROBLEM 1.20   Prove the following differentiation theorem for Fourier series:
    If $f(t)$ is continuous in $-T/2 \le t \le T/2$ with $f(-T/2) = f(T/2)$, and if its derivative $f'(t)$ is piecewise continuous and differentiable, then the Fourier series

$$f(t) = \frac{a_o}{2} + \sum_{n=1}^{\infty} (a_n \cos n\omega_o t + b_n \sin n\omega_o t) \tag{1.80}$$

can be differentiated term-by-term to yield

$$f'(t) = \sum_{n=1}^{\infty} n\omega_o (-a_n \sin n\omega_o t + b_n \cos n\omega_o t). \tag{1.81}$$

Solution: Since $f'(t)$ is piecewise continuous and differentiable, its Fourier series converges to it; hence, its Fourier series representation is

$$f'(t) = \frac{\alpha_o}{2} + \sum_{n=1}^{\infty} (\alpha_n \cos n\omega_o t + \beta_n \sin n\omega_o t), \tag{1.82}$$

where

$$\alpha_n = \frac{2}{T} \int_{-T/2}^{T/2} f'(t) \cos (n\omega_o t) \, dt, \tag{1.83}$$

$$\beta_n = \frac{2}{T} \int_{-T/2}^{T/2} f'(t) \sin (n\omega_o t) \, dt. \tag{1.84}$$

Integrating (1.83) and (1.84) by parts,

$$\alpha_n = \frac{2}{T} \left[(\cos n\omega_o t) f(t) \Big|_{-T/2}^{T/2} + n\omega_o \int_{-T/2}^{T/2} f(t) \sin (n\omega_o t) \, dt \right]$$

$$= n\omega_o \, b_n, \tag{1.85}$$

$$\beta_n = \frac{2}{T} \left[(\sin n\omega_o t) f(t) \Big|_{-T/2}^{T/2} - n\omega_o \int_{-T/2}^{T/2} f(t) \cos (n\omega_o t) \, dt \right]$$

$$= - n\omega_o \, a_n \tag{1.86}$$

since $f(-T/2) = f(T/2)$.
    It is noted that $\alpha_o = 0$. Hence,

$$f'(t) = \sum_{n=1}^{\infty} n\omega_o (-a_n \sin n\omega_o t + b_n \cos n\omega_o t),$$

which can be obtained from the Fourier series of $f(t)$ by term-by-term differentiation. (Differentiation of a function having jump discontinuities will be discussed in Sec. 2.5.)

PROBLEM 1.21   Let $f(t)$ be piecewise continuous for $-T/2 < t < T/2$, and $f(t + T) = f(t)$. Show that the Fourier series

$$f(t) = \frac{1}{2} a_o + \sum_{n=1}^{\infty} (a_n \cos n\omega_o t + b_n \sin n\omega_o t) \tag{1.87}$$

can be integrated term-by-term to yield

$$\int_{t_1}^{t_2} f(t)\,dt = \frac{1}{2} a_o (t_2 - t_1) + \sum_{n=1}^{\infty} \frac{1}{n\omega_o} [-b_n (\cos n\omega_o t_2 - \cos n\omega_o t_1)$$

$$+ a_n (\sin n\omega_o t_2 - \sin n\omega_o t_1)]. \tag{1.88}$$

Solution: Since $f(t)$ is piecewise continuous and from the result of Prob. 1.6, the function $F(t)$ defined by

$$F(t) = \int_0^t f(\tau)\,d\tau - \frac{1}{2} a_o t \tag{1.89}$$

is continuous and periodic with period T. Since

$$F'(t) = f(t) - \frac{1}{2} a_o, \tag{1.90}$$

$F'(t)$ is also continuous. Let the Fourier series expansion of $F(t)$ be

$$F(t) = \frac{1}{2} \alpha_o + \sum_{n=1}^{\infty} (\alpha_n \cos n\omega_o t + \beta_n \sin n\omega_o t). \tag{1.91}$$

Then, for $n \geq 1$,

$$\alpha_n = \frac{2}{T} \int_{-T/2}^{T/2} F(t) \cos (n\omega_o t)\,dt$$

$$= \frac{2}{n\omega_o T} F(t) \sin n\omega_o t \Big|_{-T/2}^{T/2} - \frac{2}{n\omega_o T} \int_{-T/2}^{T/2} F'(t) \sin (n\omega_o t)\,dt$$

$$= -\frac{2}{n\omega_o T} \int_{-T/2}^{T/2} [f(t) - \frac{1}{2} a_o] \sin (n\omega_o t)\,dt$$

$$= -\frac{1}{n\omega_o} b_n, \tag{1.92}$$

$$\beta_n = \frac{2}{T} \int_{-T/2}^{T/2} F(t) \sin (n\omega_o t)\,dt$$

$$= -\frac{2}{n\omega_o T} F(t) \cos n\omega_o t \Big|_{-T/2}^{T/2} + \frac{2}{n\omega_o T} \int_{-T/2}^{T/2} F'(t) \cos (n\omega_o t)\,dt$$

$$= \frac{2}{n\omega_o T} \int_{-T/2}^{T/2} [f(t) - \frac{1}{2} a_o] \cos (n\omega_o t)\,dt$$

$$= \frac{1}{n\omega_o} a_n. \tag{1.93}$$

Hence,

$$F(t) = \frac{1}{2} \alpha_o + \sum_{n=1}^{\infty} \frac{1}{n\omega_o} (-b_n \cos n\omega_o t + a_n \sin n\omega_o t). \tag{1.94}$$

Now,

$$F(t_2) - F(t_1) = \int_{t_1}^{t_2} f(\tau)\, d\tau - \frac{1}{2} a_o\, (t_2 - t_1). \qquad (1.95)$$

Hence,

$$\int_{t_1}^{t_2} f(t)\, dt = F(t_2) - F(t_1) + \frac{1}{2} a_o\, (t_2 - t_1)$$

$$= \frac{1}{2} a_o\, (t_2 - t_1) + \sum_{n=1}^{\infty} \frac{1}{n\omega_o} [-b_n\, (\cos n\omega_o t_2 - \cos n\omega_o t_1)$$

$$+ a_n\, (\sin n\omega_o t_2 - \sin n\omega_o t_1)]$$

which can be obtained from the Fourier series of $f(t)$ by term-by-term integration.

PROBLEM 1.22   Show that the integral of a periodic function whose average value is nonzero is not a periodic function.

Solution: From the result of Prob. 1.21,

$$\int_0^t f(\tau)\, d\tau = \frac{1}{2} a_o t + \sum_{n=1}^{\infty} \left[\frac{1}{n\omega_o} (a_n \sin n\omega_o t - b_n \cos n\omega_o t + b_n) \right]. \quad (1.96)$$

The term $\frac{1}{2} a_o t$ is not periodic, and therefore the integral is not periodic. We note that integrating the Fourier series of $f(t)$ term-by-term will yield the Fourier series of the integral of $f(t)$ only if $a_o = 0$; i.e., only if the average value of $f(t)$ is zero. This is proved in Prob. 1.5.

PROBLEM 1.23   Let $f(t)$ be continuous and $f'(t)$ be piecewise continuous in $-T/2 < t < T/2$. Multiply

$$f(t) = \frac{1}{2} a_o + \sum_{n=1}^{\infty} (a_n \cos n\omega_o t + b_n \sin n\omega_o t) \qquad (1.97)$$

by $f(t)$, integrate term-by-term, and show that

$$\frac{1}{T} \int_{-T/2}^{T/2} [f(t)]^2\, dt = \frac{1}{4} a_o^2 + \frac{1}{2} \sum_{n=1}^{\infty} (a_n^2 + b_n^2). \qquad (1.98)$$

(Cf., Parseval's theorem – Prob. 1.17.)

Solution: Using (1.27) and (1.28),

$$\int_{-T/2}^{T/2} [f(t)]^2\, dt = \frac{1}{2} a_o \int_{-T/2}^{T/2} f(t)\, dt + \sum_{n=1}^{\infty} \left[a_n \int_{-T/2}^{T/2} f(t) \cos (n\omega_o t)\, dt \right.$$

$$\left. + b_n \int_{-T/2}^{T/2} f(t) \sin (n\omega_o t)\, dt \right]$$

$$= \frac{1}{4} a_o^2 T + \frac{T}{2} \left[\sum_{n=1}^{\infty} (a_n^2 + b_n^2) \right]. \qquad (1.99)$$

Thus,

$$\frac{1}{T} \int_{-T/2}^{T/2} [f(t)]^2\, dt = \frac{1}{4} a_o^2 + \frac{1}{2} \sum_{n=1}^{\infty} (a_n^2 + b_n^2).$$

1.8 Supplementary Problems

PROBLEM 1.24 Find the period of the following functions:

(a) $\cos nt$, (b) $\cos 2\pi t$, (c) $\sin(2\pi t/k)$, (d) $\sin t + \sin(t/3) + \sin(t/5)$,
(e) $|\sin \omega_0 t|$.

Answer: (a) $2\pi/n$, (b) 1, (c) k, (d) 30π, (e) π/ω_0.

PROBLEM 1.25 Show that the function $f(t) = $ constant is a periodic function of period T for any positive value of T

PROBLEM 1.26 If $f(t)$ is a periodic function of t with period T, show that $f(at)$ for $a \neq 0$ is a periodic function of t with period T/a.

PROBLEM 1.27 If $f(t)$ is a periodic function of t with period T and integrable,

show that $f_a(t) = \dfrac{1}{2a} \displaystyle\int_{t-a}^{t+a} f(\tau)\,d\tau$ is also periodic with period T.

PROBLEM 1.28 Show that if $f(t)$ and $g(t)$ are piecewise continuous in the interval $(-T/2, T/2)$ and periodic with period T, then the function

$$h(t) = \frac{1}{T} \int_{-T/2}^{T/2} f(t - \tau)\,g(\tau)\,d\tau$$

is continuous and periodic with period T.

PROBLEM 1.29 Find the Fourier series for the function $f(t)$ defined by $f(t) = 1$ for $-\pi < t < 0$, $f(t) = 0$ for $0 < t < \pi$, and $f(t + 2\pi) = f(t)$. (See Fig. 1.6.)

Answer: $\dfrac{1}{2} - \dfrac{2}{\pi} \displaystyle\sum_{n=1}^{\infty} \dfrac{\sin(2n-1)t}{2n-1}$.

PROBLEM 1.30 Find the Fourier series of the function $f(t)$ defined by $f(t) = t$ for the interval $(-\pi, \pi)$ and $f(t + 2\pi) = f(t)$. (See Fig. 1.7.)

Answer: $2 \displaystyle\sum_{n=1}^{\infty} \dfrac{(-1)^{n-1}}{n} \sin nt$.

PROBLEM 1.31 Find the Fourier series for the function $f(t)$ defined by $f(t) = t$ for the interval $(-\pi, \pi)$ and $f(t + 2\pi) = f(t)$. (See Fig. 1.8.)

Answer: $\dfrac{1}{3}\pi^2 + 4 \displaystyle\sum_{n=1}^{\infty} \dfrac{(-1)^n}{n^2} \cos nt$.

PROBLEM 1.32 Find the Fourier series for the function $f(t)$ defined by $f(t) = e^t$ for the interval $(-\pi, \pi)$ and $f(t + 2\pi) = f(t)$. (See Fig. 1.9.)

Answer: $\dfrac{2 \sinh \pi}{\pi} \left[\dfrac{1}{2} + \displaystyle\sum_{n=1}^{\infty} \dfrac{(-1)^n}{1 + n^2} (\cos nt - n \sin nt) \right]$.

PROBLEM 1.33 Find the Fourier series for the function $f(t) = |A \sin \omega_0 t|$. (See Fig. 1.10.)

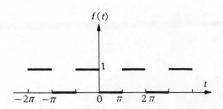

Fig. 1.6 The function $f(t)$ of Prob. 1.29.

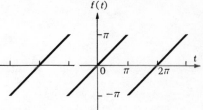

Fig. 1.7 The function $f(t)$ of Prob. 1.30.

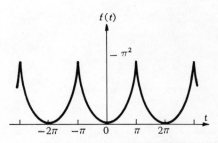

Fig. 1.8 The function $f(t)$ of Prob. 1.31.

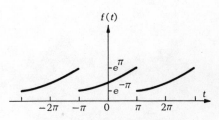

Fig. 1.9 The function $f(t)$ of Prob. 1.32.

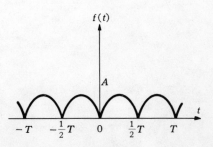

Fig. 1.10 The function $f(t)$ of Prob. 1.33.

Answer: $\dfrac{2A}{\pi} + \dfrac{4A}{\pi} \displaystyle\sum_{n=1}^{\infty} \dfrac{1}{1-4n^2} \cos(2n\omega_0 t).$

PROBLEM 1.34 Expand $f(t) = \sin^2 t \cos^3 t$ in Fourier series.

Answer: $\dfrac{1}{16} (2 \cos t - \cos 3t - \cos 5t).$

PROBLEM 1.35 Expand $f(t) = e^{r \cos t} \cos(r \sin t)$ in Fourier series.
[Hint: Use the power series for e^z when $z = re^{jt}$.]

Answer: $1 + \displaystyle\sum_{n=1}^{\infty} \dfrac{r^n}{n!} \cos nt.$

PROBLEM 1.36 Approximate the function $f(t) = t$ in the interval $(-\pi, \pi)$ with a finite Fourier series to five nonvanishing terms. Also, calculate the mean-square error in the approximation.

Answer: $2 \displaystyle\sum_{n=1}^{5} \left[\dfrac{(-1)^{n-1}}{n} \sin nt \right], \quad E_5 = 0.363.$

PROBLEM 1.37 Using the Fourier series expansion of Prob. 1.10, show that

$$\frac{\pi}{4} = 1 - \frac{1}{3} + \frac{1}{5} - \frac{1}{7} + \cdots .$$

[Hint: Set $t = \dfrac{1}{4} T$ in (1.34).]

PROBLEM 1.38 Prove that

$$\sum_{n=1}^{\infty} \frac{1}{n^2} = 1 + \frac{1}{4} + \frac{1}{9} + \frac{1}{16} + \cdots = \frac{\pi^2}{6} .$$

[Hint: Set $t = \pi$ in the result of Prob. 1.31.]

PROBLEM 1.39 Find the sum $\displaystyle\sum_{n=1}^{\infty} \dfrac{1}{(2n-1)^2}.$
[Hint: Set $t = 0$ in (1.40) of Prob. 1.11.]

Answer: $\pi^2/8.$

PROBLEM 1.40 If the periodic function $f(t)$ has continuous derivatives up to order k and a piecewise continuous derivative of order $k + 1$, show that there exists a bound B dependent only on $f(t)$ and k such that

$$|a_n| < \frac{B}{n^{k+1}} \quad \text{and} \quad |b_n| < \frac{B}{n^{k+1}} ,$$

where a_n and b_n are the Fourier coefficients of $f(t)$.

PROBLEM 1.41 Let $f(t)$ and $g(t)$ be piecewise continuous with period T, and let a_n, b_n and α_n, β_n be the respective Fourier coefficients of $f(t)$ and $g(t)$. Show that

$$\frac{2}{T} \int_{-T/2}^{T/2} f(t)\, g(t)\, dt = \frac{1}{2} a_0 \alpha_0 + \sum_{n=1}^{\infty} (a_n \alpha_n + b_n \beta_n).$$

PROBLEM 1.42 If $f(t)$ is an integrable periodic function with period T, show that

$$\frac{1}{T}\int_0^T f(t)\left(\frac{T}{2} - t\right) dt = \sum_{n=1}^{\infty} \frac{b_n}{n\omega_0} \, ,$$

where b_n is a Fourier coefficient of $f(t)$ and $\omega_0 = 2\pi/T$.

[Hint: Expand $\left(\frac{1}{2}T - t\right)$ for $0 < t < T$ in Fourier series.]

PROBLEM 1.43 Integrate the Fourier series for t^2 in Prob. 1.31 to obtain

$$\sum_{n=1}^{\infty} (-1)^n \frac{\sin nt}{n^3} = \frac{1}{12} t(t^2 - \pi) \qquad \text{and} \qquad \sum_{n=1}^{\infty} \frac{1}{n^6} = \frac{\pi^6}{945} \, .$$

PROBLEM 1.44 Use Parseval's theorem (1.72) to prove that $\displaystyle\sum_{n=1}^{\infty} \frac{1}{(2n-1)^2} = \frac{\pi^2}{8}$.

[Hint: Use the result of Prob. 1.10.]

PROBLEM 1.45 A set of infinite real functions $\{\phi_n(t)\}$, where $n = 1, 2, \cdots$, is said to be an *orthonormal* set on the interval (a, b) if

$$\int_a^b \phi_n(t)\phi_m(t)\, dt = \delta_{mn} \, ,$$

where δ_{mn} is the Kronecker's delta. Let $f(t)$ be a function defined on the interval (a, b) and suppose that $f(t)$ can be represented as

$$f(t) = c_1\phi_1(t) + c_2\phi_2(t) + \cdots + c_n\phi_n(t) + \cdots = \sum_{n=1}^{\infty} c_n\phi_n(t)$$

on (a, b) everywhere, where c_n are constants. Show that

$$c_n = \int_a^b f(t)\phi_n(t)\, dt, \quad n = 1, 2, \cdots .$$

The coefficients c_n are called the *Fourier coefficients of $f(t)$ with respect to the orthonormal set $\{\phi_n(t)\}$.*

PROBLEM 1.46 If $f(t)$ of Prob. 1.45 is approximated by $f_k(t) = \displaystyle\sum_{n=1}^{k} c_n\phi_n(t)$, show that the mean-square error $\displaystyle\frac{1}{b-a}\int_a^b [f(t) - f_k(t)]^2\, dt$ is a minimum.

PROBLEM 1.47 Show that if c_n are the Fourier coefficients of $f(t)$ with respect to the orthonormal set $\{\phi_n(t)\}$, then

$$\int_a^b [f(t)]^2\, dt = \sum_{n=1}^{\infty} c_n^2 \, .$$

This is known as *Parseval's identity.*

2 | ANALYSIS OF PERIODIC WAVEFORMS

CHAPTER

2.1 Waveform Symmetry

We saw in Chap. 1 that any periodic function $f(t)$ with period T which satisfies the Dirichlet conditions, i.e., the function $f(t)$ is piecewise continuous and integrable over any interval, can be represented in terms of a Fourier series

$$f(t) = \frac{1}{2} a_0 + \sum_{n=1}^{\infty} (a_n \cos n\omega_0 t + b_n \sin n\omega_0 t), \qquad (2.1)$$

where $\omega_0 = 2\pi/T$.

In this chapter we shall discuss the effect of waveform symmetry in a Fourier series, and the use of impulses for computation of Fourier series of some waveforms.

2.1a Even and Odd Functions

A function $f(t)$ is said to be *even* when it satisfies the condition

$$f(-t) = f(t), \qquad (2.2)$$

and it is said to be *odd* if

$$f(-t) = -f(t). \qquad (2.3)$$

Illustrations of even and odd functions are shown in Fig. 2.1.

It is noted that an even function is symmetrical about the vertical axis at the origin. On the other hand, an odd function is antisymmetrical about the vertical axis at the origin. We shall now derive some properties of even and odd functions.

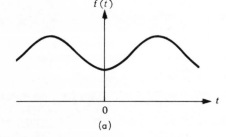

(a)

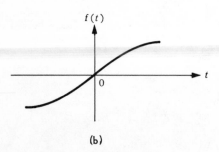

(b)

Fig. 2.1 (a) An even function.
(b) An odd function.

PROBLEM 2.1 Show that the product of two even or of two odd functions is an even function, and the product of an even and an odd function is an odd function.

Solution: Let $f(t) = f_1(t) f_2(t)$. If $f_1(t)$ and $f_2(t)$ are even functions, then

$$f(-t) = f_1(-t) f_2(-t) = f_1(t) f_2(t) = f(t),$$

and if $f_1(t)$ and $f_2(t)$ are odd functions, then

$$f(-t) = f_1(-t) f_2(-t) = -f_1(t) [-f_2(t)] = f_1(t) f_2(t) = f(t).$$

This proves that $f(t)$ is an even function.

Similarly, if $f_1(t)$ is even and $f_2(t)$ is odd, then

$$f(-t) = f_1(-t) f_2(-t) = f_1(t) [-f_2(t)] = -f_1(t) f_2(t) = -f(t).$$

This proves that $f(t)$ is an odd function.

PROBLEM 2.2 Show that any function $f(t)$ can be expressed as the sum of two component functions of which one is even and the other is odd.

Solution: Any function $f(t)$ can be expressed as

$$f(t) = \frac{1}{2}f(t) + \frac{1}{2}f(-t) + \frac{1}{2}f(t) - \frac{1}{2}f(-t)$$

$$= \frac{1}{2}[f(t) + f(-t)] + \frac{1}{2}[f(t) - f(-t)]. \qquad (2.4)$$

Let

$$\frac{1}{2}[f(t) + f(-t)] = f_e(t), \qquad (2.5)$$

$$\frac{1}{2}[f(t) - f(-t)] = f_o(t). \qquad (2.6)$$

Then,

$$f_e(-t) = \frac{1}{2}[f(-t) + f(t)] = f_e(t),$$

$$f_o(-t) = \frac{1}{2}[f(-t) - f(t)] = -\frac{1}{2}[f(t) - f(-t)] = -f_o(t).$$

Hence,

$$f(t) = f_e(t) + f_o(t),$$

where $f_e(t)$ is the even component of a given function $f(t)$, and $f_o(t)$ is the odd component of $f(t)$.

Alternate Solution: Let us assume that $f(t)$ can be expressed as

$$f(t) = f_e(t) + f_o(t), \qquad (2.7)$$

where $f_e(t)$ and $f_o(t)$ denote the even and odd components of $f(t)$, respectively. According to the definition of even and odd functions given by (2.2) and (2.3), it follows that

$$f(-t) = f_e(t) - f_o(t). \qquad (2.8)$$

Addition and subtraction of (2.7) and (2.8) yield, respectively,

$$f_e(t) = \frac{1}{2}[f(t) + f(-t)],$$

$$f_o(t) = \frac{1}{2}[f(t) - f(-t)].$$

PROBLEM 2.3 Find the even and odd components of the function defined by [Fig. 2.2(a)]:

$$f(t) = \begin{cases} e^{-t}, & t > 0 \\ 0, & t < 0. \end{cases} \qquad (2.9)$$

Solution: From (2.9),

$$f(-t) = \begin{cases} 0, & t > 0 \\ e^{t}, & t < 0. \end{cases} \qquad (2.10)$$

Hence by means of (2.5) and (2.6),

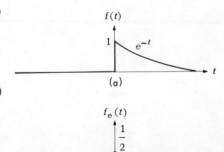

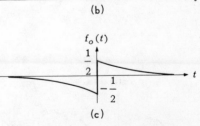

Fig. 2.2 (a) The function $f(t)$ of Prob. 2.3 (b) The even component of Fig. 2.2(a). (c) The odd component of Fig. 2.2(a).

$$f_e(t) = \frac{1}{2}[f(t) + f(-t)] = \begin{cases} \dfrac{1}{2}e^{-t}, & t > 0 \\[2mm] \dfrac{1}{2}e^{t}, & t < 0, \end{cases} \tag{2.11}$$

$$f_o(t) = \frac{1}{2}[f(t) - f(-t)] = \begin{cases} \dfrac{1}{2}e^{-t}, & t > 0 \\[2mm] -\dfrac{1}{2}e^{t}, & t < 0. \end{cases} \tag{2.12}$$

The even and odd components of $f(t)$ are shown in Figs. 2.2(b-c).

PROBLEM 2.4   If $f(t)$ is even, then show that

$$\int_{-a}^{a} f(t)\, dt = 2 \int_{0}^{a} f(t)\, dt. \tag{2.13}$$

Solution: Rewriting the left-hand side of (2.13),

$$\int_{-a}^{a} f(t)\, dt = \int_{-a}^{0} f(t)\, dt + \int_{0}^{a} f(t)\, dt.$$

Letting $t = -x$ in the first integral of the right side,

$$\int_{-a}^{0} f(t)\, dt = \int_{a}^{0} f(-x)\,(-dx) = \int_{0}^{a} f(-x)\, dx.$$

Since $f(t)$ is even, i.e., $f(-x) = f(x)$,

$$\int_{0}^{a} f(-x)\, dx = \int_{0}^{a} f(x)\, dx = \int_{0}^{a} f(t)\, dt.$$

This is true because any symbol may be used to represent the "dummy" variable. Hence,

$$\int_{-a}^{a} f(t)\, dt = \int_{0}^{a} f(t)\, dt + \int_{0}^{a} f(t)\, dt = 2 \int_{0}^{a} f(t)\, dt.$$

PROBLEM 2.5   If $f(t)$ is odd, then show that

$$\int_{-a}^{a} f(t)\, dt = 0, \tag{2.14}$$

$$f(0) = 0. \tag{2.15}$$

Solution: Rewriting the left-hand side of (2.14),

$$\int_{-a}^{a} f(t)\, dt = \int_{-a}^{0} f(t)\, dt + \int_{0}^{a} f(t)\, dt$$

$$= \int_{0}^{a} f(-t)\, dt + \int_{0}^{a} f(t)\, dt.$$

Since $f(t)$ is odd, i.e., $f(-t) = -f(t)$,

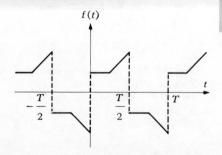

Fig. 2.3 Half-wave symmetry.

$$\int_{-a}^{a} f(t)\, dt = -\int_{0}^{a} f(t)\, dt + \int_{0}^{a} f(t)\, dt = 0.$$

In particular,

$$f(-0) = -f(0);$$

hence,

$$f(0) = 0.$$

2.1b Half-Wave Symmetry

If a function $f(t)$ is periodic with period T, then the periodic function $f(t)$ is said to have *half-wave symmetry* when it satisfies the condition

$$f(t) = -f\left(t + \frac{1}{2}T\right). \tag{2.16}$$

A waveform with half-wave symmetry is shown in Fig. 2.3. Note that the negative portion of the wave is the mirror image of the positive portion of the wave, displaced horizontally by a half period.

PROBLEM 2.6 If a periodic function $f(t)$ is half-wave symmetric, then show that

$$f(t) = -f\left(t - \frac{1}{2}T\right). \tag{2.17}$$

Solution: If $f(t)$ is half-wave symmetric, then, from (2.16),

$$f(t) = -f\left(t + \frac{1}{2}T\right).$$

Since $f(t)$ is periodic with period T,

$$f\left(t - \frac{1}{2}T\right) = f\left(t + T - \frac{1}{2}T\right) = f\left(t + \frac{1}{2}T\right).$$

Hence,

$$f(t) = -f\left(t + \frac{1}{2}T\right) = -f\left(t - \frac{1}{2}T\right).$$

2.1c Quarter-Wave Symmetry

If a periodic function $f(t)$ has half-wave symmetry and, in addition, is either an even or odd function, then $f(t)$ is said to have *even* or *odd quarter-wave symmetry*. Figure 2.4 illustrates waveforms with quarter-wave symmetry.

2.1d Hidden Symmetry

Often the symmetry of a periodic function is obscured by a constant term. The following example illustrates this point.

PROBLEM 2.7 In Fig. 2.5(a), show that if we construct a new function by subtracting a constant $A/2$ from $f(t)$, the new function is an odd function.

Solution: The subtraction of a constant $A/2$ from $f(t)$ merely shifts the horizontal axis upward by the amount $A/2$. As shown in Fig. 2.5(b), it is obvious that the new function $g(t) = f(t) - A/2$ is an odd function.

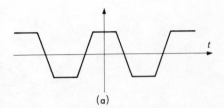
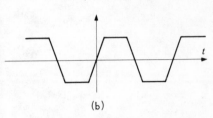

Fig. 2.4 (a) Even quarter-wave symmetry. (b) Odd quarter-wave symmetry.

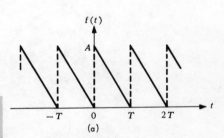

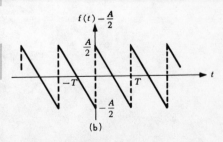

Fig. 2.5 (a) Hidden symmetry. (b) Odd symmetry.

2.2 Fourier Coefficients of Symmetrical Waveforms

The use of symmetry properties simplifies the calculation of Fourier coefficients.

PROBLEM 2.8 If $f(t)$ is an even periodic function with period T, then show that its Fourier series consists of a constant and cosine terms only; i.e.,

$$f(t) = \frac{1}{2} a_0 + \sum_{n=1}^{\infty} a_n \cos n\omega_0 t, \qquad (2.18)$$

where

$$\omega_0 = \frac{2\pi}{T},$$

and a_n is given by

$$a_n = \frac{4}{T} \int_0^{T/2} f(t) \cos (n\omega_0 t)\, dt. \qquad (2.19)$$

Solution: Fourier series expansion of $f(t)$ is

$$f(t) = \frac{1}{2} a_0 + \sum_{n=1}^{\infty} (a_n \cos n\omega_0 t + b_n \sin n\omega_0 t).$$

From (1.27) and (1.28),

$$a_n = \frac{2}{T} \int_{-T/2}^{T/2} f(t) \cos (n\omega_0 t)\, dt, \quad n = 0, 1, 2, \cdots,$$

$$b_n = \frac{2}{T} \int_{-T/2}^{T/2} f(t) \sin (n\omega_0 t)\, dt, \quad n = 1, 2, \cdots.$$

Since $\sin n\omega_0 t$ is odd and $f(t)$ is even, the product $f(t) \sin n\omega_0 t$ is an odd function. Hence, according to (2.14),

$$b_n = 0.$$

Also since $\cos n\omega_0 t$ is an even function, the product $f(t) \cos n\omega_0 t$ is an even function. Hence, from (2.13),

$$a_n = \frac{4}{T} \int_0^{T/2} f(t) \cos (n\omega_0 t)\, dt.$$

PROBLEM 2.9 If $f(t)$ is an odd periodic function with period T, then show that its Fourier series consists of sine terms only; i.e.,

$$f(t) = \sum_{n=1}^{\infty} b_n \sin n\omega_0 t, \qquad (2.20)$$

where

$$\omega_0 = \frac{2\pi}{T},$$

and b_n is given by

$$b_n = \frac{4}{T} \int_0^{T/2} f(t) \sin (n\omega_0 t) \, dt. \tag{2.21}$$

Solution: Since $f(t)$ is an odd function, the product $f(t) \cos n\omega_0 t$ is an odd function, and the product $f(t) \sin n\omega_0 t$ is an even function. Hence according to (2.13) and (2.14),

$$a_n = 0, \qquad b_n = \frac{4}{T} \int_0^{T/2} f(t) \sin (n\omega_0 t) \, dt.$$

PROBLEM 2.10 Show that the Fourier series of any periodic function $f(t)$ which has half-wave symmetry contains only odd harmonics.

Solution: The coefficient a_n in the Fourier expansion of a periodic function $f(t)$ is

$$a_n = \frac{2}{T} \int_{-T/2}^{T/2} f(t) \cos (n\omega_0 t) \, dt$$

$$= \frac{2}{T} \left[\int_{-T/2}^0 f(t) \cos (n\omega_0 t) \, dt + \int_0^{T/2} f(t) \cos (n\omega_0 t) \, dt \right].$$

Changing the variable t to $(t - \frac{1}{2} T)$ in the first integral,

$$a_n = \frac{2}{T} \left\{ \int_0^{T/2} f\left(t - \frac{1}{2} T\right) \cos \left[n\omega_0 \left(t - \frac{1}{2} T\right) \right] \, dt \right.$$

$$\left. + \int_0^{T/2} f(t) \cos (n\omega_0 t) \, dt \right\}. \tag{2.22}$$

Since $f(t)$ has half-wave symmetry, using the property $f(t) = -f(t - \frac{1}{2} T)$ from (2.17) and the fact that $\sin n\pi = 0$,

$$a_n = \frac{2}{T} \int_0^{T/2} [-f(t) \cos (n\omega_0 t) \cos n\pi + f(t) \cos (n\omega_0 t)] \, dt$$

$$= \frac{2}{T} [1 - (-1)^n] \int_0^{T/2} f(t) \cos (n\omega_0 t) \, dt$$

$$= \begin{cases} 0 & \text{for } n \text{ even} \\ \dfrac{4}{T} \displaystyle\int_0^{T/2} f(t) \cos (n\omega_0 t) \, dt & \text{for } n \text{ odd}. \end{cases} \tag{2.23}$$

A similar investigation shows that

$$b_n = \begin{cases} 0 & \text{for } n \text{ even} \\ \dfrac{4}{T} \displaystyle\int_0^{T/2} f(t) \sin (n\omega_0 t) \, dt & \text{for } n \text{ odd}. \end{cases} \tag{2.24}$$

PROBLEM 2.11 Show that the Fourier series of any periodic function $f(t)$ which has even quarter-wave symmetry consists of odd harmonics of cosine terms only; i.e.,

$$f(t) = \sum_{n=1}^{\infty} a_{2n-1} \cos [(2n-1) \omega_0 t], \tag{2.25}$$

where

$$\omega_0 = \frac{2\pi}{T},$$

$$a_{2n-1} = \frac{8}{T} \int_0^{T/4} f(t) \cos \left[(2n-1)\,\omega_0 t\right] dt. \tag{2.26}$$

Solution: Since $f(t)$ has even quarter-wave symmetry,

$$f(t) = f(-t),$$

$$f\left(t + \frac{1}{2} T\right) = -f(t).$$

Hence from the results of Probs. 2.8 and 2.10,

$$\left.\begin{array}{l} b_n = 0 \\[4pt] a_{2n} = 0 \end{array}\right\} \text{ for all } n \text{ (including } a_0), \tag{2.27}$$

$$a_{2n-1} = \frac{4}{T} \int_0^{T/2} f(t) \cos \left[(2n-1)\,\omega_0 t\right] dt$$

$$= \frac{4}{T} \left\{\int_0^{T/4} f(t) \cos \left[(2n-1)\,\omega_0 t\right] dt \right.$$

$$\left. + \int_{T/4}^{T/2} f(t) \cos \left[(2n-1)\,\omega_0 t\right] dt\right\}. \tag{2.28}$$

Changing the variable t to $(t + \frac{1}{2} T)$ in the second integral,

$$a_{2n-1} = \frac{4}{T} \left\{\int_0^{T/4} f(t) \cos \left[(2n-1)\,\omega_0 t\right] dt \right.$$

$$\left. + \int_{-T/4}^{0} f\left(t + \frac{1}{2} T\right) \cos \left[(2n-1)\omega_0 \left(t + \frac{1}{2} T\right)\right] dt\right\}. \tag{2.29}$$

Using the property $f(t) = -f(t + \frac{1}{2} T)$,

$$a_{2n-1} = \frac{4}{T} \left\{\int_0^{T/4} f(t) \cos\left[(2n-1)\omega_0 t\right] dt + \int_{-T/4}^{0} f(t) \cos \left[(2n-1)\,\omega_0 t\right] dt\right\}$$

$$= \frac{4}{T} \int_{-T/4}^{T/4} f(t) \cos \left[(2n-1)\,\omega_0 t\right] dt. \tag{2.30}$$

Since $f(-t) = f(t)$ and $f(t) \cos \left[(2n-1)\omega_0 t\right]$ is even, we obtain from (2.13),

$$a_{2n-1} = \frac{8}{T} \int_0^{T/4} f(t) \cos \left[(2n-1)\omega_0 t\right] dt.$$

PROBLEM 2.12   Show that the Fourier series of any periodic function $f(t)$ which has odd quarter-wave symmetry consists of odd harmonics of sine terms only; i.e.,

$$f(t) = \sum_{n-1}^{\infty} b_{2n-1} \sin\left[(2n-1)\,\omega_0 t\right], \tag{2.31}$$

where $\omega_0 = \dfrac{2\pi}{T}$, and

$$b_{2n-1} = \frac{8}{T} \int_0^{T/4} f(t)\,\sin\left[(2n-1)\,\omega_0 t\right]\,dt. \tag{2.32}$$

Solution: Since $f(t)$ has odd quarter-wave symmetry,

$$f(-t) = -f(t) \qquad \text{and} \qquad f\left(t + \frac{1}{2}\,T\right) = -f(t).$$

Hence, from the results of Probs. 2.9 and 2.10,

$$\left.\begin{array}{l} a_n = 0 \\[1em] b_{2n} = 0 \end{array}\right\} \text{ for all } n \text{ (including } a_0\text{)}, \tag{2.33}$$

$$b_{2n-1} = \frac{4}{T} \int_0^{T/2} f(t)\,\sin\left[(2n-1)\,\omega_0 t\right]\,dt. \tag{2.34}$$

Evaluating this integral as in Prob. 2.11,

$$b_{2n-1} = \frac{8}{T} \int_0^{T/4} f(t)\,\sin\left[(2n-1)\,\omega_0 t\right]\,dt.$$

PROBLEM 2.13   Find the Fourier series for the square wave function $f(t)$ shown in Fig. 2.6.

Solution: From Fig. 2.6,

$$f(-t) = f(t) \qquad \text{and} \qquad f\left(t + \frac{1}{2}\,T\right) = -f(t),$$

i.e., the function $f(t)$ has even quarter-wave symmetry.

Hence, from the result of Prob. 2.11,

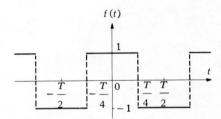

Fig. 2.6 The square wave function of Prob. 2.13.

$$f(t) = \sum_{n=1}^{\infty} a_{2n-1} \cos\left[(2n-1)\,\omega_0 t\right], \qquad \omega_0 = \frac{2\pi}{T}, \tag{2.35}$$

$$a_{2n-1} = \frac{8}{T} \int_0^{T/4} f(t)\,\cos\left[(2n-1)\,\omega_0 t\right]\,dt$$

$$= \frac{8}{T} \int_0^{T/4} \cos\left[(2n-1)\,\omega_0 t\right]\,dt$$

$$= \frac{8}{(2n-1)\,\omega_0 T} \sin\left[(2n-1)\,\omega_0 t\right]\Bigg|_0^{T/4}$$

$$= \frac{4}{(2n-1)\,\pi} \sin\left[(2n-1)\,\frac{\pi}{2}\right]$$

$$= \begin{cases} \dfrac{4}{(2n-1)\,\pi} & \text{for } (2n-1) = 1,5,\cdots \tag{2.36} \\[1.5em] \dfrac{-4}{(2n-1)\,\pi} & \text{for } (2n-1) = 3,7,\cdots. \tag{2.37} \end{cases}$$

Hence,

$$f(t) = \frac{4}{\pi}\left(\cos \omega_0 t - \frac{1}{3}\cos 3\omega_0 t + \frac{1}{5}\cos 5\omega_0 t - \cdots\right). \tag{2.38}$$

PROBLEM 2.14 Find the Fourier series for the square wave function $f(t)$ shown in Fig. 2.7.

Solution: From Fig. 2.7,

$$f(-t) = -f(t),$$

$$f\left(t + \frac{1}{2}T\right) = -f(t),$$

i.e., the function $f(t)$ has odd quarter-wave symmetry.

Hence, from the result of Prob. 2.12,

$$f(t) = \sum_{n=1}^{\infty} b_{2n-1}\sin\left[(2n-1)\,\omega_0 t\right], \qquad \omega_0 = \frac{2\pi}{T}\,, \tag{2.39}$$

$$b_{2n-1} = \frac{8}{T}\int_0^{T/4} f(t)\sin\left[(2n-1)\,\omega_0 t\right]\,dt$$

$$= \frac{8}{T}\int_0^{T/4}\sin\left[(2n-1)\,\omega_0 t\right]\,dt$$

$$= \frac{-8}{(2n-1)\,\omega_0 T}\cos\left[(2n-1)\,\omega_0 t\right]\Big|_0^{T/4}$$

$$= \frac{4}{(2n-1)\,\pi}\left\{1 - \cos\left[(2n-1)\,\frac{\pi}{2}\right]\right\}$$

$$= \frac{4}{(2n-1)\,\pi}. \tag{2.40}$$

Hence,

$$f(t) = \frac{4}{\pi}\left(\sin \omega_0 t + \frac{1}{3}\sin 3\omega_0 t + \frac{1}{5}\sin 5\omega_0 t + \cdots\right). \tag{2.41}$$

Note that this is the same result as in Prob. 1.10.

From Probs. 2.13 and 2.14, we note that by a suitable choice of origin (i.e., time displacement), we can expand the function either as a cosine series or as a sine series. The origin can, of course, be chosen anywhere, yielding in general a series containing both sine and cosine terms.

PROBLEM 2.15 Find the Fourier series for the function $f(t)$ shown in Fig. 2.8(a).

Solution: As shown in Fig. 2.8(b), the function $g(t) = \left[f(t) - \frac{1}{2}\right]$ is an odd function; hence,

$$g(t) = \sum_{n=1}^{\infty} b_n\sin n\omega_0 t, \qquad \omega_0 = \frac{2\pi}{T}, \tag{2.42}$$

$$b_n = \frac{2}{T}\int_{-T/2}^{T/2} g(t)\sin(n\omega_0 t)\,dt. \tag{2.43}$$

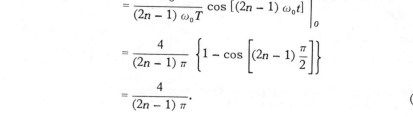

$f(t)$

1

$-\dfrac{T}{2}$ $-\dfrac{T}{4}$ $\dfrac{T}{4}$ $\dfrac{T}{2}$ T

-1

Fig. 2.7 The square wave function of Prob. 2.14.

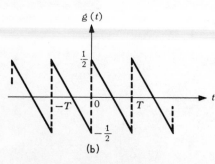

$f(t)$

1

$-T$ $\quad 0 \quad$ T $\qquad t$

(a)

$g(t)$

$\dfrac{1}{2}$

$-T$ $\quad 0 \quad$ T $\qquad t$

$-\dfrac{1}{2}$

(b)

Fig. 2.8 (a) The function $f(t)$ of Prob. 2.15. (b) The odd component of $f(t)$ of Fig. 2.8(a).

Since $g(t) \sin n\omega_0 t$ is an even function, from (2.13),

$$b_n = \frac{4}{T} \int_0^{T/2} g(t) \sin (n\omega_0 t) \, dt. \qquad (2.44)$$

Now

$$g(t) = \frac{1}{2} - \frac{1}{T} t \quad \text{for } 0 < t < T \, ;$$

then,

$$b_n = \frac{4}{T} \int_0^{T/2} \left(\frac{1}{2} - \frac{1}{T} t \right) \sin (n\omega_0 t) \, dt.$$

Integrating by parts,

$$b_n = \frac{4}{T} \left[-\left(\frac{1}{2} - \frac{1}{T} t \right) \frac{\cos n\omega_0 t}{n\omega_0} - \frac{\sin n\omega_0 t}{T(n\omega_0)^2} \right]\Bigg|_0^{T/2} = \frac{1}{n\pi}. \qquad (2.45)$$

Hence,

$$f(t) = \frac{1}{2} + g(t)$$

$$= \frac{1}{2} + \frac{1}{\pi} \sum_{n=1}^{\infty} \frac{1}{n} \sin n\omega_0 t$$

$$= \frac{1}{2} + \frac{1}{\pi} \left(\sin \omega_0 t + \frac{1}{2} \sin 2\omega_0 t + \frac{1}{3} \sin 3\omega_0 t + \cdots \right). \qquad (2.46)$$

PROBLEM 2.16   Using the result of Prob. 2.15, find the Fourier series for the function $f(t)$ shown in Fig. 2.9(a).

Solution: From Fig. 2.9(b) and the result of Prob. 2.15,

$$f_1(t) = 1 - f(t) = \frac{1}{2} + \frac{1}{\pi} \sum_{n=1}^{\infty} \frac{1}{n} \sin n\omega_0 t. \qquad (2.47)$$

Hence,

$$f(t) = 1 - f_1(t)$$

$$= 1 - \frac{1}{2} - \frac{1}{\pi} \sum_{n=1}^{\infty} \frac{1}{n} \sin n\omega_0 t$$

$$= \frac{1}{2} - \frac{1}{\pi} \left(\sin \omega_0 t + \frac{1}{2} \sin 2\omega_0 t + \frac{1}{3} \sin 3\omega_0 t + \cdots \right). \qquad (2.48)$$

2.3 Fourier Expansion of a Function Over a Finite Interval

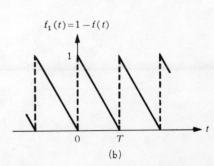

Fig. 2.9 (a) The function $f(t)$ of Prob. 2.16. (b) The function $f_1(t)$ of Prob. 2.16.

A nonperiodic function $f(t)$ defined over a certain finite interval $(0, \tau)$ can be expanded into a Fourier series which is defined only in the interval $(0, \tau)$. It is possible to expand $f(t)$ by a Fourier series with any desired fundamental frequency. Furthermore, $f(t)$ can be represented by sine or cosine terms alone. This can be done by constructing a proper periodic function which will be identical to $f(t)$ over the interval $(0, \tau)$, and satisfying such symmetry conditions as to yield the desired form of Fourier series. This is illustrated in Fig. 2.10.

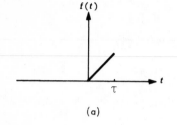

(a)

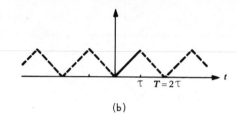

(b)

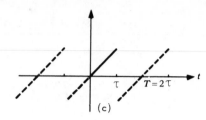

(c)

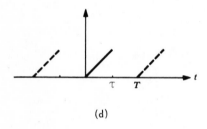

(d)

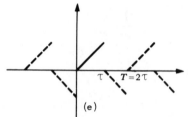

(e)

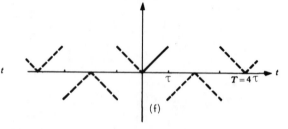

(f)

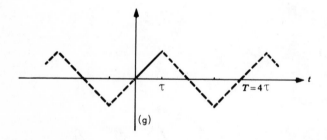

(g)

Fig. 2.10 (a) Given $f(t)$. (b) Even symmetry: cosine terms, $\omega_0 = \pi/\tau$. (c) Odd symmetry: sine terms, $\omega_0 = \pi/\tau$. (d) Sine and cosine terms, $\omega_0 = 2\pi/T$ (T: arbitrary). (e) Half-wave symmetry: sine and cosine terms, and odd harmonics, $\omega_0 = \pi/\tau$. (f) Even quarter-wave symmetry: cosine terms and odd harmonics, $\omega_0 = \pi/(2\tau)$. (g) Odd quarter-wave symmetry: sine terms and odd harmonics, $\omega_0 = \pi/(2\tau)$.

2.3a Half-Range Expansions

Let $f(t)$ have period $T = 2\tau$. If $f(t)$ is even, then from (2.18) and (2.19), we obtain the Fourier cosine series

$$f(t) = \frac{1}{2} a_0 + \sum_{n=1}^{\infty} a_n \cos \frac{n\pi}{\tau} t \qquad (2.49)$$

with coefficients

$$a_n = \frac{2}{\tau} \int_0^{\tau} f(t) \cos \left(\frac{n\pi}{\tau} t \right) dt. \qquad (2.50)$$

If $f(t)$ is odd, then from (2.20) and (2.21), we have the Fourier sine series

$$f(t) = \sum_{n=1}^{\infty} b_n \sin \frac{n\pi}{\tau} t \qquad (2.51)$$

with

$$b_n = \frac{2}{\tau} \int_0^{\tau} f(t) \sin \left(\frac{n\pi}{\tau} t \right) dt. \qquad (2.52)$$

Both series, (2.49) and (2.51), represent the same given function $f(t)$ in the interval $(0, \tau)$. Outside this interval, the series (2.49) will represent the even periodic extension of $f(t)$ having period $T = 2\tau$ [Fig. 2.10(b)], and (2.51) will represent the odd periodic extension of $f(t)$ having period $T = 2\tau$ [Fig. 2.10(c)]. The series (2.49) and (2.51) with coefficients given by (2.50) and (2.52) are called the *half-range expansions* of the given function $f(t)$.

PROBLEM 2.17   Given the function (Fig. 2.11)

$$f(t) = \begin{cases} 0 & \text{for} \quad 0 < t < \frac{1}{2}\pi \\ \\ 1 & \text{for} \quad \frac{1}{2}\pi < t < \pi, \end{cases} \tag{2.53}$$

expand $f(t)$ in a Fourier cosine series and draw the corresponding periodic extension of $f(t)$.

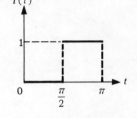

Fig. 2.11   The function $f(t)$ of Prob. 2.17.

Solution: The graph of the even periodic extension of $f_e(t)$ is shown in Fig. 2.12. Since $f(t)$ is extended to be even,

$$b_n = 0, \qquad n = 1, 2, \cdots.$$

From (2.50),

$$a_n = \frac{2}{\pi} \int_0^\pi f(t) \cos(nt)\, dt = \frac{2}{\pi} \int_{\pi/2}^\pi \cos(nt)\, dt$$

$$= \frac{2}{n\pi} \sin nt \Big|_{\pi/2}^\pi$$

$$= -\frac{2}{n\pi} \sin \frac{n\pi}{2}; \tag{2.54}$$

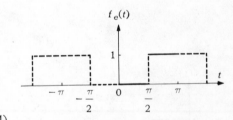

Fig. 2.12   The even periodic extension of $f(t)$ of Fig. 2.11.

that is,

$$a_n = \begin{cases} 0, & n \text{ even } (n \neq 0) \\ \\ -\dfrac{2}{n\pi}, & n = 1, 5, \cdots \\ \\ \dfrac{2}{n\pi}, & n = 3, 7, \cdots. \end{cases}$$

For $n = 0$,

$$a_0 = \frac{2}{\pi} \int_{\pi/2}^\pi dt = 1. \tag{2.55}$$

Thus,

$$f_e(t) = \frac{1}{2} - \frac{2}{\pi} \left(\cos t - \frac{1}{3} \cos 3t + \frac{1}{5} \cos 5t - \cdots \right) \tag{2.56}$$

for $0 < t < \pi$.

PROBLEM 2.18   Expand $f(t)$ of (2.53) in a Fourier sine series and draw the corresponding periodic extension of $f(t)$.

Solution: The graph of the odd periodic extension of $f_o(t)$ is shown in Fig. 2.13.

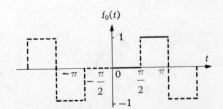

Fig. 2.13   The odd periodic extension of $f(t)$ of Fig. 2.11.

Since $f(t)$ is extended to be odd,

$$a_n = 0, \quad n = 0,1,2,\cdots.$$

From (2.52),

$$b_n = \frac{2}{\pi} \int_0^\pi f(t) \sin(nt)\, dt$$

$$= \frac{2}{\pi} \int_{\pi/2}^\pi \sin(nt)\, dt$$

$$= -\frac{2}{n\pi} \cos nt \bigg|_{\pi/2}^\pi$$

$$= -\frac{2}{n\pi} \left(\cos n\pi - \cos \frac{1}{2} n\pi\right); \qquad (2.57)$$

that is,

$$b_n = \begin{cases} \dfrac{2}{n\pi}, & n = 1,3,5,\cdots \\[2ex] -\dfrac{4}{n\pi}, & n = 2,6,10,\cdots \\[2ex] 0, & n = 4,8,12,\cdots. \end{cases}$$

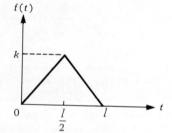

Fig. 2.14 The function $f(t)$ of Prob. 2.19.

Therefore,

$$f_o(t) = \frac{2}{\pi} \left(\sin t + \frac{1}{3} \sin 3t + \frac{1}{5} \sin 5t + \cdots\right)$$

$$- \frac{2}{\pi} \left(\sin 2t + \frac{1}{3} \sin 6t + \frac{1}{5} \sin 10t + \cdots\right) \qquad (2.58)$$

for $< 0 < t < \pi$.

PROBLEM 2.19 Given the function (Fig. 2.14)

$$f(t) = \begin{cases} \dfrac{2k}{l} t & \text{for } 0 < t < \dfrac{1}{2} l \\[2ex] \dfrac{2k}{l} (l - t) & \text{for } \dfrac{1}{2} l < t < l, \end{cases} \qquad (2.59)$$

expand $f(t)$ in a Fourier sine series.

Solution: The odd periodic extension of $f(t)$ is shown in Fig. 2.15.
Since $f(t)$ is extended to be odd,

$$a_n = 0, \quad n = 0,1,2,\cdots.$$

From (2.52),

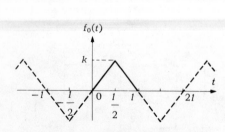

Fig. 2.15 The odd periodic extension of Fig. 2.14.

$$b_n = \frac{2}{l} \int_0^l f(t) \sin\left(\frac{n\pi}{l} t\right) dt$$

$$= \frac{2}{l} \left[\frac{2k}{l} \int_0^{l/2} t \sin\left(\frac{n\pi}{l} t\right) dt + \frac{2k}{l} \int_{l/2}^l (l - t) \sin\left(\frac{n\pi}{l} t\right) dt\right]. \qquad (2.60)$$

Now integrating by parts,

$$\int_0^{l/2} t \sin\left(\frac{n\pi}{l}t\right) dt = -\frac{lt}{n\pi}\cos\frac{n\pi}{l}t \Big|_0^{l/2} + \frac{l}{n\pi}\int_0^{l/2}\cos\left(\frac{n\pi}{l}t\right) dt$$

$$= -\frac{l^2}{2n\pi}\cos\frac{1}{2}n\pi + \frac{l^2}{n^2\pi^2}\sin\frac{1}{2}n\pi. \tag{2.61}$$

Similarly,

$$\int_{l/2}^l (l-t)\sin\left(\frac{n\pi}{l}t\right) dt = \frac{l^2}{2n\pi}\cos\frac{1}{2}n\pi + \frac{l^2}{n^2\pi^2}\sin\frac{1}{2}n\pi. \tag{2.62}$$

Substituting (2.61) and (2.62) in (2.60),

$$b_n = \frac{8k}{n^2\pi^2}\sin\frac{1}{2}n\pi. \tag{2.63}$$

Thus,

$$f(t) = \frac{8k}{\pi^2}\left(\sin\frac{\pi}{l}t - \frac{1}{3^2}\sin 3\frac{\pi}{l}t + \frac{1}{5^2}\sin 5\frac{\pi}{l}t - \cdots\right). \tag{2.64}$$

2.4 The Impulse Function

The *unit impulse function* $\delta(t)$, also known as the *delta function*, may be defined in many ways. Usually it is expressed by the relation

$$\delta(t) = \begin{cases} 0 & \text{if } t \neq 0, \\ \infty & \text{if } t = 0, \end{cases} \tag{2.65}$$

$$\int_{-\infty}^{\infty}\delta(t)\,dt = \int_{-\epsilon}^{\epsilon}\delta(t)\,dt = 1, \quad \epsilon > 0. \tag{2.66}$$

Equation (2.65) indicates that $\delta(t)$ is zero except at $t = 0$, where it becomes infinite in such a way that (2.66) is satisfied.

The delta function can also be defined in terms of its integral properties alone. This is the definition we shall use. In the following, $\delta(t)$ will be defined in the sense of a so-called *generalized* (or *symbolic*) *function*.

Now let the function $\phi(t)$ (which is called the *testing function*) be a continuous function and vanish identically outside some finite interval. Then the δ-function is defined as a symbolic function by the relation

$$\int_{-\infty}^{\infty}\delta(t)\,\phi(t)\,dt = \phi(0). \tag{2.67}$$

Expression (2.67) has no meaning as an ordinary integral. Instead, the integral and the function $\delta(t)$ are merely defined by the number $\phi(0)$ assigned to the function $\phi(t)$.

With the above understanding, it turns out that $\delta(t)$ can be handled as if it were an ordinary function except that we shall never talk about the value of $\delta(t)$. Instead, we talk about the values of integrals involving $\delta(t)$.

PROBLEM 2.20 Prove the following relations:

$$\int_{-\infty}^{\infty}\delta(t - t_0)\,\phi(t)\,dt = \int_{-\infty}^{\infty}\delta(t)\,\phi(t + t_0)\,dt = \phi(t_0), \tag{2.68}$$

$$\int_{-\infty}^{\infty} \delta(at)\phi(t)\, dt = \frac{1}{|a|} \int_{-\infty}^{\infty} \delta(t)\phi\left(\frac{t}{a}\right) dt = \frac{1}{|a|}\phi(0). \qquad (2.69)$$

Solution: With a formal change in the independent variable, i.e., $t - t_0 = \tau$, and hence, $t = \tau + t_0$, $dt = d\tau$,

$$\int_{-\infty}^{\infty} \delta(t - t_0)\phi(t)\, dt = \int_{-\infty}^{\infty} \delta(\tau)\phi(\tau + t_0)\, d\tau = \int_{-\infty}^{\infty} \delta(t)\phi(t + t_0)\, dt;$$

then, by (2.67),

$$\int_{-\infty}^{\infty} \delta(t)\phi(t + t_0)\, dt = \phi(t + t_0)\Big|_{t=0} = \phi(t_0).$$

Similarly, with $at = \tau$, $t = \tau/a$, $dt = \frac{1}{a}d\tau$, we have if $a > 0$,

$$\int_{-\infty}^{\infty} \delta(at)\phi(t)\, dt = \frac{1}{a} \int_{-\infty}^{\infty} \delta(\tau)\phi\left(\frac{\tau}{a}\right) d\tau$$

$$= \frac{1}{a} \int_{-\infty}^{\infty} \delta(t)\phi\left(\frac{t}{a}\right) dt = \frac{1}{a}\phi\left(\frac{t}{a}\right)\Big|_{t=0}$$

$$= \frac{1}{|a|}\phi(0);$$

if $a < 0$,

$$\int_{-\infty}^{\infty} \delta(at)\phi(t)\, dt = \frac{1}{a} \int_{\infty}^{-\infty} \delta(\tau)\phi\left(\frac{\tau}{a}\right) d\tau$$

$$= \frac{1}{-a} \int_{-\infty}^{\infty} \delta(t)\phi\left(\frac{t}{a}\right) dt$$

$$= \frac{1}{|a|}\phi(0).$$

PROBLEM 2.21   Consider a function $g(t)$ continuous at $t = t_0$. If $a < b$, then show that

$$\int_{a}^{b} \delta(t - t_0)g(t)\, dt = \begin{cases} g(t_0) & \text{for } a < t_0 < b \\[2mm] 0 & \text{for } b < t_0 < a. \end{cases} \qquad (2.70)$$

Solution: Here the expression

$$\int_{a}^{b} \delta(t - t_0)g(t)\, dt$$

will be interpreted as follows: If we select the testing function $\phi(t)$ such that

$$\phi(t) = \begin{cases} g(t) & \text{for } a < t < b \\[2mm] 0 & \text{for } b < t_0 < a, \end{cases} \qquad (2.71)$$

then, from (2.68),

$$\int_{a}^{b} \delta(t - t_0)g(t)\, dt = \int_{-\infty}^{\infty} \delta(t - t_0)\phi(t)\, dt = \phi(t_0) = \begin{cases} g(t_0) & \text{for } a < t_0 < b \\[2mm] 0 & \text{for } b < t_0 < a. \end{cases}$$

PROBLEM 2.22 If $a < b$, show that

$$\int_a^b \delta(t - t_0)\, dt = \begin{cases} 1 & \text{for } a < t_0 < b \\ 0 & \text{for } b < t_0 < a. \end{cases} \tag{2.72}$$

Solution: Here again, the interpretation of the expression

$$\int_a^b \delta(t - t_0)\, dt$$

is as follows: If we select the testing function $\phi(t)$ such that

$$\phi(t) = \begin{cases} 1 & \text{for } a < t < b \\ 0 & \text{for } b < t_0 < a; \end{cases} \tag{2.73}$$

then, from (2.68),

$$\int_a^b \delta(t - t_0)\, dt = \int_{-\infty}^{\infty} \delta(t - t_0)\,\phi(t)\, dt$$

$$= \phi(t_0)$$

$$= \begin{cases} 1 & \text{for } a < t_0 < b \\ 0 & \text{for } b < t_0 < a. \end{cases}$$

PROBLEM 2.23 Show that

$$f(t)\,\delta(t) = f(0)\,\delta(t), \tag{2.74}$$

where $f(t)$ is continuous at $t = 0$. Hence, show that

$$t\,\delta(t) = 0, \tag{2.75}$$

$$\delta(at) = \frac{1}{|a|}\,\delta(t), \tag{2.76}$$

$$\delta(-t) = \delta(t). \tag{2.77}$$

Solution: If $f(t)$ is a continuous function, then

$$\int_{-\infty}^{\infty} [f(t)\,\delta(t)]\,\phi(t)\, dt = \int_{-\infty}^{\infty} \delta(t)\,[f(t)\,\phi(t)]\, dt$$

$$= f(0)\,\phi(0)$$

$$= f(0)\int_{-\infty}^{\infty} \delta(t)\,\phi(t)\, dt$$

$$= \int_{-\infty}^{\infty} [f(0)\,\delta(t)]\,\phi(t)\, dt. \tag{2.78}$$

Since $\phi(t)$ is an arbitrary testing function, we conclude that $f(t)\,\delta(t) = f(0)\,\delta(t)$. From this result it is obvious that

$$t\,\delta(t) = 0.$$

From (2.69),

$$\int_{-\infty}^{\infty} \delta(at)\,\phi(t)\, dt = \frac{1}{|a|}\,\phi(0) = \frac{1}{|a|}\int_{-\infty}^{\infty} \delta(t)\,\phi(t)\, dt = \int_{-\infty}^{\infty} \frac{1}{|a|}\,\delta(t)\,\phi(t)\, dt.$$

Hence,

$$\delta(at) = \frac{1}{|a|} \delta(t).$$

Setting $a = -1$ in the above result,

$$\delta(-t) = \frac{1}{|-1|} \delta(t) = \delta(t),$$

which shows that $\delta(t)$ is an even function.

2.4a Derivatives of the δ-function

The derivative $\delta'(t)$ of $\delta(t)$ is defined by the integral relationship

$$\int_{-\infty}^{\infty} \delta'(t) \phi(t)\, dt = - \int_{-\infty}^{\infty} \delta(t) \phi'(t)\, dt = - \phi'(0), \qquad (2.79)$$

where

$$\delta'(t) = \frac{d\,\delta(t)}{dt}, \quad \phi'(0) = \frac{d\phi}{dt}\bigg|_{t=0}. \qquad (2.80)$$

Equation (2.79) shows that $\delta'(t) = d\,\delta(t)/dt$ is a generalized function which assigns the value $-\phi'(0)$ to a testing function $\phi(t)$.

The n-th derivative of the δ-function

$$\delta^{(n)}(t) = \frac{d^n\,\delta(t)}{dt^n}$$

can be similarly defined by a repeated application of (2.79); i.e.,

$$\int_{-\infty}^{\infty} \delta^{(n)}(t) \phi(t)\, dt = (-1)^n \phi^{(n)}(0), \qquad (2.81)$$

where

$$\phi^{(n)}(0) = \frac{d^n \phi(t)}{dt^n}\bigg|_{t=0}.$$

PROBLEM 2.24 Show that the expression

$$\int_{-\infty}^{\infty} f'(t) \phi(t)\, dt = - \int_{-\infty}^{\infty} f(t) \phi'(t)\, dt \qquad (2.82)$$

is consistent to an ordinary definition of a derivative of $f(t)$ if $f(t)$ is an ordinary function with a continuous first derivative.

Solution: Consider the integral given by

$$\int_{-\infty}^{\infty} f'(t) \phi(t)\, dt.$$

Integrating by parts,

$$\int_{-\infty}^{\infty} f'(t) \phi(t)\, dt = f(t) \phi(t)\bigg|_{-\infty}^{\infty} - \int_{-\infty}^{\infty} f(t) \phi'(t)\, dt. \qquad (2.83)$$

Recalling that the testing function $\phi(t)$ is such that it vanishes outside of some interval, i.e., it is zero at $t = \pm\infty$,

$$\int_{-\infty}^{\infty} f'(t)\,\phi(t)\,dt = -\int_{-\infty}^{\infty} f(t)\,\phi'(t)\,dt.$$

It will be noted that the derivative $f'(t)$ of an arbitrary generalized function $f(t)$ is defined by (2.82).

PROBLEM 2.25 If $f(t)$ is a continuous differentiable function, then show that the product rule

$$[f(t)\,\delta(t)]' = f(t)\,\delta'(t) + f'(t)\,\delta(t) \tag{2.84}$$

remains valid.

Solution: Making use of (2.82),

$$\int_{-\infty}^{\infty} [f(t)\,\delta(t)]'\,\phi(t)\,dt = -\int_{-\infty}^{\infty} [f(t)\,\delta(t)]\,\phi'(t)\,dt$$

$$= -\int_{-\infty}^{\infty} \delta(t)\,[f(t)\,\phi'(t)]\,dt$$

$$= -\int_{-\infty}^{\infty} \delta(t)\,\{[f(t)\,\phi(t)]' - f'(t)\,\phi(t)\}\,dt$$

$$= -\int_{-\infty}^{\infty} \delta(t)\,[f(t)\,\phi(t)]'\,dt + \int_{-\infty}^{\infty} \delta(t)\,[f'(t)\,\phi(t)]\,dt$$

$$= \int_{-\infty}^{\infty} \delta'(t)\,[f(t)\,\phi(t)]\,dt + \int_{-\infty}^{\infty} [\delta(t)\,f'(t)]\,\phi(t)\,dt$$

$$= \int_{-\infty}^{\infty} [\delta'(t)\,f(t) + \delta(t)\,f'(t)]\,\phi(t)\,dt. \tag{2.85}$$

Hence,

$$[f(t)\,\delta(t)]' = f(t)\,\delta'(t) + f'(t)\,\delta(t).$$

PROBLEM 2.26 Prove that

$$f(t)\,\delta'(t) = f(0)\,\delta'(t) - f'(0)\,\delta(t). \tag{2.86}$$

Solution: From (2.84),

$$f(t)\,\delta'(t) = [f(t)\,\delta(t)]' - f'(t)\,\delta(t). \tag{2.87}$$

Since, from (2.74), $f(t)\,\delta(t) = f(0)\,\delta(t)$,

$$f'(t)\,\delta(t) = f'(0)\,\delta(t),$$

$$[f(0)\,\delta(t)]' = f(0)\,\delta'(t).$$

Substituting in (2.87),

$$f(t)\,\delta'(t) = f(0)\,\delta'(t) - f'(0)\,\delta(t).$$

PROBLEM 2.27 Show that the δ-function is the derivative of the function $u(t)$, which is defined by the relation

$$\int_{-\infty}^{\infty} u(t)\,\phi(t)\,dt = \int_{0}^{\infty} \phi(t)\,dt. \tag{2.88}$$

Solution: From (2.82),

$$\int_{-\infty}^{\infty} u'(t)\,\phi(t)\,dt = -\int_{-\infty}^{\infty} u(t)\,\phi'(t)\,dt.$$

But from (2.88),

$$\int_{-\infty}^{\infty} u'(t)\,\phi(t)\,dt = -\int_{0}^{\infty} \phi'(t)\,dt = -[\phi(\infty) - \phi(0)] = \phi(0),$$

because $\phi(\infty) = 0$. Then,

$$\int_{-\infty}^{\infty} u'(t)\,\phi(t)\,dt = \int_{-\infty}^{\infty} \delta(t)\,\phi(t)\,dt. \qquad (2.89)$$

Consequently,

$$u'(t) = \frac{du(t)}{dt} = \delta(t). \qquad (2.90)$$

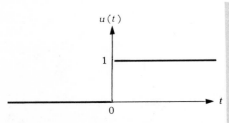

$u(t)$

1

0

Fig. 2.16 The Heaviside unit function or unit step function.

The generalized function (or symbolic function) $u(t)$ defined by (2.88) is known as the *Heaviside unit function* or *unit-step function*. It is customarily defined as (Fig. 2.16)

$$u(t) = \begin{cases} 1 & \text{for } t > 0 \\ 0 & \text{for } t < 0. \end{cases} \qquad (2.91)$$

It is not defined at $t = 0$.

Note that the derivative of the function $u(t)$ is zero for $t < 0$ and for $t > 0$.

PROBLEM 2.28 Let $f(t)$ be a piecewise continuous function having jump discontinuities $a_1, a_2, \cdots$ at $t_1, t_2, \cdots$ (Fig. 2.17). Let $f'(t)$ be defined everywhere except at these discontinuities, finite in number. Find the generalized derivative of $f(t)$.

Solution: Consider the function

$$g(t) = f(t) - \sum_{k} a_k\, u(t - t_k), \qquad (2.92)$$

where

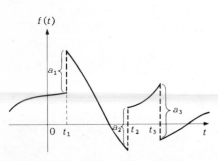

$f(t)$

a_1

a_3

0 t_1 a_2 t_2 t_3 t

Fig. 2.17 A piecewise continuous function having jump discontinuities.

$$u(t - t_k) = \begin{cases} 1 & \text{for } t > t_k \\ 0 & \text{for } t < t_k. \end{cases}$$

The function $g(t)$ is obviously everywhere continuous, and it has, except at a finite number of points, a derivative equal to $f'(t)$.

Hence, differentiation of (2.92) gives

$$g'(t) = f'(t) - \sum_{k} a_k\, \delta(t - t_k) \qquad (2.93)$$

with the use of (2.90). From (2.93),

$$f'(t) = g'(t) + \sum_{k} a_k\, \delta(t - t_k). \qquad (2.94)$$

Equation (2.94) shows that the generalized derivative of a piecewise differentiable function with jumps is the ordinary derivative, where it exists, plus the sum of δ-functions at the discontinuities multiplied by the magnitude of the jumps.

2.5 Fourier Series of Derivatives of Discontinuous Periodic Functions

A sequence of a generalized function $\{f_n(t)\}$, $n = 1, 2, \cdots$, is said to converge to the generalized function $f(t)$ if and only if

$$\lim_{n \to \infty} \int_{-\infty}^{\infty} f_n(t)\, \phi(t)\, dt = \int_{-\infty}^{\infty} f(t)\, \phi(t)\, dt \qquad (2.95)$$

for every testing function $\phi(t)$.

Similarly, a series

$$\sum_{n=1}^{k} f_n(t)$$

of generalized functions which converge to the generalized function $f(t)$ can be differentiated term-by-term. In other words,

$$f'(t) = \sum_{n=1}^{k} f'_n(t). \qquad (2.96)$$

In this case, we say that the series converges in the sense of generalized functions, though in the ordinary sense, the derivative of a convergent series of differentiable functions may not, in general, converge. This point is illustrated in Prob. 2.29.

In Prob. 1.20, we showed that if $f(t)$ is periodic and continuous and given by

$$f(t) = \frac{1}{2} a_0 + \sum_{n=1}^{\infty} (a_n \cos n\omega_0 t + b_n \sin n\omega_0 t), \qquad (2.97)$$

then $f'(t)$ is also periodic and can be obtained by term-by-term differentiation; i.e.,

$$f'(t) = \sum_{n=1}^{\infty} (-n\omega_0\, a_n \sin n\omega_0 t + n\omega_0\, b_n \cos n\omega_0 t). \qquad (2.98)$$

With the concept of the δ-function and generalized derivatives, we can now investigate the Fourier series of derivatives of waveforms with a finite number of discontinuities in one period.

PROBLEM 2.29 Find the Fourier series of the derivative of the waveform of Fig. 2.18.

Solution: From the result of Prob. 2.15, the Fourier series of $f(t)$ is given by

$$f(t) = \frac{1}{2} + \frac{1}{\pi} \sum_{n=1}^{\infty} \frac{1}{n} \sin n\omega_0 t$$

$$= \frac{1}{2} + \frac{1}{\pi} \sum_{n=1}^{\infty} \frac{1}{n} \sin \frac{n2\pi}{T} t. \qquad (2.99)$$

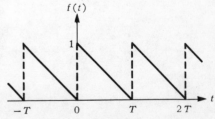

Fig. 2.18 The waveform of Prob. 2.29.

By term-by-term differentiation,

$$f'(t) = \frac{2}{T} \sum_{n=1}^{\infty} \cos \frac{n2\pi}{T} t. \tag{2.100}$$

On the other hand, from (2.94),

$$f'(t) = -\frac{1}{T} + \sum_{n=-\infty}^{\infty} \delta(t - nT). \tag{2.101}$$

We observe that the Fourier series (2.100) is not a converging series in the ordinary sense, but we can say that the series (2.100) converges to the generalized function (2.101) in the sense of a generalized function.

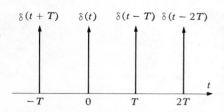

$$\delta(t + T) \quad \delta(t) \quad \delta(t - T) \quad \delta(t - 2T)$$

Fig. 2.19 A periodic train of unit impulses.

Equating (2.100) and (2.101), we obtain an interesting result, namely, the Fourier series expression for a periodic train of unit impulses (Fig. 2.19); i.e.,

$$-\frac{1}{T} + \sum_{n=-\infty}^{\infty} \delta(t - nT) = \frac{2}{T} \sum_{n=1}^{\infty} \cos \frac{n2\pi}{T} t. \tag{2.102}$$

Hence,

$$\sum_{n=-\infty}^{\infty} \delta(t - nT) = \frac{1}{T} + \frac{2}{T} \sum_{n=1}^{\infty} \cos n\omega_0 t, \tag{2.103}$$

where $\omega_0 = \frac{2\pi}{T}$.

Equation (2.103) shows that the periodic train of unit impulses consists of a constant term $1/T$ and a sum of harmonics all with exactly the same amplitude of $2/T$.

The periodic train of unit impulses is a very useful function and hence it is convenient to denote this function by a special symbol $\delta_T(t)$. Thus,

$$\delta_T(t) = \sum_{n=-\infty}^{\infty} \delta(t - nT). \tag{2.104}$$

PROBLEM 2.30 Derive the Fourier series for a periodic train of unit impulses $\delta_T(t)$ by the formal application of (1.27) and (1.28).

Solution: Assume that

$$\delta_T(t) = \frac{1}{2} a_0 + \sum_{n=1}^{\infty} (a_n \cos n\omega_0 t + b_n \sin n\omega_0 t). \tag{2.105}$$

Applying (1.27) and (1.28) with the use of (2.70) and (2.72),

$$\frac{1}{2} a_0 = \frac{1}{T} \int_{-T/2}^{T/2} \delta_T(t)\, dt = \frac{1}{T} \int_{-T/2}^{T/2} \delta(t)\, dt = \frac{1}{T}, \tag{2.106}$$

$$a_n = \frac{2}{T} \int_{-T/2}^{T/2} \delta_T(t) \cos(n\omega_0 t)\, dt = \frac{2}{T} \int_{-T/2}^{T/2} \delta(t) \cos(n\omega_0 t)\, dt = \frac{2}{T} \cos n\omega_0 t \Big|_{t=0}$$

$$= \frac{2}{T}, \tag{2.107}$$

$$b_n = \frac{2}{T} \int_{-T/2}^{T/2} \delta_T(t) \sin(n\omega_0 t)\, dt = \frac{2}{T} \int_{-T/2}^{T/2} \delta(t) \sin(n\omega_0 t)\, dt$$

$$= \frac{2}{T} \sin n\omega_0 t \Big|_{t=0}$$

$$= 0. \tag{2.108}$$

Hence,

$$\sum_{n=-\infty}^{\infty} \delta(t - nT) = \frac{1}{T} + \frac{2}{T} \sum_{n=1}^{\infty} \cos n\omega_0 t, \qquad \omega_0 = \frac{2\pi}{T}. \tag{2.109}$$

2.6 Evaluation of Fourier Coefficients by Differentiation

The use of the δ-function in conjunction with differentiation may facilitate the computation of the coefficients of the Fourier series of certain functions.

PROBLEM 2.31 Find the Fourier series for the waveform of Fig. 2.20(a) by first differentiating $f(t)$.

Solution: Let

$$f(t) = \frac{1}{2} a_0 + \sum_{n=1}^{\infty} (a_n \cos n\omega_0 t + b_n \sin n\omega_0 t), \tag{2.110}$$

$$f'(t) = \frac{1}{2} \alpha_0 + \sum_{n=1}^{\infty} (\alpha_n \cos n\omega_0 t + \beta_n \sin n\omega_0 t), \tag{2.111}$$

where

$$\omega_0 = \frac{2\pi}{T}.$$

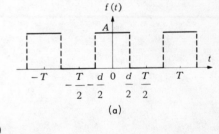

(a)

Differentiating (2.110) term-by-term and equating to (2.111),

$$\alpha_n = n\omega_0 b_n, \qquad \beta_n = -n\omega_0 a_n. \tag{2.112}$$

Hence,

$$a_n = -\frac{\beta_n}{n\omega_0}, \qquad b_n = \frac{\alpha_n}{n\omega_0}. \tag{2.113}$$

Since $f'(t)$ is an odd generalized function [Fig. 2.20(b)],

$$\alpha_n = 0, \qquad n = 1, 2, \cdots, \tag{2.114}$$

$$\beta_n = \frac{4}{T} \int_0^{T/2} f'(t) \sin(n\omega_0 t)\, dt = \frac{4}{T} \int_0^{T/2} \left[-A\, \delta\left(t - \frac{1}{2} d \right) \right] \sin(n\omega_0 t)\, dt$$

$$= -\frac{4A}{T} \sin n\omega_0 t \Big|_{t = \frac{1}{2} d}$$

$$= -\frac{4A}{T} \sin\left(\frac{n\omega_0 d}{2} \right). \tag{2.115}$$

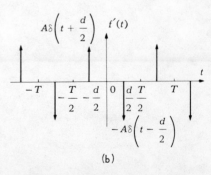

(b)

Fig. 2.20 (a) The waveform of Prob. 2.31. (b) The first derivative of the waveform in Fig. 2.20(a).

Accordingly, from (2.113),

$$a_n = -\frac{\beta_n}{n\omega_0} = \frac{4A}{n\omega_0 T} \sin\left(\frac{n\omega_0 d}{2}\right) = \frac{2Ad}{T} \frac{\sin\left(\frac{n\omega_0 d}{2}\right)}{\left(\frac{n\omega_0 d}{2}\right)} = \frac{2Ad}{T} \frac{\sin\left(\frac{n\pi d}{T}\right)}{\left(\frac{n\pi d}{T}\right)}, \quad (2.116)$$

$$b_n = 0. \quad (2.117)$$

Since the constant term $\frac{1}{2} a_0$ vanishes with the differentiation process, using (1.23),

$$\frac{1}{2} a_0 = \frac{1}{T} \int_{-T/2}^{T/2} f(t)\, dt = \frac{Ad}{T}. \quad (2.118)$$

Hence,

$$f(t) = \frac{Ad}{T} + \frac{2Ad}{T} \sum_{n=1}^{\infty} \frac{\sin\left(\frac{n\pi d}{T}\right)}{\left(\frac{n\pi d}{T}\right)} \cos\left(n\frac{2\pi}{T} t\right). \quad (2.119)$$

PROBLEM 2.32   Using the Fourier series of periodic train of unit impulses (2.103), rework Prob. 2.31.

Solution: The derivative $f'(t)$ of Fig. 2.20(b) can be expressed as

$$f'(t) = A \left[\sum_{n=-\infty}^{\infty} \delta\left(t + \frac{1}{2} d - nT\right) \right] - A \left[\sum_{n=-\infty}^{\infty} \delta\left(t - \frac{1}{2} d - nT\right) \right]. \quad (2.120)$$

From (2.103),

$$\sum_{n=-\infty}^{\infty} \delta\left(t + \frac{1}{2} d - nT\right) = \frac{1}{T} + \frac{2}{T} \sum_{n=1}^{\infty} \cos\left[n\omega_0\left(t + \frac{1}{2} d\right)\right], \quad (2.121)$$

$$\sum_{n=-\infty}^{\infty} \delta\left(t - \frac{1}{2} d - nT\right) = \frac{1}{T} + \frac{2}{T} \sum_{n=1}^{\infty} \cos\left[n\omega_0\left(t - \frac{1}{2} d\right)\right], \quad (2.122)$$

where $\omega_0 = \frac{2\pi}{T}$. Substituting (2.121) and (2.122) into (2.120) and using the trigonometric identity $\cos(A + B) - \cos(A - B) = -2 \sin A \sin B$,

$$f'(t) = \frac{2A}{T} \sum_{n=1}^{\infty} \left[\cos\left(n\omega_0 t + \frac{n\pi d}{T}\right) - \cos\left(n\omega_0 t - \frac{n\pi d}{T}\right) \right]$$

$$= -\frac{4A}{T} \sum_{n=1}^{\infty} \sin\left(\frac{n\pi d}{T}\right) \sin(n\omega_0 t). \quad (2.123)$$

Hence,

$$\beta_n = -\frac{4A}{T} \sin\left(\frac{n\pi d}{T}\right), \qquad \alpha_n = 0. \quad (2.124)$$

Thus,

$$a_n = -\frac{\beta_n}{n\omega_0} = \frac{4A}{n\omega_0 T} \sin\left(\frac{n\pi d}{T}\right)$$

$$= \frac{2A}{n\pi} \sin\left(\frac{n\pi d}{T}\right)$$

$$= \frac{2Ad}{T} \frac{\sin\left(\frac{n\pi d}{T}\right)}{\left(\frac{n\pi d}{T}\right)} \qquad (2.125)$$

$$b_n = 0. \qquad (2.126)$$

PROBLEM 2.33 Find the Fourier series for the waveform of Fig. 2.21(a) by differentiation.

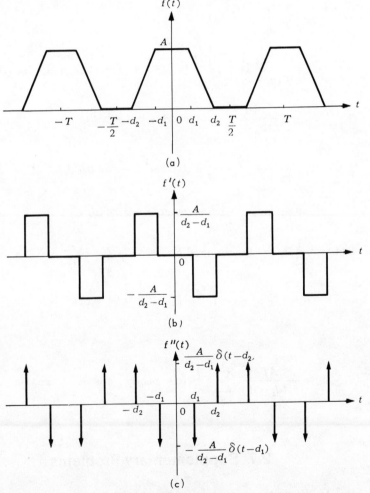

(a)

(b)

(c)

Fig. 2.21 (a) The waveform of Prob. 2.33. (b) The first derivative of the waveform in Fig. 2.21(a). (c) An even generalized function $f''(t)$ of $f(t)$ of Fig. 2.21(a).

Solution: If $f(t)$ is expanded in a Fourier series

$$f(t) = \frac{1}{2} a_0 + \sum_{n=1}^{\infty} (a_n \cos n\omega_0 t + b_n \sin n\omega_0 t), \qquad (2.127)$$

where $\omega_0 = 2\pi/T$, then

$$f'(t) = \sum_{n=1}^{\infty} (-n\omega_0 \, a_n \, \sin n\omega_0 t + n\omega_0 \, b_n \, \cos n\omega_0 t), \qquad (2.128)$$

$$f''(t) = \sum_{n=1}^{\infty} [-(n\omega_0)^2 \, a_n \, \cos n\omega_0 t - (n\omega_0)^2 \, b_n \, \sin n\omega_0 t]. \qquad (2.129)$$

[See Fig. 2.21(b).] Now from Fig. 2.21(c), $f''(t)$ is an even generalized function and

$$f''(t) = \frac{A}{d_2 - d_1} [-\delta(t - d_1) + \delta(t - d_2)], \qquad 0 < t < \frac{1}{2} T. \qquad (2.130)$$

Hence,

$$-(n\omega_0)^2 \, b_n = 0, \qquad b_n = 0, \qquad (2.131)$$

$$-(n\omega_0)^2 \, a_n = \frac{4}{T} \int_0^{T/2} f''(t) \cos (n\omega_0 t) \, dt$$

$$= \frac{4A}{T(d_2 - d_1)} \int_0^{T/2} [-\delta(t - d_1) + \delta(t - d_2)] \cos (n\omega_0 t) \, dt$$

$$= -\frac{4A}{T(d_2 - d_1)} (\cos n\omega_0 d_1 - \cos n\omega_0 d_2), \qquad (2.132)$$

$$a_n = \frac{4A}{(n\omega_0)^2 \, T(d_2 - d_1)} (\cos n\omega_0 d_1 - \cos n\omega_0 d_2)$$

$$= \frac{AT}{n^2 \pi^2 (d_2 - d_1)} (\cos n\omega_0 d_1 - \cos n\omega_0 d_2). \qquad (2.133)$$

The constant term $\frac{1}{2} a_0$ can be obtained as

$$\frac{1}{2} a_0 = \frac{1}{T} \int_{-T/2}^{T/2} f(t) \, dt = \frac{A}{T} (d_1 + d_2). \qquad (2.134)$$

Therefore,

$$f(t) = \frac{A}{T} (d_1 + d_2) + \frac{AT}{\pi^2 (d_2 - d_1)} \sum_{n=1}^{\infty} \frac{1}{n^2} (\cos n\omega_0 d_1 - \cos n\omega_0 d_2) \cos n\omega_0 t. \qquad (2.135)$$

2.7 Supplementary Problems

PROBLEM 2.34 Prove that the zero function is the only function which is simultaneously even and odd.

PROBLEM 2.35 If a function $f(t)$ is odd, prove that $|f(t)|$ is even.

PROBLEM 2.36 Let a function $f(t)$ be differentiable in the interval $(-a, a)$. Show that its derivative $f'(t)$ is odd whenever $f(t)$ is even, and even whenever $f(t)$ is odd.

PROBLEM 2.37 Find the even and odd components of the following functions:

(a) e^t, (b) $\dfrac{t+1}{t-1}$, (c) $t \sin t - \sin 2t$.

Answer: (a) $f_e(t) = \cosh t$, $f_0(t) = \sinh t$, (b) $f_e(t) = \dfrac{t^2+1}{t^2-1}$, $f_0(t) = \dfrac{2t}{t^2-1}$,

(c) $f_e(t) = t \sin t$, $f_0(t) = -\sin 2t$.

PROBLEM 2.38 Find the Fourier series expansion of the function $f(t)$ defined by $f(t) = |t|$ for $(-\pi, \pi)$ and $f(t + 2\pi) = f(t)$. (See Fig. 2.22.)

Answer: $\dfrac{\pi}{2} - \dfrac{4}{\pi} \displaystyle\sum_{n=1}^{\infty} \dfrac{1}{(2n-1)^2} \cos(2n-1)\,t$.

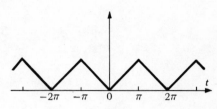

Fig. 2.22 The function $f(t)$ of Prob. 2.38.

PROBLEM 2.39 Let $f(t)$ be a periodic function with period T defined over $(-T/2, T/2)$, whose Fourier series is

$$f(t) = \frac{a_0}{2} + \sum_{n=1}^{\infty} (a_n \cos n\omega_0 t + b_n \sin n\omega_0 t), \quad \omega_0 = \frac{2\pi}{T}.$$

If $f_e(t)$ and $f_0(t)$ are the even and odd components of $f(t)$, show that $f_e(t)$ and $f_0(t)$ have the Fourier series

$$f_e(t) = \frac{a_0}{2} + \sum_{n=1}^{\infty} a_n \cos n\omega_0 t \quad \text{and} \quad f_0(t) = \sum_{n=1}^{\infty} b_n \sin n\omega_0 t.$$

PROBLEM 2.40 Use the result of Prob. 2.39 to find the Fourier series expansion of each of the following functions defined over $(-\pi, \pi)$ with period 2π: (a) $\cosh t$, (b) $\sinh t$.
[Hint: Use the result of Prob. 1.32.]

Answer: (a) $\dfrac{2 \sinh \pi}{\pi} \left[\dfrac{1}{2} + \displaystyle\sum_{n=1}^{\infty} \dfrac{(-1)^n}{1 + n^2} \cos nt \right]$,

(b) $\dfrac{2 \sinh \pi}{\pi} \displaystyle\sum_{n=1}^{\infty} \dfrac{(-1)^{n+1}}{1 + n^2} n \sin nt$.

PROBLEM 2.41 Show that the mean-squared value of $f(t)$ is equal to the sum of the mean squared values of its even and odd components; that is,

$$\frac{1}{T} \int_{-T/2}^{T/2} [f(t)]^2 \, dt = \frac{1}{T} \int_{-T/2}^{T/2} [f_e(t)]^2 \, dt + \frac{1}{T} \int_{-T/2}^{T/2} [f_0(t)]^2 \, dt.$$

PROBLEM 2.42 Let the function $f(t)$ be periodic with period T. If $f(\tfrac{1}{2}T - t) = f(t)$, determine the behavior of the Fourier coefficients a_n and b_n of $f(t)$. Illustrate $f(t)$ graphically.

Answer: $a_{2n+1} = 0$, $b_{2n} = 0$.

PROBLEM 2.43 If the periodic function $f(t)$ with period T satisfies $f(\tfrac{1}{2}T - t) = -f(t)$, determine the behavior of the Fourier coefficients of a_n and b_n of $f(t)$. Illustrate $f(t)$ graphically.

Answer: $a_{2n} = 0$, $b_{2n+1} = 0$.

PROBLEM 2.44 Suppose $f(t) = 0$ for $-\frac{1}{2}T < t < 0$. If the Fourier series expansion of $f(t)$ on the interval $(-T/2,\ T/2)$ is

$$\frac{1}{2}a_0 + \sum_{n=1}^{\infty} (a_n \cos n\omega_0 t + b_n \sin n\omega_0 t), \quad \omega_0 = 2\pi/T,$$

show that the Fourier cosine series and the Fourier sine series of $f(t)$ on the interval $(0,\ T/2)$ are

$$a_0 + \sum_{n=1}^{\infty} 2a_n \cos n\omega_0 t \quad \text{and} \quad \sum_{n=1}^{\infty} 2b_n \sin n\omega_0 t.$$

PROBLEM 2.45 Represent the following functions $f(t)$ by a Fourier cosine series and graph the corresponding periodic continuation of $f(t)$:

(a) $f(t) = t,\ \ 0 < t < \pi,$ (b) $f(t) = \sin \frac{\pi}{l} t,\ \ 0 < t < l.$

Answer: (a) $\dfrac{\pi}{2} - \dfrac{4}{\pi} \displaystyle\sum_{n=1}^{\infty} \dfrac{1}{(2n-1)^2} \cos(2n-1)t,$

(b) $\dfrac{2}{\pi} - \dfrac{4}{\pi}\left[\dfrac{1}{1\cdot 3}\cos\left(\dfrac{2\pi}{l}\right)t + \dfrac{1}{3\cdot 5}\cos\left(\dfrac{4\pi}{l}\right)t + \dfrac{1}{5\cdot 7}\cos\left(\dfrac{6\pi}{l}\right)t + \cdots \right].$

PROBLEM 2.46 Represent the following functions $f(t)$ by a Fourier sine series and graph the corresponding periodic continuation of $f(t)$:

(a) $f(t) = \cos t,\ \ 0 < t < \pi,$ (b) $\pi - t,\ \ 0 < t < \pi.$

Answer: (a) $\dfrac{8}{\pi} \displaystyle\sum_{n=1}^{\infty} \dfrac{n}{4n^2-1}\sin 2nt,$ (b) $2 \displaystyle\sum_{n=1}^{\infty} \dfrac{1}{n}\sin nt.$

PROBLEM 2.47 Find the Fourier cosine and sine series of

$$f(t) = \frac{1}{4}\pi t \qquad \text{for } 0 < t < \frac{1}{2}\pi$$

$$= \frac{1}{4}\pi t(\pi - t) \quad \text{for } \frac{1}{2}\pi < t < \pi.$$

Answer: $\dfrac{\pi^2}{16} - \displaystyle\sum_{n=1}^{\infty} \dfrac{1}{n}\cos nt, \quad \displaystyle\sum_{n=1}^{\infty} \dfrac{(-1)^{n+1}}{(2n-1)^2}\sin(2n-1)t.$

PROBLEM 2.48 Let $\phi_n(t) = \sqrt{(2/\tau)}\sin(n\pi/\tau)t$, where $n = 1, 2, \cdots$. Show that the functions $\{\phi_n(t)\}$ form an orthonormal set in the interval $(0,\ \tau)$.

PROBLEM 2.49 Let $f(t)$ be defined over $(0,\ \tau)$. Show that Fourier series of $f(t)$ with respect to the orthonormal set $\{\phi_n(t)\}$ of Prob. 2.48 is the Fourier sine series of $f(t)$ over $(0,\ \tau)$.

[Hint: Use the result of Prob. 1.45.]

PROBLEM 2.50 Show that

(a) $f(t)\delta(t - t_0) = f(t_0)\delta(t - t_0),$ (b) $t\delta'(t) = -\delta(t),$

(c) $\delta'(-t) = -\delta'(t),$ (d) $\delta^n(-t) = (-1)^n \delta^n(t).$

PROBLEM 2.51 Show that $\delta[f(t)] = \sum_{t_n} \dfrac{1}{|f'(t_n)|} \delta(t - t_n)$, where t_n are the zeros of $f(t)$.

[Hint: Set $f(t) = \tau$ and form $\psi(\tau) \doteq \phi(t)/|f'(t)|.$]

PROBLEM 2.52 Show that

(a) $\delta(t^2 - a^2) = \dfrac{1}{2|a|}\{\delta(t - a) + \delta(t + a)\}$, (b) $\delta(\sin t) = \delta_\pi(t) = \sum_{n=-\infty}^{\infty} \delta(t - n\pi)$.

[Hint: Use the result of Prob. 2.51.]

PROBLEM 2.53 Use differentiation to find the Fourier coefficients for the function $f(t)$ defined by $f(t) = t$ for $(-\pi, \pi)$ and $f(t + 2\pi) = f(t)$.

Answer: See Prob. 1.30.

PROBLEM 2.54 Using the Fourier series of the periodic train of unit impulses (2.103) and differentiation, find the Fourier coefficients for the function $f(t)$ defined by $f(t) = e^t$ for $(-\pi, \pi)$ and $f(t + 2\pi) = f(t)$.

Answer: See Prob. 1.32.

PROBLEM 2.55 Use differentiation to find the Fourier coefficients for the full rectified sine wave $f(t) = |A \sin \omega_0 t|$.

Answer: See Prob. 1.33.

PROBLEM 2.56 Use differentiation to find the Fourier coefficients for the function whose waveform is shown in Fig. 1.3.

Answer: Equation (1.40).

PROBLEM 2.57 Use differentiation to find the Fourier coefficients for the half rectified sine wave of Fig. 1.4.

Answer: Equation (1.49).

PROBLEM 2.58 Use the result of Prob. 2.55 to deduce the Fourier series for the half rectified sine wave of Fig. 1.4.

[Hint: Note that $f(t)$ can be expressed as $f(t) = \dfrac{1}{2} A \sin \omega_0 t + \dfrac{1}{2} |A \sin \omega_0 t|.$]

PROBLEM 2.59 Let $f(t) = f_e(t) + f_o(t)$, where $f_e(t)$ and $f_o(t)$ are the even and odd components of $f(t)$, respectively. Show that

$$\frac{1}{T}\int_{-T/2}^{T/2} f(t)f(t-\tau)\,dt = \frac{1}{T}\int_{-T/2}^{T/2} f_e(t)f_e(t-\tau)\,dt + \frac{1}{T}\int_{-T/2}^{T/2} f_o(t)f_o(t-\tau)\,dt.$$

PROBLEM 2.60 Show that if $f(t)$ is a continuous differentiable function, then

$$f(t)\delta'(t - t_o) = f(t_o)\delta'(t - t_o) - f'(t_o)\delta(t - t_o).$$

DISCRETE
FREQUENCY SPECTRA

3.1 Introduction

The representation of a periodic function as a Fourier series implies that the specification of its Fourier coefficients uniquely determines the function. In this chapter we shall further explore the use of Fourier coefficients for the study of periodic functions, and introduce the concept of frequency spectra of periodic signals.

3.2 Complex Form of Fourier Series

In many applications of Fourier series, it is convenient to express the Fourier series in terms of the complex exponentials $e^{\pm jn\omega_0 t}$.

Now let us consider the Fourier series of a periodic function $f(t)$ to be

$$f(t) = \frac{1}{2}a_0 + \sum_{n=1}^{\infty} (a_n \cos n\omega_0 t + b_n \sin n\omega_0 t), \qquad (3.1)$$

where $\omega_0 = 2\pi/T$. The cosine and sine may be expressed in terms of the exponentials as

$$\cos n\omega_0 t = \frac{1}{2}(e^{jn\omega_0 t} + e^{-jn\omega_0 t}), \qquad (3.2)$$

$$\sin n\omega_0 t = \frac{1}{2j}(e^{jn\omega_0 t} - e^{-jn\omega_0 t}). \qquad (3.3)$$

Substituting (3.2) and (3.3) into (3.1),

$$f(t) = \frac{1}{2}a_0 + \sum_{n=1}^{\infty} \left[a_n \frac{1}{2}(e^{jn\omega_0 t} + e^{-jn\omega_0 t}) + b_n \frac{1}{2j}(e^{jn\omega_0 t} - e^{-jn\omega_0 t}) \right]. \qquad (3.4)$$

Noting that $1/j = -j$, (3.4) can be rewritten as

$$f(t) = \frac{1}{2}a_0 + \sum_{n=1}^{\infty} \left[\frac{1}{2}(a_n - jb_n) e^{jn\omega_0 t} + \frac{1}{2}(a_n + jb_n) e^{-jn\omega_0 t} \right]. \qquad (3.5)$$

If we let

$$c_0 = \frac{1}{2}a_0, \qquad c_n = \frac{1}{2}(a_n - jb_n), \qquad c_{-n} = \frac{1}{2}(a_n + jb_n), \qquad (3.6)$$

then

$$f(t) = c_0 + \sum_{n=1}^{\infty} \left(c_n\, e^{jn\omega_0 t} + c_{-n}\, e^{-jn\omega_0 t} \right)$$

$$= c_0 + \sum_{n=1}^{\infty} c_n\, e^{jn\omega_0 t} + \sum_{n=-1}^{-\infty} c_n\, e^{jn\omega_0 t}$$

$$= \sum_{n=-\infty}^{\infty} c_n\, e^{jn\omega_0 t}. \tag{3.7}$$

Equation (3.7) is called the complex form of the Fourier series of $f(t)$ or the *complex Fourier series* of $f(t)$.

The coefficients c_n can be easily evaluated in terms of a_n and b_n, which we already know. In fact,

$$c_0 = \frac{1}{2}\, a_0 = \frac{1}{T} \int_{-T/2}^{T/2} f(t)\, dt, \tag{3.8}$$

$$c_n = \frac{1}{2}(a_n - jb_n)$$

$$= \frac{1}{T} \left[\int_{-T/2}^{T/2} f(t) \cos(n\omega_0 t)\, dt - j \int_{-T/2}^{T/2} f(t) \sin(n\omega_0 t)\, dt \right]$$

$$= \frac{1}{T} \left\{ \int_{-T/2}^{T/2} f(t) \left[\cos(n\omega_0 t) - j \sin(n\omega_0 t) \right] dt \right\}$$

$$= \frac{1}{T} \int_{-T/2}^{T/2} f(t)\, e^{-jn\omega_0 t}\, dt, \tag{3.9}$$

$$c_{-n} = \frac{1}{2}(a_n + jb_n) = \frac{1}{T} \int_{-T/2}^{T/2} f(t)\, e^{jn\omega_0 t}\, dt. \tag{3.10}$$

If $f(t)$ is real, then

$$c_{-n} = c_n^*, \tag{3.11}$$

where * indicates the complex conjugate.

Equations (3.8), (3.9), and (3.10) may be combined into a single formula; i.e.,

$$c_n = \frac{1}{T} \int_{-T/2}^{T/2} f(t)\, e^{-jn\omega_0 t}\, dt, \qquad n = 0,\ \pm 1,\ \pm 2, \cdots. \tag{3.12}$$

Since $f(t)\, e^{-jn\omega_0 t}$ is periodic with period T, and in view of (1.10), c_n also can be found from the formula

$$c_n = \frac{1}{T} \int_{0}^{T} f(t)\, e^{-jn\omega_0 t}\, dt. \tag{3.13}$$

Next, if

$$c_n \left| c_n \right| e^{j\phi_n}, \qquad c_{-n} = c_n^* = \left| c_n \right| e^{-j\phi_n}, \tag{3.14}$$

then

$$\left| c_n \right| = \frac{1}{2} \sqrt{a_n^2 + b_n^2}, \tag{3.15}$$

$$\phi_n = \tan^{-1}\left(-\frac{b_n}{a_n}\right) \tag{3.16}$$

for all n except $n = 0$. In that case, c_0 is real and

$$c_0 = \frac{1}{2} a_0. \tag{3.17}$$

PROBLEM 3.1 Find the complex Fourier series of the saw-tooth wave function $f(t)$ shown in Fig. 3.1 and defined by

$$f(t) = \frac{A}{T} t, \qquad 0 < t < T, \qquad f(t + T) = f(t). \tag{3.18}$$

Solution: The complex Fourier series representation of $f(t)$ is given by

$$f(t) = \sum_{n=-\infty}^{\infty} c_n e^{jn\omega_0 t}, \qquad \omega_0 = \frac{2\pi}{T}. \tag{3.19}$$

The coefficients c_n may be found from (3.13); thus,

$$c_n = \frac{1}{T} \int_0^T f(t) e^{-jn\omega_0 t} dt$$

$$= \frac{A}{T^2} \int_0^T t e^{-jn\omega_0 t} dt$$

$$= \frac{A}{T^2} \left(\frac{t e^{-jn\omega_0 t}}{-jn\omega_0} \Big|_0^T + \frac{1}{jn\omega_0} \int_0^T e^{-jn\omega_0 t} dt \right)$$

$$= \frac{A}{T^2} \left[\frac{T e^{-jn 2\pi}}{-jn\omega_0} - \frac{1}{(jn\omega_0)^2} (e^{-jn 2\pi} - 1) \right]. \tag{3.20}$$

Since $e^{-jn 2\pi} = 1$,

$$c_n = j \frac{A}{n\omega_0 T} = j \frac{A}{2\pi n} = \frac{A}{2\pi n} e^{j\frac{\pi}{2}}. \tag{3.21}$$

Certainly this has no meaning for $n = 0$. Therefore for $n = 0$, from (3.8),

$$c_0 = \frac{1}{T} \int_0^T f(t) dt = \frac{A}{T^2} \int_0^T t dt = \frac{1}{2} A. \tag{3.22}$$

Hence,

$$f(t) = \frac{A}{2} + j \frac{A}{2\pi} \sum_{n=-\infty}^{\infty}{}' \frac{1}{n} e^{jn\omega_0 t} \tag{3.23a}$$

$$= \frac{A}{2} + \frac{A}{2\pi} \sum_{n=-\infty}^{\infty}{}' \frac{1}{n} e^{j\left(n\omega_0 t + \frac{\pi}{2}\right)}, \tag{3.23b}$$

where $\displaystyle\sum_{n=-\infty}^{\infty}{}'$ means the summation is over nonzero integers.

PROBLEM 3.2 Reduce the result of Prob. 3.1 to the trigonometric form of the Fourier series.

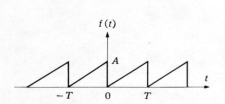

$f(t)$

A

$-T$ 0 T t

Fig. 3.1 The saw-tooth wave function.

Solution: Since from (3.6),

$$c_0 = \frac{1}{2} a_0, \qquad c_n = \frac{1}{2}(a_n - jb_n), \qquad c_{-n} = c_n^* = \frac{1}{2}(a_n + jb_n),$$

we have

$$a_0 = 2c_0, \tag{3.24}$$

$$a_n = c_n + c_{-n} = c_n + c_n^* = 2\,Re[c_n], \tag{3.25}$$

$$b_n = j(c_n - c_{-n}) = j(c_n - c_n^*) = -2\,Im[c_n], \tag{3.26}$$

where Re and Im denote "the real part of" and "the imaginary part of," respectively.

Then from (3.21) and (3.22),

$$a_0 = A, \qquad a_n = 0, \qquad b_n = -\frac{A}{n\pi}. \tag{3.27}$$

Hence,

$$f(t) = \frac{1}{2} a_0 + \sum_{n=1}^{\infty} (a_n \cos n\omega_0 t + b_n \sin n\omega_0 t)$$

$$= \frac{A}{2} - \frac{A}{\pi} \sum_{n=1}^{\infty} \frac{1}{n} \sin n\omega_0 t$$

$$= \frac{A}{2} - \frac{A}{\pi} \left(\sin \omega_0 t + \frac{1}{2} \sin 2\omega_0 t + \frac{1}{3} \sin 3\omega_0 t + \cdots \right). \tag{3.28}$$

PROBLEM 3.3 Find the complex Fourier series of a rectified sine wave periodic function $f(t)$ shown in Fig. 3.2 and defined by

$$f(t) = A \sin \pi t, \qquad 0 < t < 1, \qquad f(t + T) = f(t), \qquad T = 1. \tag{3.29}$$

Solution: Since the period $T = 1$, ω_0 is given by

$$\omega_0 = \frac{2\pi}{T} = 2\pi; \tag{3.30}$$

hence, the complex Fourier series is given by

$$f(t) = \sum_{n=-\infty}^{\infty} c_n e^{j2\pi nt}. \tag{3.31}$$

From (3.13), the coefficients c_n are

$$c_n = \frac{1}{T} \int_0^T f(t) e^{-j2\pi nt}\, dt$$

$$= \int_0^1 A \sin \pi t\, e^{-j2\pi nt}\, dt$$

$$= A \int_0^1 \frac{1}{2j} (e^{j\pi t} - e^{-j\pi t}) e^{-j2\pi nt}\, dt$$

$$= \frac{A}{2j} \int_0^1 [e^{-j\pi(2n-1)t} - e^{-j\pi(2n+1)t}]\, dt$$

$$= \frac{A}{2j} \left[\frac{e^{-j\pi(2n-1)t}}{-j\pi(2n-1)} - \frac{e^{-j\pi(2n+1)t}}{-j\pi(2n+1)} \right] \Bigg|_0^1.$$

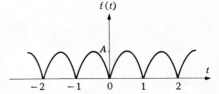

$$f(t)$$

Fig. 3.2 A rectified sine wave periodic function.

Since $e^{\pm j 2\pi n} = 1$ and $e^{\pm j\pi} = e^{-j\pi}$,

$$c_n = \frac{-2A}{\pi(4n^2 - 1)}.$$

(3.32)

We can use (3.8) to check this result for $n = 0$; thus,

$$c_0 = \frac{1}{T} \int_0^T f(t)\,dt$$

$$= \frac{2A}{\pi}.$$

(3.33)

Hence,

$$f(t) = -\frac{2A}{\pi} \sum_{n=-\infty}^{\infty} \frac{1}{4n^2 - 1} e^{j 2\pi n t}.$$

(3.34)

PROBLEM 3.4   Reduce the result of Prob. 3.3 to the trigonometric form of the Fourier series.

Solution: Equation (3.34) can be rewritten as

$$f(t) = \frac{2A}{\pi} - \frac{2A}{\pi} \left(\frac{1}{3} e^{j 2\pi t} + \frac{1}{15} e^{j 4\pi t} + \frac{1}{35} e^{j 6\pi t} + \cdots \right)$$

$$- \frac{2A}{\pi} \left(\frac{1}{3} e^{-j 2\pi t} + \frac{1}{15} e^{-j 4\pi t} + \frac{1}{35} e^{-j 6\pi t} + \cdots \right)$$

$$= \frac{2A}{\pi} - \frac{4A}{\pi} \left[\frac{1}{3} \frac{1}{2} (e^{j 2\pi t} + e^{-j 2\pi t}) + \frac{1}{15} \frac{1}{2} (e^{j 4\pi t} + e^{-j 4\pi t}) \right.$$

$$\left. + \frac{1}{35} \frac{1}{2} (e^{j 6\pi t} + e^{-j 6\pi t}) + \cdots \right]$$

$$= \frac{2A}{\pi} - \frac{4A}{\pi} \left(\frac{1}{3} \cos 2\pi t + \frac{1}{15} \cos 4\pi t + \frac{1}{35} \cos 6\pi t + \cdots \right).$$

(3.35)

Or using (3.25) and (3.26),

$$a_n = 2\,Re\,[c_n]$$

$$= -\frac{4A}{\pi(4n^2 - 1)},$$

(3.36)

$$b_n = -2\,Im\,[c_n] = 0.$$

(3.37)

Hence,

$$f(t) = \frac{1}{2} a_0 + \sum_{n=1}^{\infty} (a_n \cos n\omega_0 t + b_n \sin n\omega_0 t)$$

$$= \frac{2A}{\pi} - \frac{4A}{\pi} \sum_{n=1}^{\infty} \frac{1}{(4n^2 - 1)} \cos n 2\pi t$$

$$= \frac{2A}{\pi} - \frac{4A}{\pi} \left(\frac{1}{3} \cos 2\pi t + \frac{1}{15} \cos 4\pi t + \frac{1}{35} \cos 6\pi t + \cdots \right).$$

(3.38)

3.3 Orthogonality of Complex Fourier Series Functions

The orthogonality of the sine and cosine functions has been demonstrated in Sec. 1.3. However, for functions which assume complex values, the concept of orthogonality has to be slightly modified. We call the set of complex valued functions $\{f_n(t)\}$ *orthogonal* over the interval $a < t < b$ if

$$\int_a^b f_n(t) f_m^*(t)\, dt = \begin{cases} 0 & \text{for } n \neq m \\ \\ r_n & \text{for } n = m, \end{cases} \tag{3.39}$$

where $f_m^*(t)$ is the complex conjugate of $f_m(t)$. For example, if

$$f_m(t) = e^{jm\omega_0 t} = \cos m\omega_0 t + j \sin m\omega_0 t,$$

then its complex conjugate is

$$f_m^*(t) = e^{-jm\omega_0 t} = \cos m\omega_0 t - j \sin m\omega_0 t.$$

PROBLEM 3.5 Show that the set of complex Fourier series functions $\{e^{jn\omega_0 t}\}$, $n = 0, \pm 1, \pm 2, \cdots$, obeys the orthogonality condition for $n \neq m$ for $-\frac{1}{2}T < t < \frac{1}{2}T$, where $\omega_0 = \frac{2\pi}{T}$.

Solution: Since $e^{jm\omega_0 t}\big|_{m=0} = 1$,

$$\int_{-T/2}^{T/2} e^{jn\omega_0 t} \cdot 1\, dt = \frac{1}{jn\omega_0} e^{jn\omega_0 t}\bigg|_{-T/2}^{T/2}$$

$$= \frac{1}{jn\omega_0}(e^{jn\pi} - e^{-jn\pi})$$

$$= 0 \quad \text{for } n \neq 0, \tag{3.40}$$

$$\int_{-T/2}^{T/2} e^{jn\omega_0 t}(e^{jm\omega_0 t})^*\, dt = \int_{-T/2}^{T/2} e^{jn\omega_0 t} e^{-jm\omega_0 t}\, dt$$

$$= \int_{-T/2}^{T/2} e^{j(n-m)\omega_0 t}\, dt$$

$$= \frac{1}{j(n-m)\omega_0} e^{j(n-m)\omega_0 t}\bigg|_{-T/2}^{T/2}$$

$$= \frac{1}{j(n-m)\omega_0}(e^{j(n-m)\pi} - e^{-j(n-m)\pi})$$

$$= \frac{1}{j(n-m)\omega_0}[(-1)^{n-m} - (-1)^{n-m}]$$

$$= 0 \quad \text{for } n \neq m. \tag{3.41}$$

PROBLEM 3.6 Using the orthogonality of the complex Fourier series functions set $\{e^{jn\omega_0 t}\}$, determine the coefficients of the complex Fourier series.

Solution: Let $f(t)$ be a periodic function with period T, and let the complex exponential Fourier series corresponding to this function be given by

$$f(t) = \sum_{n=-\infty}^{\infty} c_n e^{jn\omega_0 t}, \qquad \omega_0 = \frac{2\pi}{T}. \tag{3.42}$$

Now multiplying both sides by $e^{-jm\omega_0 t}$, and integrating over $\left[-\frac{1}{2}T, \frac{1}{2}T\right]$,

$$\int_{-T/2}^{T/2} f(t)\, e^{-jm\omega_0 t}\, dt = \int_{-T/2}^{T/2} \left(\sum_{n=-\infty}^{\infty} c_n e^{jn\omega_0 t} \right) e^{-jm\omega_0 t}\, dt$$

$$= \sum_{n=-\infty}^{\infty} c_n \left[\int_{-T/2}^{T/2} e^{j(n-m)\omega_0 t}\, dt \right]. \tag{3.43}$$

In view of (3.41), the quantity in the bracket is zero except when $n = m$; therefore,

$$\int_{-T/2}^{T/2} f(t)\, e^{-jm\omega_0 t}\, dt = c_m \int_{-T/2}^{T/2} e^{j \cdot 0}\, dt$$

$$= c_m \int_{-T/2}^{T/2} dt$$

$$= c_m T. \tag{3.44}$$

Hence, by changing m to n,

$$c_n = \frac{1}{T} \int_{-T/2}^{T/2} f(t)\, e^{-jn\omega_0 t}\, dt. \tag{3.45}$$

3.4 Complex Frequency Spectra

A plot of the magnitude of the complex coefficients c_n in the series (3.7) versus the frequency ω (angular frequency) is called the *amplitude spectrum* of the periodic function $f(t)$. A plot of the phase angle ϕ_n of c_n [see (3.14)] versus ω is called the *phase spectrum* of $f(t)$. Since the index n assumes only integers, the amplitude and phase spectra are not continuous curves but appear only at the discrete variable $n\omega_0$. These are, therefore, referred to as *discrete frequency spectra* or *line spectra*. The representation of the complex coefficients c_n versus the discrete variable $n\omega_0$ specifies the periodic function $f(t)$ in the so-called frequency domain just as $f(t)$ versus t specifies it in the time domain.

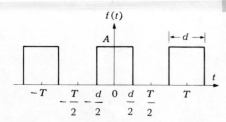

Fig. 3.3 A train of identical rectangular pulses.

PROBLEM 3.7 Find the frequency spectrum for the periodic function $f(t)$ shown in Fig. 3.3, which consists of a train of identical rectangular pulses of magnitude A and duration d.

Solution: The function $f(t)$ can be expressed over one period as follows:

$$f(t) = \begin{cases} A & \text{for } -\frac{1}{2}d < t < \frac{1}{2}d \\[2mm] 0 & \text{for } -\frac{1}{2}T < t < -\frac{1}{2}d, \ \ \frac{1}{2}d < t < \frac{1}{2}T, \end{cases} \tag{3.46}$$

Then from (3.12), with $\omega_0 = \dfrac{2\pi}{T}$,

$$c_n = \frac{1}{T} \int_{-T/2}^{T/2} f(t)\, e^{-jn\omega_0 t}\, dt$$

$$= \frac{A}{T} \int_{-d/2}^{d/2} e^{-jn\omega_0 t}\, dt$$

$$= \frac{A}{T}\, \frac{1}{-jn\omega_0}\, e^{-jn\omega_0 t} \bigg|_{-d/2}^{d/2}$$

$$= \frac{A}{T}\, \frac{1}{jn\omega_0}\, (e^{jn\omega_0 d/2} - e^{-jn\omega_0 d/2})$$

$$= \frac{Ad}{T}\, \frac{1}{\left(\dfrac{n\omega_0 d}{2}\right)}\, \frac{1}{2j}\, (e^{jn\omega_0 d/2} - e^{-jn\omega_0 d/2})$$

$$= \frac{Ad}{T}\, \frac{\sin\left(\dfrac{n\omega_0 d}{2}\right)}{\left(\dfrac{n\omega_0 d}{2}\right)}. \tag{3.47}$$

But $n\omega_0 d/2 = n\pi d/T$; hence,

$$c_n = \frac{Ad}{T}\, \frac{\sin\left(\dfrac{n\pi d}{T}\right)}{\left(\dfrac{n\pi d}{T}\right)}. \tag{3.48}$$

It is obvious from (3.47) or (3.48) that c_n is real and hence the phase spectrum is zero. The amplitude spectrum is obtained by plotting (3.47) or (3.48) versus the discrete variable $n\omega_0$. Equation (3.47) has values only for the discrete frequency $n\omega_0$; i.e., the frequency spectrum is a discrete function and exists only at

$$\omega = 0, \quad \frac{\pm 2\pi}{T}, \quad \frac{\pm 4\pi}{T}, \cdots, \text{ etc.}$$

We shall consider the spectrum for some specific values of d and T. For $d = 1/20$ and $T = 1/4$ second,

$$\omega_0 = \frac{2\pi}{T} = 8\pi.$$

Hence the amplitude spectrum exists at

$$\omega = 0, \quad \pm 8\pi, \quad \pm 16\pi, \cdots, \text{ etc.},$$

and is shown in Fig. 3.4(a).

Since $d/T = 1/5$, the amplitude spectrum becomes zero at the value of $n\omega_0$, for which

$$n\omega_0 \frac{d}{2} = m\pi \qquad \text{or} \qquad n\pi \frac{d}{T} = n\pi\left(\frac{1}{5}\right) = m\pi \quad (m = \pm 1, \pm 2, \cdots),$$

i.e., at $\omega = \pm 5\omega_0 = \pm 40\pi$, $\pm 10\omega_0 = \pm 80\pi$, $\pm 15\omega_0 = \pm 120\pi$, $\cdots$.

The next case we will consider has $d = 1/20$ and $T = 1/2$ second, and

$$\omega_0 = \frac{2\pi}{T} = 4\pi, \qquad \frac{d}{T} = \frac{1}{10}.$$

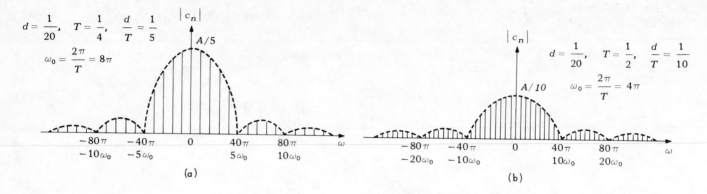

Fig. 3.4 The amplitude spectra.

Hence, the amplitude spectrum exists at

$$\omega = 0, \quad \pm 4\pi, \quad \pm 8\pi, \cdots,$$

and becomes zero at the value of $n\omega_0$ for which

$$n\omega_0 \frac{d}{2} = m\pi \qquad \text{or} \qquad n\pi \frac{d}{T} = n\pi\left(\frac{1}{10}\right) = m\pi \quad (m = \pm 1, \pm 2, \cdots),$$

i.e., at $\omega = \pm 10\omega_0 = \pm 40\pi$, $\pm 20\omega_0 = \pm 80\pi$, $\pm 30\omega_0 = \pm 120\pi$, $\cdots$. The amplitude spectrum for this case is shown in Fig. 3.4(b).

It should be noted that the phase spectrum in Prob. 3.7 is zero because of the symmetry of the rectangular pulses in Fig. 3.3 about a vertical center line, and because of the particular location chosen for the origin. The following example will illustrate the case in which the origin is shifted back by $\frac{1}{2}d$.

PROBLEM 3.8 Find the frequency spectrum for the periodic function $f(t)$ shown in Fig. 3.5.

Solution: From (3.13), with $\omega_0 = \dfrac{2\pi}{T}$,

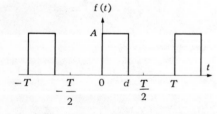

Fig. 3.5 The function $f(t)$ of Prob. 3.8.

$$c_n = \frac{1}{T} \int_0^T f(t)\, e^{-jn\omega_0 t}\, dt = \frac{A}{T} \int_0^d e^{-jn\omega_0 t}\, dt$$

$$= \frac{A}{T} \frac{1}{-jn\omega_0} e^{-jn\omega_0 t} \bigg|_0^d$$

$$= \frac{A}{T} \frac{1}{jn\omega_0} (1 - e^{-jn\omega_0 d})$$

$$= \frac{A}{T} \frac{1}{jn\omega_0} e^{-jn\omega_0 d/2} (e^{jn\omega_0 d/2} - e^{-jn\omega_0 d/2})$$

$$= \frac{Ad}{T} \frac{\sin\left(\dfrac{n\omega_0 d}{2}\right)}{\left(\dfrac{n\omega_0 d}{2}\right)} e^{-jn\omega_0 d/2}$$

$$= |c_n| e^{j\phi_n}. \tag{3.49}$$

Hence,

$$|c_n| = \frac{Ad}{T} \frac{\sin\left(\dfrac{n\omega_0 d}{2}\right)}{\left(\dfrac{n\omega_0 d}{2}\right)}, \tag{3.50}$$

$$\phi_n = -\frac{n\omega_0 d}{2} = -n\pi\left(\frac{d}{T}\right). \tag{3.51}$$

The amplitude spectrum is exactly the same as that of Prob. 3.7 and is not affected by the shift of the origin, but the phase spectrum is now equal to $-n\omega_0 d/2 = -n\pi d/T$ radians.

PROBLEM 3.9 Show that the time displacement in a periodic function has no effect on the magnitude spectrum, but changes the phase spectrum by an amount of $-n\omega_0\tau$ radians for the component at the frequency $n\omega_0$ if the time displacement is τ.

Solution: Let $f(t)$ be a periodic function with period T, and let its complex Fourier series be given by

$$f(t) = \sum_{n=-\infty}^{\infty} c_n e^{jn\omega_0 t}. \tag{3.52}$$

From (3.52),

$$f(t - \tau) = \sum_{n=-\infty}^{\infty} c_n e^{jn\omega_0(t-\tau)}$$

$$= \sum_{n=-\infty}^{\infty} c_n e^{-jn\omega_0\tau} e^{jn\omega_0 t}$$

$$= \sum_{n=-\infty}^{\infty} c_n' e^{jn\omega_0 t}, \tag{3.53}$$

where

$$c_n' = c_n e^{-jn\omega_0\tau}. \tag{3.54}$$

Hence, if

$$c_n = |c_n| e^{j\phi_n}, \tag{3.55}$$

then

$$c_n' = |c_n| e^{j(\phi_n - n\omega_0\tau)}. \tag{3.56}$$

From (3.55) and (3.56), it is obvious that the magnitude spectra of $f(t)$ and $f(t - \tau)$ are the same; however, the phases are different. The time displacement τ causes a lag of phase by an amount of $n\omega_0\tau$ radians in the frequency component $n\omega_0$.

In (3.47) or (3.48), if

$$\frac{n\omega_0 d}{2} = \frac{n\pi d}{T} = x_n,$$

then

$$c_n = \frac{Ad}{T} \frac{\sin x_n}{x_n}.$$ (3.57)

The envelope of c_n is a continuous function found by replacing $n\omega_0$ with ω or replacing x_n by x. In frequency analysis, the function

$$Sa(x) = \frac{\sin x}{x}$$ (3.58)

plays an important role and is known as the *sampling function*. The sampling function is shown in Fig. 3.6. Note that the function has zeros at $x = \pm n\pi$, $n = 1, 2, \cdots$, etc.

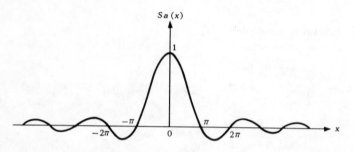

Fig. 3.6 The sampling function.

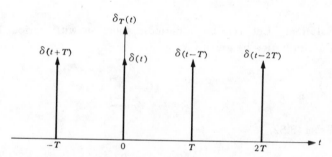

Fig. 3.7 A periodic train of unit impulses.

3.5 Evaluation of Complex Fourier Coefficients by Use of δ-Function

In Sec. 2.6 we saw that the evaluation of the Fourier coefficients of certain functions was greatly facilitated by the use of the δ-function. Here we shall apply the same technique to the evaluation of complex Fourier coefficients.

PROBLEM 3.10 Derive the complex Fourier series of the periodic train of unit impulses of Fig. 3.7.

Solution: A periodic train $\delta_T(t)$ of unit impulses can be expressed as

$$\left. \begin{aligned} \delta_T(t) &= \sum_{n=-\infty}^{\infty} \delta(t - nT), \quad -\frac{T}{2} < t < \frac{T}{2} \\[2mm] &= \delta(t), \qquad\qquad -\frac{T}{2} < t < \frac{T}{2}. \end{aligned} \right\}$$ (3.59)

Hence, with $\omega_0 = \dfrac{2\pi}{T}$,

$$c_n = \frac{1}{T} \int_{-T/2}^{T/2} \delta_T(t) e^{-jn\omega_0 t} dt = \frac{1}{T} \int_{-T/2}^{T/2} \delta(t) e^{-jn\omega_0 t} dt$$

$$= \frac{1}{T} e^{-jn\omega_0 t} \Big|_{t=0}$$

$$= \frac{1}{T} . \tag{3.60}$$

Therefore,

$$\sum_{n=-\infty}^{\infty} \delta(t - nT) = \frac{1}{T} \sum_{n=-\infty}^{\infty} e^{jn\omega_0 t} = \frac{1}{T} \sum_{n=-\infty}^{\infty} e^{jn\frac{2\pi}{T}t}. \tag{3.61}$$

PROBLEM 3.11 Prove that (2.103) is equal to (3.61).

Solution: From (3.61),

$$\sum_{n=-\infty}^{\infty} \delta(t - nT) = \frac{1}{T} \sum_{n=-\infty}^{\infty} e^{jn\omega_0 t}$$

$$= \frac{1}{T} \left(\sum_{n=-\infty}^{-1} e^{jn\omega_0 t} + e^{j0} + \sum_{n=1}^{\infty} e^{jn\omega_0 t} \right)$$

$$= \frac{1}{T} \left[1 + \sum_{n=1}^{\infty} (e^{jn\omega_0 t} + e^{-jn\omega_0 t}) \right]$$

$$= \frac{1}{T} + \frac{2}{T} \sum_{n=1}^{\infty} \frac{1}{2} (e^{jn\omega_0 t} + e^{-jn\omega_0 t})$$

$$= \frac{1}{T} + \frac{2}{T} \sum_{n=1}^{\infty} \cos n\omega_0 t$$

$$= \frac{1}{T} + \frac{2}{T} \sum_{n=1}^{\infty} \cos n\frac{2\pi}{T}t, \tag{3.62}$$

which is exactly (2.103).

PROBLEM 3.12 Find the complex Fourier coefficients for the function $f(t)$ shown in Fig. 3.8(a).

Solution: Assume that

$$f(t) = \sum_{n=-\infty}^{\infty} c_n e^{jn\omega_0 t}, \quad \omega_0 = \frac{2\pi}{T}. \tag{3.63}$$

By term-by-term differentiation, as shown in Fig. 3.8(b-c),

$$f'(t) = \sum_{n=-\infty}^{\infty} (jn\omega_0) c_n e^{jn\omega_0 t}, \tag{3.64}$$

$$f''(t) = \sum_{n=-\infty}^{\infty} (jn\omega_0)^2 c_n e^{jn\omega_0 t} = - \sum_{n=-\infty}^{\infty} (n\omega_0)^2 c_n e^{jn\omega_0 t}. \tag{3.65}$$

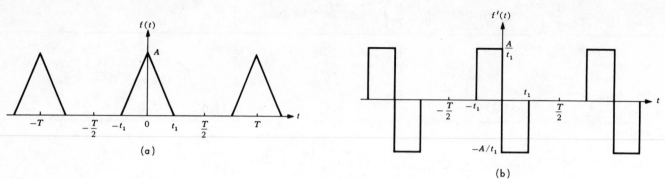

(a)

(b)

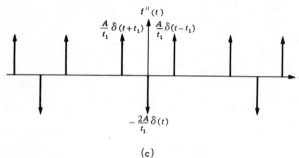

(c)

Fig. 3.8 (a) The function $f(t)$ of Prob. 3.12. (b) The first derivative of $f(t)$ of Fig. 3.8(a). (c) The second derivative of $f(t)$ of Fig. 3.8(a).

In the interval $-T/2 < t < T/2$, from Fig. 3.8(c),

$$f''(t) = \frac{A}{t_1} \delta(t + t_1) - \frac{2A}{t_1} \delta(t) + \frac{A}{t_1} \delta(t - t_1);$$ (3.66)

hence,

$$-(n\omega_0)^2 c_n = \frac{1}{T} \int_{-T/2}^{T/2} f''(t) e^{-jn\omega_0 t} dt$$

$$= \frac{A}{Tt_1} \int_{-T/2}^{T/2} [\delta(t + t_1) - 2\delta(t) + \delta(t - t_1)] e^{-jn\omega_0 t} dt$$

$$= \frac{A}{Tt_1} (e^{jn\omega_0 t_1} - 2 + e^{-jn\omega_0 t_1})$$

$$= \frac{2A}{Tt_1} (\cos n\omega_0 t_1 - 1).$$ (3.67)

Using the trigonometric identity $1 - \cos \theta = 2 \sin^2\left(\dfrac{\theta}{2}\right)$,

$$-(n\omega_0)^2 c_n = -\frac{4A}{Tt_1} \sin^2\left(\frac{n\omega_0 t_1}{2}\right).$$ (3.68)

Hence,

$$c_n = \frac{4A}{Tt_1} \left[\frac{\sin\left(\dfrac{n\omega_0 t_1}{2}\right)}{n\omega_0}\right]^2$$

$$= A \frac{t_1}{T} \left[\frac{\sin\left(\dfrac{n\omega_0 t_1}{2}\right)}{\left(\dfrac{n\omega_0 t_1}{2}\right)}\right]^2.$$ (3.69)

PROBLEM 3.13 Rework Prob. 3.12 by using the complex Fourier series (3.61) of a periodic train of unit impulses.

Solution: From Fig. 3.8(c), $f''(t)$ can be expressed as

$$f''(t) = \frac{A}{t_1} \sum_{n=-\infty}^{\infty} \delta(t + t_1 - nT) - \frac{2A}{t_1} \sum_{n=-\infty}^{\infty} \delta(t - nT) + \frac{A}{t_1} \sum_{n=-\infty}^{\infty} \delta(t - t_1 - nT). \quad (3.70)$$

From (3.61),

$$\sum_{n=-\infty}^{\infty} \delta(t - nT) = \frac{1}{T} \sum_{n=-\infty}^{\infty} e^{jn\omega_0 t}, \qquad \omega_0 = \frac{2\pi}{T}. \quad (3.71)$$

Changing t to $t + t_1$ and $t - t_1$, respectively, in the above expression,

$$\sum_{n=-\infty}^{\infty} \delta(t + t_1 - nT) = \frac{1}{T} \sum_{n=-\infty}^{\infty} e^{jn\omega_0(t+t_1)} = \frac{1}{T} \sum_{n=-\infty}^{\infty} e^{jn\omega_0 t_1} e^{jn\omega_0 t}, \quad (3.72)$$

$$\sum_{n=-\infty}^{\infty} \delta(t - t_1 - nT) = \frac{1}{T} \sum_{n=-\infty}^{\infty} e^{jn\omega_0(t-t_1)} = \frac{1}{T} \sum_{n=-\infty}^{\infty} e^{-jn\omega_0 t_1} e^{jn\omega_0 t}. \quad (3.73)$$

Substituting (3.71), (3.72), and (3.73) into (3.70),

$$f''(t) = \frac{A}{Tt_1} \sum_{n=-\infty}^{\infty} (e^{jn\omega_0 t_1} + e^{-jn\omega_0 t_1} - 2) e^{jn\omega_0 t}$$

$$= \frac{2A}{Tt_1} \sum_{n=-\infty}^{\infty} (\cos n\omega_0 t_1 - 1) e^{jn\omega_0 t}. \quad (3.74)$$

Therefore,

$$-(n\omega_0)^2 c_n = \frac{2A}{Tt_1}(\cos n\omega_0 t_1 - 1); \quad (3.75)$$

hence,

$$c_n = A \frac{t_1}{T} \left[\frac{\sin\left(\dfrac{n\omega_0 t_1}{2}\right)}{\left(\dfrac{n\omega_0 t_1}{2}\right)} \right]^2. \quad (3.76)$$

3.6 Power Content of a Periodic Function: Parseval's Theorem

The *power content* of a periodic function $f(t)$ in the period T is defined as the mean-square value

$$\frac{1}{T} \int_{-T/2}^{T/2} [f(t)]^2 \, dt. \quad (3.77)$$

If we assume the function $f(t)$ is a voltage or a current waveform, then (3.77) represents the average power delivered by $f(t)$ to a 1-Ω resistor.

PROBLEM 3.14 Let $f_1(t)$ and $f_2(t)$ be two periodic functions having the same period T. Show that

$$\frac{1}{T} \int_{-T/2}^{T/2} f_1(t) f_2(t) \, dt = \sum_{n=-\infty}^{\infty} (c_1)_n (c_2)_{-n}, \tag{3.78}$$

where $(c_1)_n$ and $(c_2)_n$ are the complex Fourier coefficients of $f_1(t)$ and $f_2(t)$, respectively.

Solution: Let

$$f_1(t) = \sum_{n=-\infty}^{\infty} (c_1)_n \, e^{jn\omega_0 t}, \qquad \omega_0 = \frac{2\pi}{T}, \tag{3.79}$$

where

$$(c_1)_n = \frac{1}{T} \int_{-T/2}^{T/2} f_1(t) \, e^{-jn\omega_0 t} \, dt.. \tag{3.80}$$

Let

$$f_2(t) = \sum_{n=-\infty}^{\infty} (c_2)_n \, e^{jn\omega_0 t}, \tag{3.81}$$

where

$$(c_2)_n = \frac{1}{T} \int_{-T/2}^{T/2} f_2(t) \, e^{-jn\omega_0 t} \, dt. \tag{3.82}$$

Then,

$$\int_{-T/2}^{T/2} f_1(t) f_2(t) \, dt = \frac{1}{T} \int_{-T/2}^{T/2} \left[\sum_{n=-\infty}^{\infty} (c_1)_n \, e^{jn\omega_0 t} \ f_2(t) \, dt \right]$$

$$= \sum_{n=-\infty}^{\infty} (c_1)_n \left[\frac{1}{T} \int_{-T/2}^{T/2} f_2(t) \, e^{jn\omega_0 t} \, dt \right]. \tag{3.83}$$

In view of (3.82),

$$\frac{1}{T} \int_{-T/2}^{T/2} f_2(t) \, e^{jn\omega_0 t} \, dt = \frac{1}{T} \int_{-T/2}^{T/2} f_2(t) \, e^{-j(-n)\omega_0 t} \, dt$$

$$= (c_2)_{-n}. \tag{3.84}$$

Hence,

$$\frac{1}{T} \int_{-T/2}^{T/2} f_1(t) f_2(t) \, dt = \sum_{n=-\infty}^{\infty} (c_1)_n (c_2)_{-n}.$$

> *Parseval's theorem* states that if $f(t)$ is a real periodic function with period T, then
>
> $$\frac{1}{T} \int_{-T/2}^{T/2} [f(t)]^2 \, dt = \sum_{n=-\infty}^{\infty} |c_n|^2, \tag{3.85}$$
>
> where the c's are the complex Fourier coefficients of the function $f(t)$.

PROBLEM 3.15 Prove Parseval's theorem.

Solution: By putting $f_1(t) = f_2(t) = f(t)$ in the result (3.78) of Prob. 3.14,

$$\frac{1}{T} \int_{-T/2}^{T/2} [f(t)]^2 \, dt = \sum_{n=-\infty}^{\infty} c_n \, c_{-n} \, . \tag{3.86}$$

If $f(t)$ is real, then, from (3.11),

$$c_{-n} = c_n^* \, .$$

Hence,

$$\frac{1}{T} \int_{-T/2}^{T/2} [f(t)]^2 \, dt = \sum_{n=-\infty}^{\infty} c_n \, c_n^*$$

$$= \sum_{n=-\infty}^{\infty} |c_n|^2 \, .$$

PROBLEM 3.16 From the result (3.85) of Prob. 3.15, derive Parseval's identity

$$\frac{1}{T} \int_{-T/2}^{T/2} [f(t)]^2 \, dt = \frac{1}{4} a_0^2 + \frac{1}{2} \sum_{n=1}^{\infty} (a_n^2 + b_n^2), \tag{1.72}$$

where the a's and b's are the Fourier coefficients of $f(t)$. (Cf., Prob. 1.17.)

Solution: From (3.6),

$$c_0 = \frac{1}{2} a_0, \qquad c_n = \frac{1}{2} (a_n - jb_n), \qquad c_{-n} = \frac{1}{2} (a_n + jb_n);$$

hence,

$$c_0^2 = \frac{1}{4} a_0^2 . \qquad |c_n|^2 = \frac{1}{4} (a_n^2 + b_n^2) = |c_{-n}|^2 . \tag{3.87}$$

Substituting (3.87) into (3.85),

$$\frac{1}{T} \int_{-T/2}^{T/2} [f(t)]^2 \, dt = \sum_{n=-\infty}^{\infty} |c_n|^2$$

$$= |c_0|^2 + 2 \sum_{n=1}^{\infty} |c_n|^2$$

$$= \frac{1}{4} a_0^2 + \frac{1}{2} \sum_{n=1}^{\infty} (a_n^2 + b_n^2). \tag{3.88}$$

PROBLEM 3.17 Show that the mean-square value of a periodic function $f(t)$ is the sum of the mean-square values of its harmonics.

Solution: From (1.12),

$$f(t) = C_0 + \sum_{n=1}^{\infty} C_n \cos (n\omega_0 t - \theta_n).$$

For the n-th harmonic of $f(t)$,

$$f_n(t) = C_n \cos(n\omega_0 t - \theta_n).$$

The rms (root-mean-square) value is $C_n/\sqrt{2}$; hence, the mean-square value of the n-th harmonic is $(C_n/\sqrt{2})^2$.

In view of (1.14),

$$C_n = \sqrt{a_n^2 + b_n^2} = 2\left|c_n\right|, \qquad C_0 = \frac{1}{2}a_0 = \left|c_0\right|;$$

hence,

$$\left|c_n\right|^2 = \frac{1}{4}C_n^2, \qquad \left|c_0\right|^2 = C_0^2.$$

Then, from (3.88),

$$\frac{1}{T}\int_{-T/2}^{T/2}[f(t)]^2\,dt = \left|c_0\right|^2 + 2\sum_{n=1}^{\infty}\left|c_n\right|^2$$

$$= C_0^2 + \sum_{n=1}^{\infty}\left|\frac{C_n}{\sqrt{2}}\right|^2. \tag{3.89}$$

Equation (3.89) indicates that the mean-square value of a periodic function $f(t)$ is the sum of the mean-square values of its harmonics. It is noted that the power content (mean-square value) of a periodic function depends only on the amplitudes of its harmonics and is independent of their phases.

3.7 Supplementary Problems

PROBLEM 3.18 Show that the complex Fourier coefficients of an even periodic function are real and those of an odd periodic function are pure imaginary.

PROBLEM 3.19 If $f(t)$ and $g(t)$ are periodic functions with period T and their Fourier expansions are

$$f(t) = \sum_{n=-\infty}^{\infty} c_n e^{jn\omega_0 t}, \qquad g(t) = \sum_{n=-\infty}^{\infty} d_n e^{jn\omega_0 t} \qquad \text{for} \quad \omega_0 = \frac{2\pi}{T},$$

show that the function

$$h(t) = \frac{1}{T}\int_{-T/2}^{T/2} f(t-\tau)g(\tau)\,d\tau$$

is a periodic function with the same period T and can be expressed as

$$h(t) = \sum_{n=-\infty}^{\infty} c_n d_n e^{jn\omega_0 t}.$$

PROBLEM 3.20 If $f(t)$ and $g(t)$ are periodic functions with period T and their Fourier expansions are

$$f(t) = \sum_{n=-\infty}^{\infty} c_n e^{jn\omega_0 t}, \qquad g(t) = \sum_{n=-\infty}^{\infty} d_n e^{jn\omega_0 t} \qquad \text{for} \quad \omega_0 = \frac{2\pi}{T},$$

show that the function $h(t) = f(t) g(t)$ is a periodic function with the same period T and can be expressed as

$$h(t) = \sum_{n=-\infty}^{\infty} \alpha_n e^{jn\omega_0 t},$$

where $\alpha_n = \sum_{k=-\infty}^{\infty} c_{n-k} d_k.$

[Hint: Show that $\alpha_n = \sum_{k=-\infty}^{\infty} c_{n-k} d_k$ are the Fourier coefficients of $h(t)$.]

PROBLEM 3.21 If $f(t)$ is a periodic function with period T and has complex Fourier coefficients c_n, show that the complex Fourier coefficients of the periodically amplitude-modulated carrier function $f(t) \cos m\omega_0 t$ is $\frac{1}{2}(c_{n-m} + c_{n+m})$.

PROBLEM 3.22 If $f(t)$ is integrable over the finite interval $(-\frac{1}{2}T, \frac{1}{2}T)$ and ω is real, show that

$$\lim_{|\omega| \to \infty} \int_{-T/2}^{T/2} f(t) e^{-j\omega t} dt = 0.$$

[Hint: Use Prob. 1.19.]

PROBLEM 3.23 Find the complex Fourier series for the function $f(t)$ defined by $f(t) = \sin^4 t$ for $(0, \pi)$ and $f(t + \pi) = f(t)$.

Answer: $\frac{1}{16}(e^{4jt} - 4e^{2jt} + 6 - 4e^{-2jt} + e^{-4jt})$.

PROBLEM 3.24 Find the complex Fourier series for the function $f(t)$ defined by $f(t) = e^t$ for $(0, 2\pi)$ and $f(t + 2\pi) = f(t)$ by direct integration.

Answer: $\dfrac{e^{2\pi} - 1}{2\pi} \sum_{n=-\infty}^{\infty} \dfrac{1}{1 - jn} e^{jnt}$.

PROBLEM 3.25 Use differentiation to find the complex Fourier series for the function of Prob. 3.24. Note that $f'(t) = f(t) - (e^{2\pi} - 1) \delta_{2\pi}(t)$, where

$$\delta_{2\pi}(t) = \sum_{n=-\infty}^{\infty} \delta(t - 2\pi n).$$

PROBLEM 3.26 Reduce the result of Prob. 3.24 to the trigonometric form of the Fourier series.

Answer: $\dfrac{e^{2\pi} - 1}{\pi} \left[\dfrac{1}{2} + \sum_{n=1}^{\infty} \dfrac{1}{1 + n^2} (\cos nt - n \sin nt) \right]$.

PROBLEM 3.27 Show that if $\omega_0 = 2\pi/T$,

$$\delta_T'(t) = \sum_{n=-\infty}^{\infty} \delta'(t - nT) = \frac{j\omega_0^2}{2\pi} \sum_{n=-\infty}^{\infty} n e^{jn\omega_0 t} = -\frac{\omega_0^2}{\pi} \sum_{n=1}^{\infty} n \sin n\omega_0 t.$$

PROBLEM 3.28 Find the complex Fourier coefficients and sketch the frequency spectra for a half-rectified sine wave $f(t)$ defined by

$$f(t) = \begin{cases} A \sin \omega_0 t & \text{for } 0 < t < T/2 \\ 0 & \text{for } T/2 < t < T \end{cases}$$

and $f(t + T) = f(t)$, where $\omega_0 = 2\pi/T$.

Answer: $c_n = \dfrac{1}{2\pi(1 - n^2)}(1 + e^{-jn\pi})$, and note that $c_1 = c_{-1} = -\dfrac{j}{4}$ and $c_{2m+1} = 0$, where $m = 1, 2, \cdots$.

PROBLEM 3.29 Find the complex Fourier coefficients and sketch the frequency spectra for the saw-tooth wave function $f(t)$ defined by $f(t) = -\dfrac{1}{T}t + \dfrac{1}{2}$ for $0 < t < T$ and $f(t + T) = f(t)$.

Answer: $c_n = \dfrac{1}{j2\pi n}$, $c_0 = 0$.

PROBLEM 3.30 Apply Parseval's theorem (3.85) to the result of Prob. 3.29 to prove that

$$\sum_{n=1}^{\infty} \frac{1}{n^2} = \frac{\pi^2}{6}.$$

PROBLEM 3.31 Use differentiation to find the complex Fourier series of the saw-tooth wave function of Fig. 3.1.

Answer: Equations (3.23a-b).

PROBLEM 3.32 Use differentiation to find the complex Fourier series of the full rectified sine wave of Fig. 3.2.

Answer: Equation (3.34).

PROBLEM 3.33 Show that if $f(t)$ is a real periodic function with period T, then

$$\frac{1}{T}\int_{-T/2}^{T/2} [f(t)]^2\, dt = c_0 + 2\sum_{n=1}^{\infty} |c_n|^2,$$

where c_n's are the complex Fourier coefficients of the function $f(t)$.
[Hint: Use the result of Prob. 3.15.]

PROBLEM 3.34 Let $f_1(t)$ and $f_2(t)$ be two periodic functions having the same period T. Show that

$$\frac{1}{T}\int_{-T/2}^{T/2} f_1(t + \tau) f_2(t)\, dt = \sum_{n=-\infty}^{\infty} (c_1)_n (c_2)_{-n}\, e^{jn\omega_0 \tau},$$

where $(c_1)_n$ and $(c_2)_n$ are the complex Fourier coefficients of $f_1(t)$ and $f_2(t)$, respectively, and $\omega_0 = 2\pi/T$.

PROBLEM 3.35 Show that if $f(t)$ is a real periodic function with period T, then

$$\frac{1}{T}\int_{-T/2}^{T/2} f(t + \tau) f(t)\, dt = \sum_{n=-\infty}^{\infty} |c_n|^2\, e^{jn\omega_0 \tau},$$

where c_n's are the complex Fourier coefficients of $f(t)$, and $\omega_0 = 2\pi/T$.

FOURIER INTEGRAL AND CONTINUOUS SPECTRA

4.1 Introduction

We have seen that Fourier series are a powerful tool in treating various problems involving periodic functions. Since many practical problems do not involve periodic functions, it is desirable to develop a method of Fourier analysis that includes nonperiodic functions. In this chapter, we shall discuss a frequency representation of nonperiodic functions by means of the Fourier series representation.

4.2 From Fourier Series to Fourier Integral

PROBLEM 4.1 If we start with a periodic function $f_T(t)$ of period T and let T approach infinity, then the resulting function $f(t) = \lim_{T \to \infty} f_T(t)$ is no longer periodic. Illustrate this limiting process by using a rectangular pulse train.

Solution: Consider the rectangular pulse train of Fig. 4.1(a), where

$$f_T(t) = \begin{cases} 0 & \text{for} \quad -\frac{1}{2}T < t < -\frac{1}{2}d \\ 1 & \text{for} \quad -\frac{1}{2}d < t < \frac{1}{2}d \\ 0 & \text{for} \quad \frac{1}{2}d < t < \frac{1}{2}T, \end{cases} \tag{4.1}$$

$$f_T(t + T) = f_T(t), \quad T > d.$$

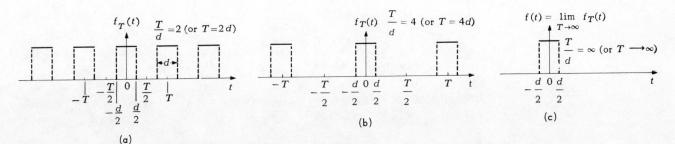

Fig. 4.1 The limiting process as T increases to infinity.

For $T \longrightarrow \infty$, we obtain the function

$$f(t) = \lim_{T \to \infty} f_T(t) = \begin{cases} 1 & \text{when } -\frac{1}{2}d < t < \frac{1}{2}d \\ \\ 0 & \text{otherwise.} \end{cases} \tag{4.2}$$

It is evident that $f(t)$ is not a periodic function. Figure 4.1 illustrates the limiting process as T increases and finally becomes infinite.

PROBLEM 4.2 Using the rectangular pulse train of Fig. 4.1 as an example, discuss the effects of increasing the period on the spectrum of a periodic function.

Solution: The frequency spectrum of the periodic rectangular pulse has been found in Prob. 3.7. From Fig. 3.4, we observe that when the discrete spectrum of a periodic function with period T is plotted as a function of frequency, the distance between neighboring harmonics is the fundamental frequency $\omega_0 = 2\pi/T$. Thus as the period T increases, ω_0 decreases, and the lines in the spectrum move closer to each other. Consequently, the number of lines (harmonics) in a given frequency band increases.

Next, from (3.48),

$$c_n = A \frac{d}{T} \frac{\sin\left(\dfrac{n\pi d}{T}\right)}{\left(\dfrac{n\pi d}{T}\right)}.$$

Hence, as the period T increases, the amplitudes of all harmonics decrease.

From the above discussion, we conclude that in the limit as T approaches infinity [Fig. 4.1(c)], the harmonics are infinitely close together and infinitesimal in amplitude; i.e., the discrete spectrum becomes a continuous spectrum.

PROBLEM 4.3 Let $f(t)$ be a periodic function with period T. When T approaches infinity, $f(t)$ becomes nonperiodic. Find the Fourier representation of this nonperiodic function.

Solution: We begin with the complex exponential form of the Fourier series (3.7); that is,

$$f(t) = \sum_{n=-\infty}^{\infty} c_n e^{jn\omega_0 t}, \tag{4.3}$$

where

$$c_n = \frac{1}{T} \int_{-T/2}^{T/2} f(t) e^{-jn\omega_0 t} dt, \tag{4.4}$$

$$\omega_0 = \frac{2\pi}{T}. \tag{4.5}$$

Substituting (4.4) into (4.3),

$$f(t) = \sum_{n=-\infty}^{\infty} \left[\frac{1}{T} \int_{-T/2}^{T/2} f(x) e^{-jn\omega_0 x} dx \right] e^{jn\omega_0 t}. \tag{4.6}$$

Here, the dummy integration variable x is used to avoid confusion with t. Since $1/T = \omega_0/2\pi$, (4.6) can be rewritten as

$$f(t) = \sum_{n=-\infty}^{\infty} \left[\frac{1}{2\pi} \int_{-T/2}^{T/2} f(x) e^{-jn\omega_0 x} dx \right] \omega_0 e^{jn\omega_0 t}. \tag{4.7}$$

We now let $T \longrightarrow \infty$, and thus, from (4.5), ω_0 becomes vanishingly small. Let $\omega_0 = \Delta \omega$; then, the frequency of any "harmonic" $n\omega_0$ must now correspond to the general frequency variable which describes the continuous spectrum. In other words, $n \longrightarrow \infty$ as $\omega_0 = \Delta \omega \longrightarrow 0$, such that the product is finite; that is,

$$n\omega_0 = n \Delta \omega \longrightarrow \omega.$$

Now (4.7) becomes

$$f(t) = \sum_{n=-\infty}^{\infty} \left[\frac{1}{2\pi} \int_{-T/2}^{T/2} f(x)\, e^{jn\Delta\omega x}\, dx \right] e^{jn\Delta\omega x}\, \Delta\omega. \qquad (4.8)$$

In the limit, $T \longrightarrow \infty$, $\Delta \omega \longrightarrow d\omega$, and the summation becomes an integration over ω; i.e., the nonperiodic function $f(t)$ becomes

$$f(t) = \frac{1}{2\pi} \int_{-\infty}^{\infty} \left[\int_{-\infty}^{\infty} f(x)\, e^{-j\omega x}\, dx \right] e^{j\omega t}\, d\omega. \qquad (4.9)$$

Now, if we define

$$F(\omega) = \int_{-\infty}^{\infty} f(t)\, e^{-j\omega t}\, dt, \qquad (4.10)$$

then (4.9) becomes

$$f(t) = \frac{1}{2\pi} \int_{-\infty}^{\infty} F(\omega)\, e^{j\omega t}\, d\omega. \qquad (4.11)$$

Equations (4.10) and (4.11) are the Fourier representation of the nonperiodic function.

We note that (4.11) is analogous to (4.3) and (4.10) is analogous to (4.4). The relation (4.9) is known as *Fourier's identity*.

It should be stressed that the above heuristic derivation of (4.10) and (4.11) or (4.9) does not establish their validity on a rigorous mathematical basis. However, our interest is from an engineering point of view and lies primarily in their interpretation and use.

Fourier's integral theorem states that if $f(t)$ is real,

$$f(t) = \frac{1}{\pi} \int_{0}^{\infty} \int_{-\infty}^{\infty} f(x)\, \cos \omega (t - x)\, dx\, d\omega. \qquad (4.12)$$

PROBLEM 4.4 Prove Fourier's integral theorem.

Solution: We can rewrite (4.9) as

$$f(t) = \frac{1}{2\pi} \int_{-\infty}^{\infty} \int_{-\infty}^{\infty} f(x)\, e^{j\omega(t-x)}\, dx\, d\omega. \qquad (4.13)$$

If $f(t)$ is real, we can equate real parts in the Fourier identity (4.13), which becomes

$$f(t) = \frac{1}{2\pi} \int_{-\infty}^{\infty} \int_{-\infty}^{\infty} f(x)\, \cos \omega (t - x)\, dx\, d\omega. \qquad (4.14)$$

Since $\cos \omega (t - x)$ is even with respect to ω, from (2.13),

$$f(t) = \frac{1}{\pi} \int_{0}^{\infty} \int_{-\infty}^{\infty} f(x)\, \cos \omega (t - x)\, dx\, d\omega$$

4.3 Fourier Transforms

The function $F(\omega)$ defined by (4.10) is known as the *Fourier integral* or *Fourier transform* of $f(t)$, and the integral operation is often symbolized by $\mathcal{F}$; that is,

$$F(\omega) = \mathcal{F}[f(t)] = \int_{-\infty}^{\infty} f(t)\, e^{-j\omega t}\, dt. \tag{4.15}$$

Similarly, $\mathcal{F}^{-1}$ is the symbol used to denote the inverse operation of obtaining $f(t)$ when $F(\omega)$ is given; that is,

$$f(t) = \mathcal{F}^{-1}[F(\omega)] = \frac{1}{2\pi} \int_{-\infty}^{\infty} F(\omega)\, e^{j\omega t}\, d\omega, \tag{4.16}$$

and $f(t)$ is called the *inverse Fourier transform* of $F(\omega)$. Equations (4.15) and (4.16) are often called the *Fourier transform pair*.

The condition for the existence of $F(\omega)$ is usually given as

$$\int_{-\infty}^{\infty} |f(t)|\, dt < \infty. \tag{4.17}$$

In other words, the function $f(t)$ must be absolutely integrable.

PROBLEM 4.5 Show that (4.17) is a sufficient condition for the existence of the Fourier transform of $f(t)$.

Solution: Since

$$e^{-j\omega t} = \cos \omega t - j \sin \omega t$$

and, hence,

$$|e^{-j\omega t}| = \sqrt{\cos^2 \omega t + \sin^2 \omega t} = 1,$$

$$|f(t)\, e^{-j\omega t}| = |f(t)|,$$

it follows that if

$$\int_{-\infty}^{\infty} |f(t)|\, dt = \int_{-\infty}^{\infty} |f(t)\, e^{-j\omega t}|\, dt$$

is finite, then

$$\int_{-\infty}^{\infty} f(t)\, e^{-j\omega t}\, dt$$

is finite, i.e., $\mathcal{F}[f(t)]$ exists.

It should be noted that (4.17) is a sufficient but not necessary condition for the existence of $\mathcal{F}[f(t)]$. Functions which do not satisfy (4.17) may have Fourier transforms. We shall discuss these functions in Chap. 5.

The function $F(\omega) = \mathcal{F}[f(t)]$ is, in general, complex, and

$$F(\omega) = R(\omega) + j\, X(\omega) = |F(\omega)|\, e^{j\phi(\omega)}, \tag{4.18}$$

where $|F(\omega)|$ is called the *magnitude spectrum* of $f(t)$, and $\phi(\omega)$, the *phase spectrum* of $f(t)$.

PROBLEM 4.6   If $f(t)$ is real, then show that the real and imaginary parts of $F(\omega)$ are

$$R(\omega) = \int_{-\infty}^{\infty} f(t) \cos \omega t \, dt, \tag{4.19}$$

$$X(\omega) = - \int_{-\infty}^{\infty} f(t) \sin \omega t \, dt. \tag{4.20}$$

Then, also show that $R(\omega)$ and $X(\omega)$ are even and odd functions of ω, respectively; i.e.,

$$R(\omega) = R(-\omega), \tag{4.21}$$

$$X(\omega) = -X(-\omega), \tag{4.22}$$

$$F(-\omega) = F^*(\omega), \tag{4.23}$$

where $F^*(\omega)$ denotes the complex conjugate of $F(\omega)$.

Solution: If $f(t)$ is real, then using the identity

$$e^{-j\omega t} = \cos \omega t - j \sin \omega t,$$

we can rewrite (4.15) as

$$F(\omega) = \int_{-\infty}^{\infty} f(t) \, e^{-j\omega t} \, dt$$

$$= \int_{-\infty}^{\infty} f(t) \cos \omega t \, dt - j \int_{-\infty}^{\infty} f(t) \sin \omega t \, dt$$

$$= R(\omega) + j X(\omega). \tag{4.24}$$

Equating the real and imaginary parts,

$$R(\omega) = \int_{-\infty}^{\infty} f(t) \cos \omega t \, dt,$$

$$X(\omega) = - \int_{-\infty}^{\infty} f(t) \sin \omega t \, dt.$$

Next, since $f(t)$ is real,

$$R(-\omega) = \int_{-\infty}^{\infty} f(t) \cos (-\omega t) \, dt = \int_{-\infty}^{\infty} f(t) \cos \omega t \, dt = R(\omega),$$

$$X(-\omega) = - \int_{-\infty}^{\infty} f(t) \sin (-\omega t) \, dt = \int_{-\infty}^{\infty} f(t) \sin \omega t \, dt = - X(\omega).$$

Hence, $R(\omega)$ is an even function of ω and $X(\omega)$ is an odd function of ω. From (4.21) and (4.22),

$$F(-\omega) = R(-\omega) + j \, X(-\omega) = R(\omega) - j \, X(\omega) = F^*(\omega).$$

PROBLEM 4.7   Show that (4.23) is a necessary and sufficient condition for $f(t)$ to be real.

Solution: The fact that (4.23), i.e., $F(-\omega) = F^*(\omega)$, is a necessary condition for $f(t)$ to be real has been shown in Prob. 4.6. Next, it will be proved that (4.23) is also a sufficient condition for $f(t)$ to be real.

Let

$$f(t) = f_1(t) + j\, f_2(t), \tag{4.25}$$

where $f_1(t)$ and $f_2(t)$ are real functions. Then from (4.16),

$$f(t) = f_1(t) + j\, f_2(t)$$

$$= \frac{1}{2\pi} \int_{-\infty}^{\infty} F(\omega)\, e^{j\omega t}\, d\omega$$

$$= \frac{1}{2\pi} \int_{-\infty}^{\infty} [R(\omega) + j\, X(\omega)] (\cos \omega t + j \sin \omega t)\, d\omega$$

$$= \frac{1}{2\pi} \int_{-\infty}^{\infty} [R(\omega) \cos \omega t - X(\omega) \sin \omega t]\, d\omega$$

$$+ j\, \frac{1}{2\pi} \int_{-\infty}^{\infty} [R(\omega) \sin \omega t + X(\omega) \cos \omega t]\, d\omega. \tag{4.26}$$

Hence,

$$f_1(t) = \frac{1}{2\pi} \int_{-\infty}^{\infty} [R(\omega) \cos \omega t - X(\omega) \sin \omega t]\, d\omega, \tag{4.27}$$

$$f_2(t) = \frac{1}{2\pi} \int_{-\infty}^{\infty} [R(\omega) \sin \omega t + X(\omega) \cos \omega t]\, d\omega. \tag{4.28}$$

Now, if $F(-\omega) = F^*(\omega)$, then

$$R(-\omega) = R(\omega) \qquad \text{and} \qquad X(-\omega) = -X(\omega).$$

Consequently (from the results of Prob. 2.1), $R(\omega) \sin \omega t$ and $X(\omega) \cos \omega t$ are odd functions of ω, and the integrand in (4.28) is an odd function of ω. Hence from (2.21),

$$f_2(t) = 0,$$

i.e., $f(t)$ is real.

PROBLEM 4.8 If $f(t)$ is real, then show that its magnitude spectrum $|F(\omega)|$ is an even function of ω, and its phase spectrum $\phi(\omega)$ is an odd function of ω.

Solution: If $f(t)$ is real, then, from (4.23),

$$F(-\omega) = F^*(\omega). \tag{4.29}$$

Now from (4.18),

$$F^*(\omega) = |F(\omega)|\, e^{-j\phi(\omega)}, \tag{4.30}$$

$$F(-\omega) = |F(-\omega)|\, e^{j\phi(-\omega)}. \tag{4.31}$$

Hence,

$$|F(-\omega)|\, e^{j\phi(-\omega)} = |F(\omega)|\, e^{-j\phi(\omega)}, \tag{4.32}$$

and therefore,

$$|F(-\omega)| = |F(\omega)|, \tag{4.33}$$

$$\phi(-\omega) = -\phi(\omega). \tag{4.34}$$

PROBLEM 4.9 Show that if the Fourier transform of a real function $f(t)$ is real, then $f(t)$ is an even function of t, and if the Fourier transform of a real function $f(t)$ is pure imaginary, then $f(t)$ is an odd function of t.

Solution: Let

$$\mathcal{F}[f(t)] = F(\omega) = R(\omega) + j X(\omega). \tag{4.35}$$

Then from (4.19) and (4.20),

$$R(\omega) = \int_{-\infty}^{\infty} f(t) \cos \omega t \, dt, \tag{4.36}$$

$$X(\omega) = -\int_{-\infty}^{\infty} f(t) \sin \omega t \, dt. \tag{4.37}$$

If $F(\omega) = R(\omega)$ and $X(\omega) = 0$, then the integrand of (4.37) must be odd with respect to t. Since $\sin \omega t$ is an odd function of t, $f(t)$ must be an even function of t.

Alternate Solution: From (4.27), with $X(\omega) = 0$,

$$f(t) = \frac{1}{2\pi} \int_{-\infty}^{\infty} R(\omega) \cos \omega t \, d\omega$$

$$= \frac{1}{\pi} \int_{0}^{\infty} R(\omega) \cos \omega t \, d\omega, \tag{4.38}$$

where, from (4.19),

$$R(\omega) = 2 \int_{0}^{\infty} f(t) \cos \omega t \, dt. \tag{4.39}$$

From (4.38) it is obvious that $f(-t) = f(t)$.

Similarly, if $F(\omega) = j X(\omega)$, i.e., $R(\omega) = 0$, then the integrand of (4.36) must be odd with respect to t. Since $\cos \omega t$ is an even function of t, $f(t)$ must be an odd function of t.

Or, again from (4.27) we have, if $R(\omega) = 0$,

$$f(t) = -\frac{1}{2\pi} \int_{-\infty}^{\infty} X(\omega) \sin \omega t \, d\omega$$

$$= -\frac{1}{\pi} \int_{0}^{\infty} X(\omega) \sin \omega t \, d\omega, \tag{4.40}$$

where, from (4.20),

$$X(\omega) = -2 \int_{0}^{\infty} f(t) \sin \omega t \, dt. \tag{4.41}$$

From (4.40) it is also obvious that $f(-t) = -f(t)$.

From the above results, we conclude that if $f(t)$ is a real function and

$$\mathcal{F}[f(t)] = F(\omega) = R(\omega) + j X(\omega),$$

then

$$\mathcal{F}[f_e(t)] = R(\omega), \tag{4.42}$$

$$\mathcal{F}[f_o(t)] = j X(\omega), \tag{4.43}$$

where $f(t) = f_e(t) + f_o(t)$, and $f_e(t)$ and $f_o(t)$ are the even and odd components of $f(t)$, respectively.

PROBLEM 4.10 Find the Fourier transform of the rectangular pulse $p_d(t)$ [Fig. 4.2(a)] defined by

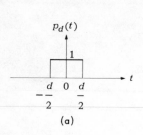

$p_d(t)$

1

$-\dfrac{d}{2}$ 0 $\dfrac{d}{2}$ t

(a)

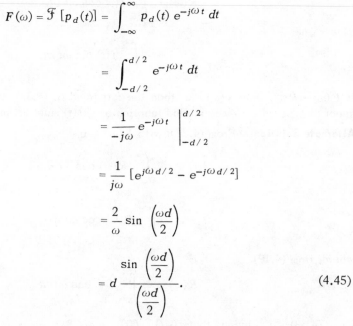

$|F(\omega)|$

d

$-\dfrac{2\pi}{d}$ 0 $\dfrac{2\pi}{d}$ ω

(b)

Fig. 4.2 (a) The rectangular pulse of Prob. 4.10. (b) Fourier transform of the rectangular pulse in Fig. 4.2(a).

$$p_d(t) = \begin{cases} 1, & |t| < \dfrac{1}{2}d \\[2mm] 0, & |t| > \dfrac{1}{2}d. \end{cases} \qquad (4.44)$$

Solution: From (4.15),

$$F(\omega) = \mathcal{F}[p_d(t)] = \int_{-\infty}^{\infty} p_d(t)\, e^{-j\omega t}\, dt$$

$$= \int_{-d/2}^{d/2} e^{-j\omega t}\, dt$$

$$= \frac{1}{-j\omega} e^{-j\omega t} \Big|_{-d/2}^{d/2}$$

$$= \frac{1}{j\omega}\left[e^{j\omega d/2} - e^{-j\omega d/2}\right]$$

$$= \frac{2}{\omega}\sin\left(\frac{\omega d}{2}\right)$$

$$= d\,\frac{\sin\left(\dfrac{\omega d}{2}\right)}{\left(\dfrac{\omega d}{2}\right)}. \qquad (4.45)$$

In Fig. 4.2(b), the solid line is the magnitude spectrum $|F(\omega)|$, and the dotted line shows $F(\omega)$.

PROBLEM 4.11 Find the Fourier transform of $f(t)$ defined by

$$f(t) = \begin{cases} e^{-\alpha t}, & t > 0 \\[2mm] 0, & t < 0, \end{cases} \qquad (4.46)$$

where $\alpha > 0$ (Fig. 4.3).

Solution: By means of (4.15),

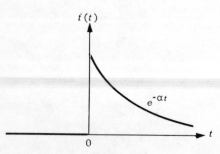

$f(t)$

$e^{-\alpha t}$

0 t

Fig. 4.3 The function $f(t)$ of Prob. 4.11.

$$F(\omega) = \int_{-\infty}^{\infty} f(t)\, e^{-j\omega t}\, dt$$

$$= \int_{0}^{\infty} e^{-\alpha t}\, e^{-j\omega t}\, dt$$

$$= \int_{0}^{\infty} e^{-(\alpha + j\omega) t}\, dt$$

$$= \frac{1}{-(\alpha + j\omega)} e^{-(\alpha + j\omega) t} \Big|_{0}^{\infty}$$

$$= \frac{1}{\alpha + j\omega}. \qquad (4.47)$$

4.4 Fourier Sine and Cosine Transforms

PROBLEM 4.12 If $f(t)$ is given only for $0 < t < \infty$, then show that $f(t)$ can be represented by

$$f(t) = \frac{2}{\pi} \int_0^\infty F_c(\omega) \cos \omega t \, d\omega, \tag{4.48}$$

where $F_c(\omega)$ is given by

$$F_c(\omega) = \int_0^\infty f(t) \cos \omega t \, dt. \tag{4.49}$$

Solution: If $f(t)$ is given only for $0 < t < \infty$, we can define $f(t)$ for negative t by the equation $f(-t) = f(t)$, so that the resulting function is even. Here we assume a convenient behavior of $f(t)$ for negative time. Of course, we are careful to remember in interpreting results that $f(t)$ is defined only for t greater than zero. Now if we define

$$F_c(\omega) = \int_0^\infty f(t) \cos \omega t \, dt,$$

then from (4.38) and (4.39),

$$f(t) = \frac{2}{\pi} \int_0^\infty F_c(\omega) \cos \omega t \, d\omega.$$

We call $F_c(\omega)$ the *Fourier cosine transform* of $f(t)$ which will be denoted by

$$\mathcal{F}_c[f(t)] = F_c(\omega) = \int_0^\infty f(t) \cos \omega t \, dt, \tag{4.50}$$

$$f(t) = \mathcal{F}_c^{-1}[F_c(\omega)] = \frac{2}{\pi} \int_0^\infty F_c(\omega) \cos \omega t \, d\omega. \tag{4.51}$$

PROBLEM 4.13 If $f(t)$ is given only for $0 < t < \infty$, then show that $f(t)$ can be represented by

$$f(t) = \frac{2}{\pi} \int_0^\infty F_s(\omega) \sin \omega t \, d\omega, \tag{4.52}$$

where $F_s(\omega)$ is given by

$$F_s(\omega) = \int_0^\infty f(t) \sin \omega t \, dt. \tag{4.53}$$

Solution: If $f(t)$ is given only for $0 < t < \infty$, we also can define $f(t)$ for negative t by the equation $f(-t) = -f(t)$, so that the resulting function is odd. Now if we define

$$F_s(\omega) = \int_0^\infty f(t) \sin \omega t \, dt,$$

then from (4.40) and (4.41),

$$f(t) = \frac{2}{\pi} \int_0^\infty F_s(\omega) \sin \omega t \, d\omega.$$

We call $F_s(\omega)$ the *Fourier sine transform* of $f(t)$ which will be denoted by

$$\mathcal{F}_s[f(t)] = F_s(\omega) = \int_0^\infty f(t) \sin \omega t \, dt, \tag{4.54}$$

$$f(t) = \mathcal{F}_s^{-1}[F_s(\omega)] = \frac{2}{\pi} \int_0^\infty F_s(\omega) \sin \omega t \, d\omega. \tag{4.55}$$

PROBLEM 4.14 Find $\mathcal{F}_c[e^{-\alpha t}]$ and $\mathcal{F}_s[e^{-\alpha t}]$ for $t > 0$, $\alpha > 0$.

Solution: The Fourier cosine and sine transforms of $e^{-\alpha t}$ are

$$\mathcal{F}_c[e^{-\alpha t}] = \int_0^\infty e^{-\alpha t} \cos \omega t \, dt,$$

$$\mathcal{F}_s[e^{-\alpha t}] = \int_0^\infty e^{-\alpha t} \sin \omega t \, dt.$$

Let $\displaystyle\int_0^\infty e^{-\alpha t} \cos \omega t \, dt = I_1$ and $\displaystyle\int_0^\infty e^{-\alpha t} \sin \omega t \, dt = I_2$; then, integrating I_1 by parts,

$$I_1 = \int_0^\infty e^{-\alpha t} \cos \omega t \, dt$$

$$= \frac{-e^{-\alpha t} \cos \omega t}{\alpha} \Big|_0^\infty - \frac{\omega}{\alpha} \int_0^\infty e^{-\alpha t} \sin \omega t \, dt$$

$$= \frac{1}{\alpha} - \frac{\omega}{\alpha} I_2. \tag{4.56}$$

Similarly, integrating I_2 by parts,

$$I_2 = \int_0^\infty e^{-\alpha t} \sin \omega t \, dt$$

$$= \frac{-e^{-\alpha t} \sin \omega t}{\alpha} \Big|_0^\infty + \frac{\omega}{\alpha} \int_0^\infty e^{-\alpha t} \cos \omega t \, dt$$

$$= \frac{\omega}{\alpha} I_1. \tag{4.57}$$

Solving (4.56) and (4.57) for I_1 and I_2 yields

$$I_1 = \frac{\alpha}{\alpha^2 + \omega^2} \qquad \text{and} \qquad I_2 = \frac{\omega}{\alpha^2 + \omega^2};$$

hence,

$$\mathcal{F}_c[e^{-\alpha t}] = \frac{\alpha}{\alpha^2 + \omega^2}, \tag{4.58}$$

$$\mathcal{F}_s[e^{-\alpha t}] = \frac{\omega}{\alpha^2 + \omega^2}. \tag{4.59}$$

4.5 Interpretation of Fourier Transforms

Assuming that $f(t)$ is periodic with period T, then $f(t)$ can be expressed as

$$f(t) = \sum_{n=-\infty}^{\infty} c_n \, e^{jn\omega_0 t}, \qquad \omega_0 = \frac{2\pi}{T}, \tag{4.60}$$

where

$$c_n = \frac{1}{T} \int_{-T/2}^{T/2} f(t) \, e^{-jn\omega_0 t} \, dt. \tag{4.61}$$

Now, if we consider that as $T \longrightarrow \infty$, $\omega_0 \longrightarrow \Delta\omega = 2\pi \, \Delta f$, $\Delta f = 1/T$, then (4.60) and (4.61) become, respectively,

$$f(t) = \sum_{n=-\infty}^{\infty} c_n \, e^{j(n \, \Delta\omega) T}, \tag{4.62}$$

$$c_n = \Delta f \int_{-T/2}^{T/2} f(t) \, e^{-j(n \, \Delta\omega) t} \, dt. \tag{4.63}$$

Following an argument similar to that in the derivation of (4.9), we observe that as $\Delta\omega \longrightarrow 0$, $n \longrightarrow \infty$, such that $n \, \Delta\omega \longrightarrow \omega$. In other words, in the limit, instead of having discrete harmonics corresponding to the $n\omega_0$, every value of ω is allowed. Thus, instead of having c_n, we have $c(\omega)$, and from (4.63),

$$\lim_{\Delta f \to 0} \frac{c(\omega)}{\Delta f} = \int_{-\infty}^{\infty} f(t) \, e^{-j\omega t} \, dt = F(\omega). \tag{4.64}$$

From (4.64), we note that

$$F(\omega) \, df = c(\omega), \tag{4.65}$$

or, since $\omega = 2\pi f$,

$$\frac{1}{2\pi} F(\omega) \, d\omega = c(\omega). \tag{4.66}$$

Then (4.62) becomes

$$f(t) = \int_{-\infty}^{\infty} \frac{1}{2\pi} F(\omega) \, d\omega \, e^{j\omega t}$$

$$= \frac{1}{2\pi} \int_{-\infty}^{\infty} F(\omega) \, e^{j\omega t} \, d\omega. \tag{4.67}$$

This equation shows that $\frac{1}{2}\pi |F(\omega)| \, d\omega$ represents the infinitesimal magnitude of a "harmonic" at the radian frequency ω. These harmonics have zero fundamental frequency ($\omega_0 \longrightarrow d\omega$) and are "spaced" infinitesimally far apart. Though $|F(\omega)| \, d\omega$ is infinitesimal, $F(\omega)$ is finite. For this reason we call the plot of $|F(\omega)|$ vs. ω a *continuous spectrum*, and $|F(\omega)|$ is often called the *magnitude spectrum* of $f(t)$.

The above representation of a nonperiodic function as a sum of exponentials with the fundamental frequency tending to zero is not an easy concept to accept. Sometimes the following interpretation of the Fourier transform pair (4.15) and (4.16) will be more direct and meaningful:

$$F(\omega) = \int_{-\infty}^{\infty} f(t) \, e^{-j\omega t} \, dt, \qquad\qquad [4.15]$$

$$f(t) = \frac{1}{2\pi} \int_{-\infty}^{\infty} F(\omega) \, e^{j\omega t} \, d\omega. \qquad\qquad [4.16]$$

Namely, we assume that any given function has two equivalent modes of representation: one in the time domain $f(t)$, and the other in the frequency domain $F(\omega)$. Equation (4.15) transforms a function $f(t)$ in the time domain into its equivalent function $F(\omega)$ in the frequency domain, and (4.16) reverses the process. Equation (4.15) analyzes the time function into a frequency spectrum, and (4.16) synthesizes the frequency spectrum to regain the time function.

4.6 Properties of Fourier Transforms

PROBLEM 4.15 If $F_1(\omega) = \mathcal{F}[f_1(t)]$ and $F_2(\omega) = \mathcal{F}[f_2(t)]$, and a_1 and a_2 are two arbitrary constants, then show that

$$\mathcal{F}[a_1 f_1(t) + a_2 f_2(t)] = a_1 F_1(\omega) + a_2 F_2(\omega). \qquad (4.68)$$

Solution: The required Fourier transform is

$$\mathcal{F}[a_1 f_1(t) + a_2 f_2(t)] = \int_{-\infty}^{\infty} [a_1 f_1(t) + a_2 f_2(t)] \, e^{-j\omega t} \, dt$$

$$= a_1 \int_{-\infty}^{\infty} f_1(t) \, e^{-j\omega t} \, dt + a_2 \int_{-\infty}^{\infty} f_2(t) \, e^{-j\omega t} \, dt$$

$$= a_1 F_1(\omega) + a_2 F_2(\omega).$$

PROBLEM 4.16 If a is a real constant and $F(\omega) = \mathcal{F}[f(t)]$, then show that

$$\mathcal{F}[f(at)] = \frac{1}{|a|} F\left(\frac{\omega}{a}\right). \qquad (4.69)$$

Solution: For $a > 0$,

$$\mathcal{F}[f(at)] = \int_{-\infty}^{\infty} f(at) \, e^{-j\omega t} \, dt.$$

Let $at = x$; then,

$$\mathcal{F}[f(at)] = \frac{1}{a} \int_{-\infty}^{\infty} f(x) \, e^{-j(\omega/a)x} \, dx.$$

Since the dummy variable can be represented by any symbol,

$$\mathcal{F}[f(at)] = \frac{1}{a} \int_{-\infty}^{\infty} f(t) \, e^{-j(\omega/a)t} \, dt$$

$$= \frac{1}{|a|} F\left(\frac{\omega}{a}\right). \qquad (4.70)$$

For $a < 0$,

$$\mathcal{F}[f(at)] = \int_{-\infty}^{\infty} f(at) \, e^{-j\omega t} \, dt.$$

Again let $at = x$; then,

$$\mathcal{F}\left[f(at)\right] = \frac{1}{a} \int_{\infty}^{-\infty} f(x)\, e^{-j(\omega/a)x}\, dx$$

$$= -\frac{1}{a} \int_{-\infty}^{\infty} f(t)\, e^{-j(\omega/a)t}\, dt$$

$$= \frac{1}{|a|}\, F\left(\frac{\omega}{a}\right). \tag{4.71}$$

Consequently,

$$\mathcal{F}\left[f(at)\right] = \frac{1}{|a|}\, F\left(\frac{\omega}{a}\right).$$

Equation (4.68) is the *linearity property* of the Fourier transform.

Equation (4.69) is the *scaling property* of the Fourier transform. The function $f(at)$ represents the function $f(t)$ compressed in the time scale by a factor of a. Similarly, the function $F(\omega/a)$ represents the function $F(\omega)$ expanded in the frequency scale by the same factor a. The scaling property therefore states that compression in the time domain is equivalent to expansion in the frequency domain and vice versa.

PROBLEM 4.17 If $\mathcal{F}\left[f(t)\right] = F(\omega)$, then show that

$$\mathcal{F}\left[f(-t)\right] = F(-\omega). \tag{4.72}$$

Solution: From (4.69),

$$\mathcal{F}\left[f(at)\right] = \frac{1}{|a|}\, F\left(\frac{\omega}{a}\right).$$

Letting $a = -1$,

$$\mathcal{F}\left[f(-t)\right] = F(-\omega).$$

Alternate Solution: The Fourier transform of $f(-t)$ is

$$\mathcal{F}\left[f(-t)\right] = \int_{-\infty}^{\infty} f(-t)\, e^{-j\omega t}\, dt.$$

Letting $-t = x$ inside the integral,

$$\mathcal{F}\left[f(-t)\right] = -\int_{\infty}^{-\infty} f(x)\, e^{j\omega x}\, dx$$

$$= \int_{-\infty}^{\infty} f(x)\, e^{-j(-\omega)x}\, dx$$

$$= \int_{-\infty}^{\infty} f(t)\, e^{-j(-\omega)t}\, dt$$

$$= F(-\omega).$$

PROBLEM 4.18 If $F(\omega) = \mathcal{F}\left[f(t)\right]$, then show that

$$\mathcal{F}\left[f(t - t_0)\right] = F(\omega)\, e^{-j\omega t_0}. \tag{4.73}$$

Solution: The required Fourier transform is

$$\mathcal{F}\left[f(t - t_0)\right] = \int_{-\infty}^{\infty} f(t - t_0)\ e^{-j\omega t}\ dt.$$

Letting $t - t_0 = x$, $dt = dx$; hence,

$$\mathcal{F}\left[f(t - t_0)\right] = \int_{-\infty}^{\infty} f(x)\ e^{-j\omega(t_0 + x)}\ dx$$

$$= e^{-j\omega t_0} \int_{-\infty}^{\infty} f(x)\ e^{-j\omega x}\ dx$$

$$= e^{-j\omega t_0}\ F(\omega).$$

PROBLEM 4.19   If ω_0 is a real constant and $F(\omega) = \mathcal{F}\left[f(t)\right]$, then show that

$$\mathcal{F}\left[f(t)\ e^{j\omega_0 t}\right] = F(\omega - \omega_0). \tag{4.74}$$

Solution: The required Fourier transform is

$$\mathcal{F}\left[f(t)\ e^{j\omega_0 t}\right] = \int_{-\infty}^{\infty} \left[f(t)\ e^{j\omega_0 t}\right] e^{-j\omega t}\ dt = \int_{-\infty}^{\infty} f(t)\ e^{-j(\omega - \omega_0)t}\ dt$$

$$= F(\omega - \omega_0).$$

Equation (4.73) is the *time-shifting property* of the Fourier transform.
Equation (4.74) is the *frequency-shifting property* of the Fourier transform.

PROBLEM 4.20   If $F(\omega) = \mathcal{F}\left[f(t)\right]$, then find the Fourier transform of $f(t) \cos \omega_0 t$.

Solution: With the identity $\cos \omega_0 t = \dfrac{1}{2}(e^{j\omega_0 t} + e^{-j\omega_0 t})$, and (4.74),

$$\mathcal{F}\left[f(t)\cos \omega_0 t\right] = \mathcal{F}\left[\frac{1}{2} f(t)\ e^{j\omega_0 t} + \frac{1}{2} f(t)\ e^{-j\omega_0 t}\right]$$

$$= \frac{1}{2}\mathcal{F}\left[f(t)\ e^{j\omega_0 t}\right] + \frac{1}{2}\mathcal{F}\left[f(t)\ e^{-j\omega_0 t}\right]$$

$$= \frac{1}{2} F(\omega - \omega_0) + \frac{1}{2} F(\omega + \omega_0). \tag{4.75}$$

PROBLEM 4.21   Find the Fourier transform of the cosine function of finite duration d.

Solution: The cosine function of finite duration d [Fig. 4.4(a)] can be expressed as a pulse-modulated function; i.e.,

$$f(t) = p_d(t) \cos \omega_0 t, \tag{4.76}$$

where

$$p_d(t) = \begin{cases} 1 & \text{for}\quad |t| < \dfrac{1}{2} d \\[2mm] 0 & \text{for}\quad |t| > \dfrac{1}{2} d. \end{cases}$$

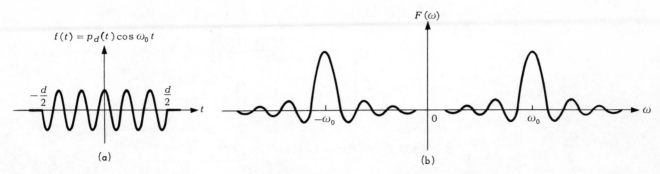

Fig. 4.4 (a) The cosine function of finite duration.   (b) The Fourier transform of the cosine function in Fig. 4.4(a).

Now from the result (4.45) of Prob. 4.10,

$$\mathcal{F}[p_d(t)] = \frac{2}{\omega} \sin\left(\frac{\omega d}{2}\right). \tag{4.77}$$

Then from (4.75),

$$F(\omega) = \mathcal{F}[p_d(t) \cos \omega_0 t]$$

$$= \frac{\sin \frac{1}{2} d (\omega - \omega_0)}{\omega - \omega_0} + \frac{\sin \frac{1}{2} d (\omega + \omega_0)}{\omega + \omega_0}. \tag{4.78}$$

The Fourier transform $F(\omega)$ is plotted in Fig. 4.4(b).

PROBLEM 4.22   If $F(\omega) = \mathcal{F}[f(t)]$, then show that

$$\mathcal{F}[F(t)] = 2\pi f(-\omega). \tag{4.79}$$

Solution: From (4.16),

$$2\pi f(t) = \int_{-\infty}^{\infty} F(\omega) e^{j\omega t} d\omega. \tag{4.80}$$

Changing t to $-t$ in the above expression,

$$2\pi f(-t) = \int_{-\infty}^{\infty} F(\omega) e^{-j\omega t} d\omega. \tag{4.81}$$

Now interchanging t and ω in (4.81),

$$2\pi f(-\omega) = \int_{-\infty}^{\infty} F(t) e^{-j\omega t} dt = \mathcal{F}[F(t)]. \tag{4.82}$$

Equation (4.79) is the *symmetry property* of the Fourier transform.

PROBLEM 4.23   Find the Fourier transform of the function

$$f(t) = \frac{\sin at}{\pi t}. \tag{4.83}$$

Solution: From (4.45) of Prob. 4.10,

$$\mathcal{F}[p_d(t)] = \frac{2}{\omega} \sin\left(\frac{\omega d}{2}\right). \tag{4.84}$$

Now from the symmetry property of the Fourier transform (4.79),

$$\mathcal{F}\left[\frac{2}{t}\sin\left(\frac{dt}{2}\right)\right] = 2\pi\, p_d(-\omega) \tag{4.85}$$

or

$$\mathcal{F}\left[\frac{\sin\left(\frac{1}{2}dt\right)}{\pi t}\right] = p_d(-\omega). \tag{4.86}$$

Since $p_d(\omega)$ is defined by (see Prob. 4.10),

$$p_d(\omega) = \begin{cases} 1 & \text{for} \quad |\omega| < \frac{1}{2}d \\[2mm] 0 & \text{for} \quad |\omega| > \frac{1}{2}d \ , \end{cases} \tag{4.87}$$

it is an even function of ω. Hence,

$$p_d(-\omega) = p_d(\omega). \tag{4.88}$$

Letting $\frac{1}{2}d = a$ in (4.86),

$$\mathcal{F}\left(\frac{\sin at}{\pi t}\right) = p_{2a}(\omega), \tag{4.89}$$

where

$$p_{2a}(\omega) = \begin{cases} 1 & \text{for} \quad |\omega| < a \\[2mm] 0 & \text{for} \quad |\omega| > a. \end{cases} \tag{4.90}$$

Plots of $f(t) = \sin at/\pi t$ and its Fourier transform $F(\omega)$ are shown in Fig. 4.5.

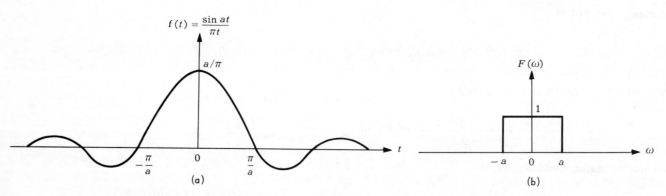

Fig. 4.5 (a) The function $f(t)$ of Prob. 4.23. (b) The Fourier transform of $f(t)$ in Fig. 4.5(a).

We now seek the relationship between the Fourier transform of a function $f(t)$ and the Fourier transform of its derivative $f'(t)$.

PROBLEM 4.24 If $\mathcal{F}[f(t)] = F(\omega)$ and $f(t) \longrightarrow 0$ as $t \longrightarrow \pm\infty$, then show that

$$\mathcal{F}[f'(t)] = j\omega\, F(\omega) = j\omega\, \mathcal{F}[f(t)]. \tag{4.91}$$

Solution: On integration by parts,

$$\mathcal{F}[f'(t)] = \int_{-\infty}^{\infty} f'(t)\, e^{-j\omega t}\, dt = f(t)\, e^{-j\omega t}\, \bigg|_{-\infty}^{\infty} + j\omega \int_{-\infty}^{\infty} f(t)\, e^{-j\omega t}\, dt. \tag{4.92}$$

Since $f(t) \longrightarrow 0$ as $t \longrightarrow \pm\infty$,

$$\mathcal{F}[f'(t)] = j\omega \int_{-\infty}^{\infty} f(t)\, e^{-j\omega t}\, dt = j\omega\, F(\omega) = j\omega\, \mathcal{F}[f(t)].$$

Problem 4.24 shows that differentiation in the time domain corresponds to multiplication of the Fourier transform by $j\omega$, provided that $f(t) \longrightarrow 0$ as $t \longrightarrow \pm\infty$.

It should be noted that if $f(t)$ has a finite number of jump discontinuities, then $f'(t)$ contains impulses (see Prob. 2.28). Then the Fourier transform of $f'(t)$ for this case must contain the Fourier transform of the impulses in $f'(t)$, which will be discussed in Chap. 5.

By repeated application of (4.91),

$$\mathcal{F}[f^{(n)}(t)] = (j\omega)^n\, F(\omega) = (j\omega)^n\, \mathcal{F}[f(t)], \quad n = 1, 2, \cdots . \tag{4.93}$$

It should be noted that (4.93) does not guarantee the existence of the Fourier transform of $f^{(n)}(t)$; it only indicates that if the transform exists, then it is given by $(j\omega)^n\, F(\omega)$.

PROBLEM 4.25 If $\mathcal{F}[f(t)] = F(\omega)$, $\omega \neq 0$, and

$$\int_{-\infty}^{\infty} f(t)\, dt = F(0) = 0, \tag{4.94}$$

then show that

$$\mathcal{F}\left[\int_{-\infty}^{t} f(x)\, dx\right] = \frac{1}{j\omega}\, F(\omega) = \frac{1}{j\omega}\, \mathcal{F}[f(t)]. \tag{4.95}$$

Solution: Consider the function

$$\phi(t) = \int_{-\infty}^{t} f(x)\, dx; \tag{4.96}$$

then $\phi'(t) = f(t)$. Hence, if $\mathcal{F}[\phi(t)] = \Phi(\omega)$, then from (4.91),

$$\mathcal{F}[\phi'(t)] = \mathcal{F}[f(t)] = j\omega\Phi(\omega) \tag{4.97}$$

provided that

$$\lim_{t \to \infty} \phi(t) = \int_{-\infty}^{\infty} f(x)\, dx = \int_{-\infty}^{\infty} f(t)\, dt = F(0) = 0. \tag{4.98}$$

Therefore,

$$\Phi(\omega) = \frac{1}{j\omega}\, \mathcal{F}[f(t)] = \frac{1}{j\omega}\, F(\omega); \tag{4.99}$$

that is,

$$\mathcal{F}\left[\int_{-\infty}^{t} f(x)\, dx\right] = \frac{1}{j\omega}\, F(\omega) = \frac{1}{j\omega}\, \mathcal{F}[f(t)].$$

Note that (4.95) applies only when $\omega \neq 0$. When $\omega = 0$,

$$\mathcal{F}[\phi(t)] = \int_{-\infty}^{\infty} \phi(t)\, dt. \tag{4.100}$$

When $F(0) = \int_{-\infty}^{\infty} f(x)\, dx \neq 0$,

$$\mathcal{F}\left[\int_{-\infty}^{t} f(x)\, dx\right] = \frac{1}{j\omega} F(\omega) + \pi F(0)\, \delta(\omega). \tag{4.101}$$

This is proved in Prob. 5.12.

PROBLEM 4.26 If $\mathcal{F}[f(t)] = F(\omega)$, then show that

$$\mathcal{F}[-jt\, f(t)] = \frac{dF(\omega)}{d\omega}. \tag{4.102}$$

Solution: Since

$$F(\omega) = \int_{-\infty}^{\infty} f(t)\, e^{-j\omega t}\, dt, \tag{4.103}$$

we have

$$\frac{dF(\omega)}{d\omega} = \frac{d}{d\omega} \int_{-\infty}^{\infty} f(t)\, e^{-j\omega t}\, dt. \tag{4.104}$$

Changing the order of differentiation and integration,

$$\frac{dF(\omega)}{d\omega} = \int_{-\infty}^{\infty} f(t)\, \frac{\partial}{\partial\omega}(e^{-j\omega t})\, dt = \int_{-\infty}^{\infty} [-jt\, f(t)]\, e^{-j\omega t}\, dt$$

$$= \mathcal{F}[-jt\, f(t)].$$

4.7 Convolution

Let $f_1(t)$ and $f_2(t)$ be two given functions. The *convolution* of $f_1(t)$ and $f_2(t)$ is defined to be the function

$$f(t) = \int_{-\infty}^{\infty} f_1(x)\, f_2(t - x)\, dx, \tag{4.105}$$

which is often expressed symbolically as

$$f(t) = f_1(t) * f_2(t). \tag{4.106}$$

An important special case is that in which

$$f_1(t) = 0 \quad \text{for} \quad t < 0, \qquad \text{and} \qquad f_2(t) = 0 \quad \text{for} \quad t < 0.$$

Then (4.105) becomes

$$f(t) = f_1(t) * f_2(t) = \int_{0}^{t} f_1(x)\, f_2(t - x)\, dx. \tag{4.107}$$

PROBLEM 4.27 Show that convolution obeys the *commutative law*; that is,

$$f_1(t) * f_2(t) = f_2(t) * f_1(t). \tag{4.108}$$

Solution: From (4.105),

$$f_1(t) * f_2(t) = \int_{-\infty}^{\infty} f_1(x)\, f_2(t - x)\, dx. \tag{4.109}$$

By changing the variable to $t - x = y$,

$$f_1(t) * f_2(t) = \int_{-\infty}^{\infty} f_1(t - y) \, f_2(y) \, dy$$

$$= \int_{-\infty}^{\infty} f_2(y) \, f_1(t - y) \, dy$$

$$= f_2(t) * f_1(t). \qquad (4.110)$$

PROBLEM 4.28   Show that convolution obeys the *associative law*; that is,

$$[f_1(t) * f_2(t)] * f_3(t) = f_1(t) * [f_2(t) * f_3(t)]. \qquad (4.111)$$

Solution: If we let $f_1(t) * f_2(t) = g(t)$, and $f_2(t) * f_3(t) = h(t)$, then (4.111) can be expressed as

$$g(t) * f_3(t) = f_1(t) * h(t). \qquad (4.112)$$

Since

$$g(t) = \int_{-\infty}^{\infty} f_1(y) \, f_2(t - y) \, dy, \qquad (4.113)$$

we have

$$g(t) * f_3(t) = \int_{-\infty}^{\infty} g(x) \, f_3(t - x) \, dx$$

$$= \int_{-\infty}^{\infty} \left[\int_{-\infty}^{\infty} f_1(y) \, f_2(x - y) \, dy \right] f_3(t - x) \, dx. \qquad (4.114)$$

Substituting $z = x - y$, and interchanging the order of integration,

$$g(t) * f_3(t) = \int_{-\infty}^{\infty} f_1(y) \left[\int_{-\infty}^{\infty} f_2(z) \, f_3(t - y - z) \, dz \right] dy. \qquad (4.115)$$

Now since

$$h(t) = \int_{-\infty}^{\infty} f_2(z) \, f_3(t - z) \, dz, \qquad (4.116)$$

we have

$$h(t - y) = \int_{-\infty}^{\infty} f_2(z) \, f_3(t - y - z) \, dz. \qquad (4.117)$$

Therefore, we identify the integral inside the bracket on the right-hand side of (4.115) as $h(t - y)$.

Hence,

$$g(t) * f_3(t) = \int_{-\infty}^{\infty} f_1(y) \, h(t - y) \, dy = f_1(t) * h(t); \qquad (4.118)$$

that is,

$$[f_1(t) * f_2(t)] * f_3(t) = f_1(t) * [f_2(t) * f_3(t)].$$

PROBLEM 4.29   Show that the convolution of a function $f(t)$ with a unit impulse function $\delta(t)$ yields the function $f(t)$ itself.

Solution: By definition (4.105),

$$f(t) * \delta(t) = \int_{-\infty}^{\infty} f(x)\, \delta(t-x)\, dx.$$

Using the commutative property (4.108),

$$f(t) * \delta(t) = \delta(t) * f(t) = \int_{-\infty}^{\infty} \delta(x)\, f(t-x)\, dx = f(t) \qquad (4.119)$$

according to (2.68).

Hence,

$$f(t) * \delta(t) = f(t).$$

PROBLEM 4.30   Show that

$$f(t) * \delta(t-T) = f(t-T), \qquad\qquad (4.120)$$

$$f(t-t_1) * \delta(t-t_2) = f(t-t_1-t_2). \qquad\qquad (4.121)$$

Solution: Proceeding as in Prob. 4.29,

$$f(t) * \delta(t-T) = \delta(t-T) * f(t) = \int_{-\infty}^{\infty} \delta(x-T)\, f(t-x)\, dx = f(t-T)$$

according to (2.68). Similarly,

$$f(t-t_1) * \delta(t-t_2) = \delta(t-t_2) * f(t-t_1) = \int_{-\infty}^{\infty} \delta(x-t_2)\, f(t-x-t_1)\, dx$$

$$= f(t-t_2-t_1)$$

$$= f(t-t_1-t_2).$$

The *time convolution theorem* states that if $\mathcal{F}[f_1(t)] = F_1(\omega)$ and $\mathcal{F}[f_2(t)] = F_2(\omega)$, then

$$\mathcal{F}[f_1(t) * f_2(t)] = F_1(\omega)\, F_2(\omega). \qquad\qquad (4.122)$$

PROBLEM 4.31   Prove the time convolution theorem.

Solution: The Fourier transform of $f_1(t) * f_2(t)$ is

$$\mathcal{F}[f_1(t) * f_2(t)] = \int_{-\infty}^{\infty} \left[\int_{-\infty}^{\infty} f_1(x)\, f_2(t-x)\, dx\right] e^{-j\omega t}\, dt.$$

Changing the order of integration,

$$\mathcal{F}[f_1(t) * f_2(t)] = \int_{-\infty}^{\infty} f_1(x) \left[\int_{-\infty}^{\infty} f_2(t-x)\, e^{-j\omega t}\, dt\right] dx. \qquad (4.123)$$

From the time-shifting property of the Fourier transform (4.73),

$$\int_{-\infty}^{\infty} f_2(t-x)\, e^{-j\omega t}\, dt = F_2(\omega)\, e^{-j\omega x}.$$

Substituting this into (4.123),

$$\mathcal{F}[f_1(t) * f_2(t)] = \int_{-\infty}^{\infty} f_1(x)\, F_2(\omega)\, e^{-j\omega x} dx = \left[\int_{-\infty}^{\infty} f_1(x)\, e^{-j\omega x}\, dx\right] F_2(\omega)$$

$$= \left[\int_{-\infty}^{\infty} f_1(t)\, e^{-j\omega t}\, dt\right] F_2(\omega)$$

$$= F_1(\omega)\, F_2(\omega).$$

The *frequency convolution theorem* states that if $\mathcal{F}^{-1}[F_1(\omega)] = f_1(t)$ and $\mathcal{F}^{-1}[F_2(\omega)] = f_2(t)$, then

$$\mathcal{F}^{-1}[F_1(\omega) * F_2(\omega)] = 2\pi f_1(t) f_2(t), \qquad (4.124)$$

or

$$\mathcal{F}[f_1(t) f_2(t)] = \frac{1}{2\pi} F_1(\omega) * F_2(\omega) = \frac{1}{2\pi} \int_{-\infty}^{\infty} F_1(y) F_2(\omega - y) \, dy. \qquad (4.125)$$

PROBLEM 4.32   Prove the frequency convolution theorem.

Solution: From (4.16),

$$\mathcal{F}^{-1}[F_1(\omega) * F_2(\omega)] = \mathcal{F}^{-1}\left[\int_{-\infty}^{\infty} F_1(y) F_2(\omega - y) \, dy\right]$$

$$= \frac{1}{2\pi} \int_{-\infty}^{\infty} \left[\int_{-\infty}^{\infty} F_1(y) F_2(\omega - y) \, dy\right] e^{j\omega t} \, d\omega. \qquad (4.126)$$

Substituting $\omega - y = x$ and interchanging the order of integration,

$$\mathcal{F}^{-1}[F_1(\omega) * F_2(\omega)] = \frac{1}{2\pi} \int_{-\infty}^{\infty} F_1(y) \left[\int_{-\infty}^{\infty} F_2(x) e^{j(x+y)t} \, dx\right] dy$$

$$= \frac{1}{2\pi} \int_{-\infty}^{\infty} F_1(y) e^{jyt} \left[\int_{-\infty}^{\infty} F_2(x) e^{jxt} \, dx\right] dy$$

$$= 2\pi \left[\frac{1}{2\pi} \int_{-\infty}^{\infty} F_1(\omega) e^{j\omega t} \, d\omega\right] \left[\frac{1}{2\pi} \int_{-\infty}^{\infty} F_2(\omega) e^{j\omega t} \, d\omega\right]$$

$$= 2\pi [f_1(t) f_2(t)] \qquad (4.127)$$

by changing the dummy variables of integration.

Equation (4.127) can be rewritten as

$$\mathcal{F}[f_1(t) f_2(t)] = \frac{1}{2\pi} F_1(\omega) * F_2(\omega) = \frac{1}{2\pi} \int_{-\infty}^{\infty} F_1(y) F_2(\omega - y) \, dy.$$

PROBLEM 4.33   Using the symmetry property (4.79) of the Fourier transform and the result (4.122) of Prob. 4.31, rework Prob. 4.32.

Solution: From (4.122),

$$\mathcal{F}[f_1(t) * f_2(t)] = F_1(\omega) F_2(\omega);$$

that is,

$$\mathcal{F}\left[\int_{-\infty}^{\infty} f_1(x) f_2(t - x) \, dx\right] = F_1(\omega) F_2(\omega). \qquad (4.128)$$

Now from the symmetry property (4.79) of the Fourier transform, we know that if $\mathcal{F}[f(t)] = F(\omega)$, then $\mathcal{F}[F(t)] = 2\pi f(-\omega)$.   Applying this result to (4.128),

$$\mathcal{F}[F_1(t) F_2(t)] = 2\pi \int_{-\infty}^{\infty} f_1(x) f_2(-\omega - x) \, dx. \qquad (4.129)$$

Substituting $x = -y$,

$$\mathcal{F}[F_1(t) \, F_2(t)] = 2\pi \int_{-\infty}^{\infty} f_1(-y) \, f_2(-\omega + y) \, dy$$

$$= 2\pi \int_{-\infty}^{\infty} f_1(-y) \, f_2[-(\omega - y)] \, dy$$

$$= \frac{1}{2\pi} \int_{-\infty}^{\infty} [2\pi \, f_1(-y)] \{2\pi \, f_2[-(\omega - y)]\} \, dy. \quad (4.130)$$

Now, remembering that $2\pi \, f_1(-\omega) = \mathcal{F}[F_1(t)]$ and $2\pi \, f_2(-\omega) = \mathcal{F}[F_2(t)]$, and changing $F_1(t)$ and $F_2(t)$ to $f_1(t)$ and $f_2(t)$, respectively, and consequently $2\pi \, f_1(-\omega)$ and $2\pi \, f_2(-\omega)$ to $F_1(\omega)$ and $F_2(\omega)$, respectively, we can rewrite (4.130) as

$$\mathcal{F}[f_1(t) \, f_2(t)] = \frac{1}{2\pi} \int_{-\infty}^{\infty} F_1(y) \, F_2(\omega - y) \, dy = \frac{1}{2\pi} F_1(\omega) * F_2(\omega).$$

PROBLEM 4.34   Use convolution to find $f(t) = \mathcal{F}^{-1}\left[\dfrac{1}{(1 + j\omega)^2}\right]$.

Solution: The Fourier transform of $f(t)$ is

$$F(\omega) = \mathcal{F}[f(t)] = \frac{1}{(1 + j\omega)^2} = \frac{1}{(1 + j\omega)} \times \frac{1}{(1 + j\omega)}.$$

From (4.47), we recall that

$$\mathcal{F}^{-1}\left[\frac{1}{1 + j\omega}\right] = e^{-t} \, u(t).$$

Hence, from (4.122),

$$f(t) = \int_{-\infty}^{\infty} e^{-x} \, u(x) \, e^{-(t - x)} \, u(t - x) \, dx. \quad (4.131)$$

In the above integral, the integrand includes the factor $u(x) u(t - x)$. Since $u(x) = 0$ for $x < 0$, and $u(t - x) = 0$ for $x > t$,

$$u(x) u(t - x) = \begin{cases} 0 & \text{for } 0 > x \text{ and } x > t \\ 1 & \text{for } 0 < x < t. \end{cases}$$

Hence,

$$f(t) = \int_{0}^{t} e^{-x} \, e^{-(t - x)} \, dx = e^{-t} \int_{0}^{t} dx = t \, e^{-t} \, u(t). \quad (4.132)$$

4.8 Parseval's Theorem and Energy Spectrum

PROBLEM 4.35   If $\mathcal{F}[f_1(t)] = F_1(\omega)$ and $\mathcal{F}[f_2(t)] = F_2(\omega)$, then show that

$$\int_{-\infty}^{\infty} [f_1(t) \, f_2(t)] \, dt = \frac{1}{2\pi} \int_{-\infty}^{\infty} F_1(\omega) \, F_2(-\omega) \, d\omega. \quad (4.133)$$

Solution: From (4.125),

$$\mathcal{F}[f_1(t)\, f_2(t)] = \frac{1}{2\pi} \int_{-\infty}^{\infty} F_1(y)\, F_2(\omega - y)\, dy;$$

that is,

$$\int_{-\infty}^{\infty} [f_1(t)\, f_2(t)]\, e^{-j\omega t}\, dt = \frac{1}{2\pi} \int_{-\infty}^{\infty} F_1(y)\, F_2(\omega - y)\, dy. \qquad (4.134)$$

Now, letting $\omega = 0$,

$$\int_{-\infty}^{\infty} [f_1(t)\, f_2(t)]\, dt = \frac{1}{2\pi} \int_{-\infty}^{\infty} F_1(y)\, F_2(-y)\, dy$$

$$= \frac{1}{2\pi} \int_{-\infty}^{\infty} F_1(\omega)\, F_2(-\omega)\, d\omega$$

by changing the dummy variable of integration.

PROBLEM 4.36 If the functions $f_1(t)$ and $f_2(t)$ are real, $\mathcal{F}[f_1(t)] = F_1(\omega)$, and $\mathcal{F}[f_2(t)] = F_2(\omega)$, then show that

$$\int_{-\infty}^{\infty} f_1(t)\, f_2(t)\, dt = \frac{1}{2\pi} \int_{-\infty}^{\infty} F_1(\omega)\, F_2^*(\omega)\, d\omega, \qquad (4.135)$$

where $F_2^*(\omega)$ denotes the complex conjugate of $F_2(\omega)$.

Solution: If $f(t)$ is real, then from (4.23),

$$F(-\omega) = F^*(\omega).$$

Consequently from (4.133),

$$\int_{-\infty}^{\infty} f_1(t)\, f_2(t)\, dt = \frac{1}{2\pi} \int_{-\infty}^{\infty} F_1(\omega)\, F_2(-\omega)\, d\omega$$

$$= \frac{1}{2\pi} \int_{-\infty}^{\infty} F_1(\omega)\, F_2^*(\omega)\, d\omega.$$

Parseval's theorem states that if $\mathcal{F}[f(t)] = F(\omega)$, then

$$\int_{-\infty}^{\infty} |f(t)|^2\, dt = \frac{1}{2\pi} \int_{-\infty}^{\infty} |F(\omega)|^2\, d\omega. \qquad (4.136)$$

PROBLEM 4.37 Prove Parseval's theorem.

Solution: If $\mathcal{F}[f(t)] = F(\omega)$, then

$$\mathcal{F}[f^*(t)] = \int_{-\infty}^{\infty} f^*(t)\, e^{-j\omega t}\, dt = \int_{-\infty}^{\infty} [f(t)\, e^{j\omega t}]^*\, dt$$

$$= \left[\int_{-\infty}^{\infty} f(t)\, e^{-j(-\omega)t}\, dt \right]^*$$

$$= F^*(-\omega). \qquad (4.137)$$

Hence, in (4.133), if we let $f_1(t) = f(t)$, and $f_2(t) = f^*(t)$, then

$$\int_{-\infty}^{\infty} f(t)\, f^*(t)\, dt = \frac{1}{2\pi} \int_{-\infty}^{\infty} F(\omega)\, F^*[-(-\omega)]\, d\omega$$

$$= \frac{1}{2\pi} \int_{-\infty}^{\infty} F(\omega)\, F^*(\omega)\, d\omega. \qquad (4.138)$$

Since $f(t)\, f^*(t) = |f(t)|^2$ and $F(\omega)\, F^*(\omega) = |F(\omega)|^2$,

$$\int_{-\infty}^{\infty} |f(t)|^2\, dt = \frac{1}{2\pi} \int_{-\infty}^{\infty} |F(\omega)|^2\, d\omega.$$

If $f(t)$ is real, then (4.136) can be obtained simply from (4.135).

In Sec. 3.6 we saw that for a periodic function, the power in a signal can be associated with the power contained in each discrete frequency component. The same concept can be extended to nonperiodic functions. A useful concept for a nonperiodic function is its *energy content E*, defined by

$$E = \int_{-\infty}^{\infty} |f(t)|^2\, dt. \qquad (4.139)$$

Indeed, if we assume $f(t)$ to be the voltage of a source across a 1-Ω resistance, then the quantity $\int_{-\infty}^{\infty} |f(t)|^2\, dt$ equals the total energy delivered by the source.

Now from Parseval's theorem (4.136),

$$E = \int_{-\infty}^{\infty} |f(t)|^2\, dt = \frac{1}{2\pi} \int_{-\infty}^{\infty} |F(\omega)|^2\, d\omega = \int_{-\infty}^{\infty} |F(\omega)|^2\, df. \qquad (4.140)$$

This equation states that the energy content of $f(t)$ is given by $\frac{1}{2}\pi$ times the area under the $|F(\omega)|^2$ curve. For this reason, the quantity $|F(\omega)|^2$ is called the *energy spectrum* or *energy spectral density function* of $f(t)$.

4.9 Correlation Functions

The function

$$R_{12}(\tau) = \int_{-\infty}^{\infty} f_1(t)\, f_2(t - \tau)\, dt \qquad (4.141)$$

is known as the *cross-correlation function* between functions $f_1(t)$ and $f_2(t)$. In a similar way, we define

$$R_{21}(\tau) = \int_{-\infty}^{\infty} f_2(t)\, f_1(t - \tau)\, dt. \qquad (4.142)$$

The cross-correlation function $R_{12}(\tau)$ or $R_{21}(\tau)$ provides a measure of the similarity or interdependence between functions $f_1(t)$ and $f_2(t)$ as a function of the parameter τ (the shift of one function with respect to the other). If the cross-correlation function is identically zero for all τ, then the two functions are said to be uncorrelated.

If $f_1(t)$ and $f_2(t)$ are identical, then the correlation function

$$R_{11}(\tau) = \int_{-\infty}^{\infty} f_1(t) \, f_1(t - \tau) \, dt \tag{4.143}$$

is termed the *autocorrelation function* of $f_1(t)$.

PROBLEM 4.38 Show that

$$R_{12}(\tau) = \int_{-\infty}^{\infty} f_1(t) \, f_2(t - \tau) \, dt = \int_{-\infty}^{\infty} f_1(t + \tau) \, f_2(t) \, dt, \tag{4.144}$$

$$R_{21}(\tau) = \int_{-\infty}^{\infty} f_2(t) \, f_1(t - \tau) \, dt = \int_{-\infty}^{\infty} f_2(t + \tau) \, f_1(t) \, dt, \tag{4.145}$$

$$R_{11}(\tau) = \int_{-\infty}^{\infty} f_1(t) \, f_1(t - \tau) \, dt = \int_{-\infty}^{\infty} f_1(t + \tau) \, f_1(t) \, dt. \tag{4.146}$$

Solution: By changing the variable t to $(t + \tau)$ in (4.141), (4.142), and (4.143),

$$R_{12}(\tau) = \int_{-\infty}^{\infty} f_1(t + \tau) \, f_2(t) \, dt,$$

$$R_{21}(\tau) = \int_{-\infty}^{\infty} f_2(t + \tau) \, f_1(t) \, dt,$$

$$R_{11}(\tau) = \int_{-\infty}^{\infty} f_1(t + \tau) \, f_1(t) \, dt.$$

From the above results, we note that it is immaterial whether we shift the function $f_1(t)$ by an amount τ in the negative direction or shift the function $f_2(t)$ by the same amount in the positive direction.

PROBLEM 4.39 Show that

$$R_{12}(\tau) = R_{21}(-\tau), \tag{4.147}$$

$$R_{11}(\tau) = R_{11}(-\tau). \tag{4.148}$$

Solution: From (4.145),

$$R_{21}(\tau) = \int_{-\infty}^{\infty} f_2(t + \tau) \, f_1(t) \, dt,$$

and hence,

$$R_{21}(-\tau) = \int_{-\infty}^{\infty} f_2(t - \tau) \, f_1(t) \, dt = \int_{-\infty}^{\infty} f_1(t) \, f_2(t - \tau) \, dt = R_{12}(\tau).$$

Similarly, from (4.146),

$$R_{11}(\tau) = \int_{-\infty}^{\infty} f_1(t + \tau) \, f_1(t) \, dt,$$

and hence,

$$R_{11}(-\tau) = \int_{-\infty}^{\infty} f_1(t - \tau) \, f_1(t) \, dt = \int_{-\infty}^{\infty} f_1(t) \, f_1(t - \tau) \, dt = R_{11}(\tau),$$

in view of (4.143).

Equation (4.148) states that the autocorrelation function is an even function of τ.

PROBLEM 4.40 Show that the cross-correlation of $f_1(t)$ and $f_2(t)$ is related to the convolution of $f_1(t)$ and $f_2(-t)$.

Solution: Let $G_{12}(t) = f_1(t) * f_2(-t)$. Then from the definition (4.105) of convolution, that is,

$$f_1(t) * f_2(t) = \int_{-\infty}^{\infty} f_1(x) f_2(t - x) \, dx,$$

we obtain

$$G_{12}(t) = \int_{-\infty}^{\infty} f_1(x) f_2[-(t - x)] \, dx$$

$$= \int_{-\infty}^{\infty} f_1(x) f_2(x - t) \, dx. \tag{4.149}$$

Changing the variable t to τ,

$$G_{12}(\tau) = \int_{-\infty}^{\infty} f_1(x) f_2(x - \tau) \, dx. \tag{4.150}$$

Again by changing the dummy variable x to t,

$$G_{12}(\tau) = \int_{-\infty}^{\infty} f_1(t) f_2(t - \tau) \, dt$$

$$= R_{12}(\tau). \tag{4.151}$$

Hence,

$$R_{12}(\tau) = G_{12}(\tau) = f_1(t) * f_2(-t)\big|_{t=\tau}. \tag{4.152}$$

PROBLEM 4.41 If $\mathcal{F}[f_1(t)] = F_1(\omega)$ and $\mathcal{F}[f_2(t)] = F_2(\omega)$, then show that

$$\mathcal{F}[R_{12}(\tau)] = F_1(\omega) F_2(-\omega), \tag{4.153}$$

$$\mathcal{F}[R_{21}(\tau)] = F_1(-\omega) F_2(\omega), \tag{4.154}$$

$$\mathcal{F}[R_{11}(\tau)] = F_1(\omega) F_1(-\omega). \tag{4.155}$$

Also, if $f_1(t)$ is real, show that

$$\mathcal{F}[R_{11}(\tau)] = |F(\omega)|^2. \tag{4.156}$$

Solution: Equation (4.72) of Prob. 4.17 shows that if $\mathcal{F}[f(t)] = F(\omega)$, then $\mathcal{F}[f(-t)] = F(-\omega)$. Thus if

$$\mathcal{F}[f_1(t)] = F_1(\omega) \text{ and } \mathcal{F}[f_2(t)] = F_2(\omega),$$

then

$$\mathcal{F}[f_1(-t)] = F_1(-\omega) \text{ and } \mathcal{F}[f_2(-t)] = F_2(-\omega).$$

Now applying the time-convolution theorem

$$\mathcal{F}[f_1(t) * f_2(t)] = F_1(\omega) F_2(\omega) \tag{4.122}$$

to (4.152),

$$\mathcal{F}[R_{12}(\tau)] = \mathcal{F}[f_1(t) * f_2(-t)] = F_1(\omega) F_2(-\omega),$$

or

$$\int_{-\infty}^{\infty} R_{12}(\tau) e^{-j\omega\tau} d\tau = F_1(\omega) F_2(-\omega). \qquad (4.157)$$

Similarly,

$$\mathcal{F}[R_{21}(\tau)] = \mathcal{F}[f_2(t) * f_1(-t)] = F_2(\omega) F_1(-\omega) = F_1(-\omega) F_2(\omega),$$

or

$$\int_{-\infty}^{\infty} R_{21}(\tau) e^{-j\omega\tau} d\tau = F_1(-\omega) F_2(\omega), \qquad (4.158)$$

and

$$\mathcal{F}[R_{11}(\tau)] = \mathcal{F}[f_1(t) * f_1(-t)] = F_1(\omega) F_1(-\omega).$$

From (4.23), if $f_1(t)$ is a real function of t, then $F_1(-\omega) = F_1^*(\omega)$. Hence,

$$\mathcal{F}[R_{11}(\tau)] = F_1(\omega) F_1^*(\omega) = |F_1(\omega)|^2$$

or

$$\int_{-\infty}^{\infty} R_{11}(\tau) e^{-j\omega\tau} d\tau = |F_1(\omega)|^2 \qquad (4.159)$$

if $f_1(t)$ is a real function of t.

PROBLEM 4.42   Derive (4.159) without the use of (4.155).

Solution: From (4.143),

$$R_{11}(\tau) = \int_{-\infty}^{\infty} f_1(t) f_1(t - \tau) \, dt.$$

Then,

$$\mathcal{F}[R_{11}(\tau)] = \int_{-\infty}^{\infty} R_{11}(\tau) e^{-j\omega t} \, d\tau$$

$$= \int_{-\infty}^{\infty} \left[\int_{-\infty}^{\infty} f_1(t) f_1(t - \tau) \, dt\right] e^{-j\omega\tau} \, d\tau$$

$$= \int_{-\infty}^{\infty} f_1(t) \left[\int_{-\infty}^{\infty} f_1(t - \tau) e^{-j\omega\tau} \, d\tau\right] dt \qquad (4.160)$$

by interchanging the order of integration.

Changing the variable $(t - \tau)$ to x in the integral within the bracket in (4.160),

$$\mathcal{F}[R_{11}(\tau)] = \int_{-\infty}^{\infty} f_1(t) \left[\int_{-\infty}^{\infty} f_1(x) e^{-j\omega(t - x)} \, dx\right] dt$$

$$= \int_{-\infty}^{\infty} f_1(t) e^{-j\omega t} \, dt \int_{-\infty}^{\infty} f_1(x) e^{j\omega x} \, dx$$

$$= F_1(\omega) F_1(-\omega)$$

$$= |F_1(\omega)|^2. \qquad (4.161)$$

It follows from (4.159) or (4.161) that the Fourier transform of the autocorrelation function $R_{11}(\tau)$ yields the energy spectrum $|F_1(\omega)|^2$ of $f_1(t)$. In other words, the autocorrelation function $R_{11}(\tau)$ and the energy spectral density $|F_1(\omega)|^2$ constitute a Fourier transform pair; i.e.,

$$|F_1(\omega)|^2 = \mathcal{F}[R_{11}(\tau)] = \int_{-\infty}^{\infty} R_{11}(\tau)\, e^{-j\omega\tau}\, d\tau, \qquad (4.162)$$

$$R_{11}(\tau) = \mathcal{F}^{-1}[|F_1(\omega)|^2] = \frac{1}{2\pi} \int_{-\infty}^{\infty} |F_1(\omega)|^2\, e^{j\omega\tau}\, d\omega. \qquad (4.163)$$

This result is known as the *Wiener-Khintchine theorem*.

PROBLEM 4.43   Show that

$$R_{11}(0) = \int_{-\infty}^{\infty} [f_1(t)]^2\, dt. \qquad (4.164)$$

Solution: From (4.143),

$$R_{11}(\tau) = \int_{-\infty}^{\infty} f_1(t)\, f_1(t-\tau)\, dt.$$

Letting $\tau = 0$,

$$R_{11}(0) = \int_{-\infty}^{\infty} f_1(t)\, f_1(t)\, dt$$

$$= \int_{-\infty}^{\infty} [f_1(t)]^2\, dt.$$

PROBLEM 4.44   From (4.163) and (4.164), derive Parseval's theorem, i.e.,

$$\int_{-\infty}^{\infty} [f_1(t)]^2\, dt = \frac{1}{2\pi} \int_{-\infty}^{\infty} |F_1(\omega)|^2\, d\omega. \qquad (4.165)$$

Solution: From (4.163),

$$R_{11}(\tau) = \frac{1}{2\pi} \int_{-\infty}^{\infty} |F_1(\omega)|^2\, e^{j\omega\tau}\, d\omega.$$

Letting $\tau = 0$,

$$R_{11}(0) = \frac{1}{2\pi} \int_{-\infty}^{\infty} |F_1(\omega)|^2\, d\omega. \qquad (4.166)$$

From (4.164),

$$R_{11}(0) = \int_{-\infty}^{\infty} [f_1(t)]^2\, dt.$$

Hence,

$$\int_{-\infty}^{\infty} [f_1(t)]^2\, dt = \frac{1}{2\pi} \int_{-\infty}^{\infty} |F_1(\omega)|^2\, d\omega.$$

4.10 Supplementary Problems

PROBLEM 4.45 Find the Fourier integral representation of the function

$$f(t) = \begin{cases} 1 & \text{for } |t| < 1 \\ 0 & \text{for } |t| > 1. \end{cases}$$

Answer: $f(t) = \dfrac{2}{\pi} \displaystyle\int_0^\infty \dfrac{\cos t\omega \sin \omega}{\omega} \, d\omega$.

PROBLEM 4.46 Use the result of Prob. 4.45 to derive

$$\int_0^\infty \frac{\sin \omega}{\omega} \, d\omega = \frac{\pi}{2} \, .$$

[Hint: Set $t = 0$ in the result of Prob. 4.45.]

PROBLEM 4.47 If $f(t)$ is pure imaginary, that is, $f(t) = jg(t)$, where $g(t)$ is real, show that the real and imaginary parts of $F(\omega)$ are

$$R(\omega) = \int_{-\infty}^\infty g(t) \sin \omega t \, dt, \qquad X(\omega) = \int_{-\infty}^\infty g(t) \cos \omega t \, dt.$$

Also show that $R(\omega)$ and $X(\omega)$ are odd and even functions of ω; that is,

$$R(-\omega) = -R(\omega), \qquad X(-\omega) = X(\omega), \qquad F(-\omega) = -F^*(\omega).$$

PROBLEM 4.48 If $\mathcal{F}[f(t)] = F(\omega)$, show that $\mathcal{F}[f^*(t)] = F^*(-\omega)$, where $f^*(t)$ is the conjugate function of $f(t)$ and $F^*(-\omega)$ is the conjugate of $F(-\omega)$.

PROBLEM 4.49 If $F(\omega) = \mathcal{F}[f(t)]$, show that

$$\mathcal{F}[f(at) e^{j\omega_0 t}] = \frac{1}{|a|} F\left(\frac{\omega - \omega_0}{a}\right).$$

PROBLEM 4.50 If $F(\omega) = \mathcal{F}[f(t)]$, find the Fourier transform of $f(t) \sin \omega_0 t$.

Answer: $\dfrac{1}{2j} [F(\omega - \omega_0) - F(\omega + \omega_0)]$.

PROBLEM 4.51 Find the Fourier transform of $f(t) = e^{-a|t|}$.

Answer: $2a/(a^2 + \omega^2)$.

PROBLEM 4.52 Find the Fourier transform of $f(t) = \dfrac{1}{a^2 + t^2}$.

[Hint: Apply symmetry property of the Fourier transform (4.79) to the result of Prob. 4.51.]

Answer: $(\pi/a) e^{-a|\omega|}$.

PROBLEM 4.53 (a) Find the Fourier transform of the pulse $f_1(t)$ shown in Fig. 4.6(a). (b) The pulse $f_2(t)$ shown in Fig. 4.6(b) is the integral of $f_1(t)$. Use the result of part (a) to obtain the Fourier transform of $f_2(t)$. Check the result by direct integration.

[Hint: For (b) use the result of Prob. 4.25.]

Answer: (a) $F_1(\omega) = -\dfrac{4A}{j\omega T} \sin^2\left(\dfrac{\omega T}{2}\right)$, (b) $F_2(\omega) = AT \dfrac{\sin^2\left(\dfrac{\omega T}{2}\right)}{\left(\dfrac{\omega T}{2}\right)^2}$.

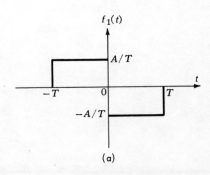

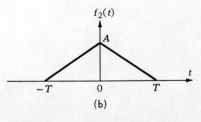

Fig. 4.6 (a) The pulse of Prob. 4.53. (b) The integral of the pulse in Fig. 4.6(a).

PROBLEM 4.54 The n-th moment m_n of a function $f(t)$ is defined by

$$m_n = \int_{-\infty}^{\infty} t^n f(t)\, dt \quad \text{for } n = 0, 1, 2, \cdots .$$

Using the result of Prob. 4.26, show that

$$m_n = (j)^n \frac{d^n F(0)}{d\omega^n} \quad \text{for } n = 0, 1, 2, \cdots ,$$

where $\dfrac{d^n F(0)}{d\omega^n} = \dfrac{d^n F(\omega)}{d\omega^n}\bigg|_{\omega=0}$ and $F(\omega) = \mathcal{F}[f(t)]$.

PROBLEM 4.55 Use the result of Prob. 4.54 to show that $F(\omega) = \mathcal{F}[f(t)]$ can be expressed as

$$F(\omega) = \sum_{n=0}^{\infty} (-j)^n m_n \frac{\omega^n}{n!} .$$

[Hint: Expand $e^{-j\omega t} = \displaystyle\sum_{n=0}^{\infty} \frac{(-j\omega t)^n}{n!}$ and integrate (4.15) termwise.]

PROBLEM 4.56 Show that if $\mathcal{F}[f(t)] = F(\omega)$, then

$$|F(\omega)| \le \int_{-\infty}^{\infty} |f(t)|\, dt, \quad |F(\omega)| \le \frac{1}{|\omega|} \int_{-\infty}^{\infty} \left| \frac{df(t)}{dt} \right| dt, \quad |F(\omega)| \le \frac{1}{\omega^2} \int_{-\infty}^{\infty} \left| \frac{d^2 f(t)}{dt^2} \right| dt.$$

These inequalities determine the upper bounds of $|F(\omega)|$.

PROBLEM 4.57 Use convolution to find $f(t) = \mathcal{F}^{-1}\left[\dfrac{1}{(1 + j\omega)(2 + j\omega)} \right]$.

Answer: $(e^{-t} - e^{-2t})\, u(t)$.

PROBLEM 4.58 Find $f(t)$ of Prob. 4.57 by expanding $F(\omega)$ in partial fractions.

[Hint: $\dfrac{1}{(j\omega + 1)(j\omega + 2)} = \dfrac{1}{j\omega + 1} + \dfrac{-1}{j\omega + 2}$ and use the result of Prob. 4.11.]

PROBLEM 4.59 Show that if $f(t)$ is band-limited, that is, $F(\omega) = \mathcal{F}[f(t)] = 0$ for $|\omega| > \omega_c$, then $f(t) * \dfrac{\sin at}{\pi t} = f(t)$ for every $a > \omega_c$.

[Hint: Use the result of Prob. 4.23 and time convolution theorem (4.122).]

PROBLEM 4.60 Let $F(\omega) = \mathcal{F}[f(t)]$ and $G(\omega) = \mathcal{F}[g(t)]$. Prove that

(a) $$\int_{-\infty}^{\infty} f(x)\, g(t - x)\, dx = \frac{1}{2\pi} \int_{-\infty}^{\infty} F(\omega)\, G(\omega)\, e^{j\omega t}\, d\omega,$$

(b) $$\int_{-\infty}^{\infty} f(t)\, g(-t)\, dt = \frac{1}{2\pi} \int_{-\infty}^{\infty} F(\omega)\, G(\omega)\, d\omega,$$

(c) $$\int_{-\infty}^{\infty} f(t)\, g^*(t)\, dt = \frac{1}{2\pi} \int_{-\infty}^{\infty} F(\omega)\, G^*(\omega)\, d\omega,$$

where * denotes complex conjugation.
[Hint: (a) Use (4.122) and (4.16); (b) deduce from (a) by setting $t = 0$; (c) deduce from (b) with the aid of (4.72) and Prob. 4.48.]

PROBLEM 4.61 Let $f_1(t)$ and $f_2(t)$ be two Gaussian functions; that is,

$$f_1(t) = \frac{1}{\sigma_1 \sqrt{2\pi}} e^{-t^2/2\sigma_1^2}, \quad f_2(t) = \frac{1}{\sigma_2 \sqrt{2\pi}} e^{-t^2/2\sigma_2^2}.$$

Show that if $f_3(t) = f_1(t) * f_2(t)$, then $f_3(t)$ is also a Gaussian function and

$$f_3(t) = \frac{1}{\sigma_3 \sqrt{2\pi}} e^{-t^2/2\sigma_3^2}, \quad \text{where} \quad \sigma_3^2 = \sigma_1^2 + \sigma_2^2.$$

PROBLEM 4.62 Show that the correlation function of any two Gaussian functions is itself a Gaussian function.

PROBLEM 4.63 If $R_{11}(\tau)$ is the autocorrelation function of $f_1(t)$, show that $R_{11}(0) \geq |R_{11}(\tau)|$.

[Hint: Expand the expression $\int_{-\infty}^{\infty} [f_1(t) \pm f_1(t+\tau)]^2 dt > 0$ for $\tau \neq 0.$]

PROBLEM 4.64 If $R_{11}(\tau)$ and $R_{22}(\tau)$ are the autocorrelation functions of $f_1(t)$ and $f_2(t)$, and $R_{12}(\tau)$ is the cross-correlation function of $f_1(t)$ and $f_2(t)$, show that $R_{11}(0) + R_{22}(0) > 2|R_{12}(\tau)|$ for all τ.

[Hint: Expand the expression $\int_{-\infty}^{\infty} [f_1(t) \pm f_2(t+\tau)]^2 dt > 0$ for all τ.]

PROBLEM 4.65 (a) Find the autocorrelation function $R_{11}(\tau)$ of the rectangular pulse $f(t)$ defined by

$$f(t) = \begin{cases} A & \text{for} \quad |t| < d/2 \\ 0 & \text{for} \quad |t| > d/2. \end{cases}$$

(b) Find the energy spectrum density $S(\omega)$ of $f(t)$ from $R_{11}(\tau)$ obtained in part (a) and also check that $S_{11}(\omega) = |F(\omega)|^2$ with the use of $F(\omega)$ given in (4.45).

Answer: (a) $R_{11}(\tau) = \begin{cases} A^2(d-|\tau|) & \text{for} \quad |\tau| < d \\ 0 & \text{for} \quad |\tau| > d, \end{cases}$ (b) $S_{11}(\omega) = A^2 d \left[\frac{\sin(\omega d/2)}{\omega d/2} \right]^2.$

PROBLEM 4.66 Let $R_{11}(\tau)$ be the autocorrelation function and $S_{11}(\omega) = |F_1(\omega)|^2$ be the energy spectrum density of the function $f_1(t)$. Show that the Wiener-Khintchine theorem (4.162-3) can be rewritten as

$$S_{11}(\tau) = \int_0^{\infty} R_{11}(\omega) \cos \omega\tau \, d\omega \quad \text{and} \quad R_{11}(\omega) = \frac{1}{\pi} \int_0^{\infty} S_{11}(\tau) \cos \omega\tau \, d\tau.$$

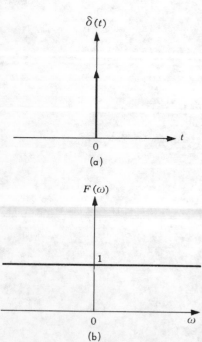

$\delta(t)$

0   t

(a)

$F(\omega)$

1

0   ω

(b)

Fig. 5.1 (a) A unit impulse function. (b) The Fourier transform of a unit impulse function.

5
CHAPTER

FOURIER TRANSFORMS OF SPECIAL FUNCTIONS

5.1 Introduction

The sufficient condition for the existence of a Fourier transform of a function $f(t)$ was given by (4.17), i.e.,

$$\int_{-\infty}^{\infty} |f(t)| \, dt < \infty. \tag{5.1}$$

In other words, the function $f(t)$ is absolutely integrable.

Functions such as $\sin \omega t$, $\cos \omega t$, the unit step function $u(t)$, etc., do not satisfy the above condition. The object of this chapter is to find the Fourier transforms of these functions, and also to define Fourier transforms of generalized functions, such as the impulse function $\delta(t)$ and its derivatives (Sec. 2.4).

5.2 The Fourier Transform of an Impulse Function

PROBLEM 5.1 Find the Fourier transform of the unit impulse function $\delta(t)$ shown in Fig. 5.1(a).

Solution: The Fourier transform of $\delta(t)$ is given by

$$\mathcal{F}[\delta(t)] = \int_{-\infty}^{\infty} \delta(t) \, e^{-j\omega t} dt. \tag{5.2}$$

From the discussion of Sec. 2.4, we are led to the definition

$$\mathcal{F}[\delta(t)] = \int_{-\infty}^{\infty} \delta(t) \, e^{-j\omega t} dt = e^{-j\omega t}\big|_{t=0} = 1. \tag{5.3}$$

Hence, the Fourier transform of the unit impulse function is unity. It is therefore evident that an impulse function has a uniform spectral density over the entire frequency interval. [See Fig. 5.1(b).]

PROBLEM 5.2 Derive the following identity:

$$\delta(t) = \frac{1}{2\pi} \int_{-\infty}^{\infty} e^{j\omega t} \, d\omega. \tag{5.4}$$

Solution: Applying the inverse Fourier transform formula (4.16) to (5.3),

$$\delta(t) = \mathcal{F}^{-1}[1] = \frac{1}{2\pi} \int_{-\infty}^{\infty} 1 \, e^{j\omega t} \, d\omega = \frac{1}{2\pi} \int_{-\infty}^{\infty} e^{j\omega t} \, d\omega.$$

It should be noted that the ordinary integration of $\int_{-\infty}^{\infty} e^{j\omega t}\,d\omega$ is meaningless

here. Instead we should interprete (5.4) as a generalized function (or symbolic function); i.e., the integration of (5.4) converges to $\delta(t)$ in the sense of a generalized function.

PROBLEM 5.3 Derive the following integral representation of $\delta(t)$:

$$\delta(t) = \frac{1}{\pi} \int_{0}^{\infty} \cos \omega t\, d\omega. \qquad (5.5)$$

Solution: From (5.4), and using the identity $e^{j\omega t} = \cos \omega t + j \sin \omega t$,

$$\delta(t) = \frac{1}{2\pi} \int_{-\infty}^{\infty} e^{j\omega t}\,d\omega$$

$$= \frac{1}{2\pi} \int_{-\infty}^{\infty} (\cos \omega t + j \sin \omega t)\,d\omega$$

$$= \frac{1}{2\pi} \int_{-\infty}^{\infty} \cos \omega t\, d\omega + j \frac{1}{2\pi} \int_{-\infty}^{\infty} \sin \omega t\, d\omega$$

$$= \frac{1}{\pi} \int_{0}^{\infty} \cos \omega t\, d\omega$$

with the use of the properties (2.13) and (2.14) of even and odd functions.

Again it is noted that the integration (5.5) converges to $\delta(t)$ in the sense of a generalized function.

With the identities (5.4) and (5.5), we can write in general,

$$\delta(y) = \frac{1}{2\pi} \int_{-\infty}^{\infty} e^{jxy}\,dx, \qquad (5.6)$$

$$\delta(y) = \frac{1}{\pi} \int_{0}^{\infty} \cos (xy)\,dx. \qquad (5.7)$$

PROBLEM 5.4 Find the Fourier transform of the shifted impulse function $\delta(t - t_0)$ shown in Fig. 5.1(a).

Solution: Using (2.68),

$$\mathcal{F}[\delta(t - t_0)] = \int_{-\infty}^{\infty} \delta(t - t_0) e^{-j\omega t}\,dt = e^{-j\omega t}\Big|_{t=t_0}$$

$$= e^{-j\omega t_0}. \qquad (5.8)$$

Alternate Solution: Since $\mathcal{F}[\delta(t)] = 1$ and from (4.73), i.e.,

$$\mathcal{F}[f(t - t_0)] = F(\omega) e^{-j\omega t_0},$$

we obtain

$$\mathcal{F}[\delta(t - t_0)] = 1 e^{-j\omega t_0} = e^{-j\omega t_0}, \qquad (5.9)$$

as shown in Fig. 5.2(b).

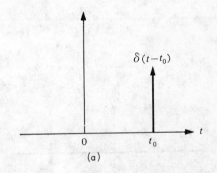

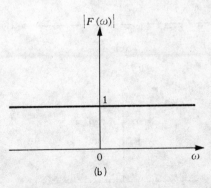

Fig. 5.2 (a) The shifted impulse function. (b) The Fourier transform of the shifted impulse function.

PROBLEM 5.5 Using the identity (5.6) and the relation (2.68), prove the inversion formula of the Fourier transform; i.e.,

$$f(t) = \mathcal{F}^{-1}[F(\omega)] = \frac{1}{2\pi} \int_{-\infty}^{\infty} F(\omega)\, e^{j\omega t}\, d\omega, \tag{5.10}$$

where

$$F(\omega) = \int_{-\infty}^{\infty} f(t)\, e^{-j\omega t}\, dt. \tag{5.11}$$

Solution: Substituting (5.11) into the right-hand side of (5.10),

$$\frac{1}{2\pi} \int_{-\infty}^{\infty} F(\omega)\, e^{j\omega t}\, d\omega = \frac{1}{2\pi} \int_{-\infty}^{\infty} \left[\int_{-\infty}^{\infty} f(y)\, e^{-j\omega y}\, dy \right] e^{j\omega t}\, d\omega. \tag{5.12}$$

Here, in order to avoid confusion, a different dummy variable y is used. Interchanging the order of integration and using (5.6),

$$\frac{1}{2\pi} \int_{-\infty}^{\infty} F(\omega)\, e^{j\omega t}\, d\omega = \int_{-\infty}^{\infty} f(y) \left[\frac{1}{2\pi} \int_{-\infty}^{\infty} e^{j\omega(t-y)}\, d\omega \right] dy$$

$$= \int_{-\infty}^{\infty} f(y)\, \delta(t-y)\, dy = f(t). \tag{5.13}$$

The last integral was obtained with the use of (2.68). Hence, (5.10) is proved.

5.3 The Fourier Transform of a Constant

Let us now find the Fourier transform of a function $f(t) = A$. It is observed that this function does not satisfy the condition of absolute integrability (5.1).

PROBLEM 5.6 Find the Fourier transform of a constant function

$$f(t) = A, \tag{5.14}$$

as shown in Fig. 5.3(a).

Solution: The Fourier transform of $f(t) = A$ is

$$\mathcal{F}[f(t)] = \mathcal{F}[A] = \int_{-\infty}^{\infty} A\, e^{-j\omega t}\, dt$$

$$= 2\pi A\, \frac{1}{2\pi} \int_{-\infty}^{\infty} e^{j(-\omega)t}\, dt. \tag{5.15}$$

Now from (5.6),

$$\delta(y) = \frac{1}{2\pi} \int_{-\infty}^{\infty} e^{jxy}\, dx. \tag{5.16}$$

Letting $x = t$ and $y = -\omega$,

$$\delta(-\omega) = \frac{1}{2\pi} \int_{-\infty}^{\infty} e^{jt(-\omega)}\, dt. \tag{5.17}$$

Substituting (5.17) into (5.15),

$$\mathcal{F}[A] = 2\pi A\, \delta(-\omega). \tag{5.18}$$

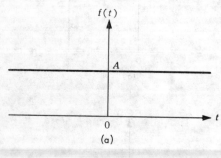

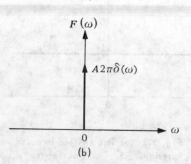

Fig. 5.3 (a) The function $f(t) = A$.
(b) The Fourier transform of $f(t) = A$.

Since from (2.77), $\delta(-\omega) = \delta(\omega)$,

$$\mathcal{F}[A] = A\, 2\pi\, \delta(\omega). \qquad (5.19)$$

Letting $A = 1$,

$$\mathcal{F}[1] = 2\pi\, \delta(\omega). \qquad (5.20)$$

Alternate Solution: From (5.3),

$$\mathcal{F}[\delta(t)] = 1.$$

Now, using the symmetry property (4.79) of the Fourier transform, i.e., if $\mathcal{F}[f(t)] = F(\omega)$, then $\mathcal{F}[F(t)] = 2\pi f(-\omega)$,

$$\mathcal{F}[1] = 2\pi\, \delta(-\omega) = 2\pi\, \delta(\omega).$$

Therefore, $\mathcal{F}[A] = A\, 2\pi\, \delta(\omega)$, as shown in Fig. 5.3(b).

It should be emphasized that $f(t) = A$ means the function $f(t)$ is constant for all t [see Fig. 5.3(a)], and is not the discontinuous step function $Au(t)$. Therefore we observe that if $f(t) = $ constant, the only frequency we can associate with it is zero frequency (pure d-c).

PROBLEM 5.7   Find the Fourier transform of $e^{j\omega_0 t}$.

Solution: From (5.20),

$$\mathcal{F}[1] = 2\pi\, \delta(\omega)$$

and from (4.74),

$$\mathcal{F}[f(t)\, e^{j\omega_0 t}] = F(\omega - \omega_0).$$

Hence, the Fourier transform of $e^{j\omega_0 t}$ is

$$\mathcal{F}[e^{j\omega_0 t}] = 2\pi\, \delta(\omega - \omega_0). \qquad (5.21)$$

PROBLEM 5.8   Find the Fourier transforms of $\cos \omega_0 t$ and $\sin \omega_0 t$.

Solution: Using the identity

$$\cos \omega_0 t = \frac{1}{2}(e^{j\omega_0 t} + e^{-j\omega_0 t})$$

and (5.21), the Fourier transform of $\cos \omega_0 t$ is

$$\mathcal{F}[\cos \omega_0 t] = \mathcal{F}\left[\frac{1}{2}(e^{j\omega_0 t} + e^{-j\omega_0 t})\right]$$

$$= \frac{1}{2}\mathcal{F}[e^{j\omega_0 t}] + \frac{1}{2}\mathcal{F}[e^{-j\omega_0 t}]$$

$$= \pi\, \delta(\omega - \omega_0) + \pi\, \delta(\omega + \omega_0). \qquad (5.22)$$

Similarly, since $\sin \omega_0 t = \dfrac{1}{2j}(e^{j\omega_0 t} - e^{-j\omega_0 t})$,

$$\mathcal{F}[\sin \omega_0 t] = \mathcal{F}\left[\frac{1}{2j}(e^{j\omega_0 t} - e^{-j\omega_0 t})\right]$$

$$= \frac{1}{2j}[2\pi\, \delta(\omega - \omega_0) - 2\pi\, \delta(\omega + \omega_0)]$$

$$= -j\pi\, \delta(\omega - \omega_0) + j\pi\, \delta(\omega + \omega_0). \qquad (5.23)$$

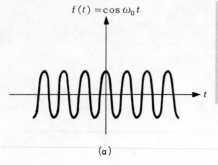

$f(t) = \cos \omega_0 t$

(a)

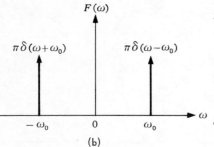

$F(\omega)$

$\pi \delta(\omega + \omega_0)$ $\pi \delta(\omega - \omega_0)$

$-\omega_0$ 0 ω_0

(b)

Fig. 5.4 (a) The function
$f(t) = \cos \omega_0 t$. (b) The
Fourier transform of
$f(t) = \cos \omega_0 t$.

It is noted that the function $e^{j\omega_0 t}$ is not a real function of time, and hence it has a spectrum (5.21) which exists at $\omega = \omega_0$ alone. We have shown that for any real function of time, the amplitude spectrum is an even function of ω (see Prob. 4.8). Hence if there is an impulse at $\omega = \omega_0$, then there must exist an impulse at $\omega = -\omega_0$ for any real function of time. This is the case for the functions $\cos \omega_0 t$ and $\sin \omega_0 t$. (See Fig. 5.4.)

5.4 The Fourier Transform of a Unit Step Function

PROBLEM 5.9 Find the Fourier transform of a unit step function $u(t)$ which is defined by (2.88) or

$$u(t) = \begin{cases} 1 & \text{for } t > 0 \\ 0 & \text{for } t < 0. \end{cases} \tag{5.24}$$

Solution: Let

$$\mathcal{F}[u(t)] = F(\omega).$$

Then from (4.72),

$$\mathcal{F}[u(-t)] = F(-\omega). \tag{5.25}$$

Since

$$u(-t) = \begin{cases} 0 & \text{for } t > 0 \\ 1 & \text{for } t < 0, \end{cases} \tag{5.26}$$

we have

$$u(t) + u(-t) = 1 \text{ (except at } t = 0).$$

From the linearity of the Fourier transform and (5.20),

$$\mathcal{F}[u(t)] + \mathcal{F}[u(-t)] = \mathcal{F}[1]; \tag{5.27}$$

that is,

$$F(\omega) + F(-\omega) = 2\pi \delta(\omega). \tag{5.28}$$

We now assume that

$$F(\omega) = k \delta(\omega) + B(\omega), \tag{5.29}$$

where $B(\omega)$ is an ordinary function and k is a constant. Then since $\delta(-\omega) = \delta(\omega)$,

$$F(\omega) + F(-\omega) = k \delta(\omega) + B(\omega) + k \delta(-\omega) + B(-\omega)$$

$$= 2k \delta(\omega) + B(\omega) + B(-\omega)$$

$$= 2\pi \delta(\omega). \tag{5.30}$$

Hence we conclude that $k = \pi$, and $B(\omega)$ is odd.

To find $B(\omega)$, we proceed as follows: From (2.90),

$$u'(t) = \frac{du(t)}{dt} = \delta(t). \tag{5.31}$$

Then according to (4.91),

$$\mathcal{F}[u'(t)] = j\omega F(\omega) = j\omega [\pi \delta(\omega) + B(\omega)]$$

$$= \mathcal{F}[\delta(t)]$$

$$= 1. \tag{5.32}$$

Now, since from (2.75), $\omega\,\delta(\omega) = 0$,

$$j\,\omega\,B(\omega) = 1. \tag{5.33}$$

Hence,

$$B(\omega) = \frac{1}{j\,\omega}. \tag{5.34}$$

Finally we obtain

$$\mathcal{F}[u(t)] = \pi\,\delta(\omega) + \frac{1}{j\,\omega}. \tag{5.35}$$

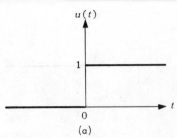

(a)

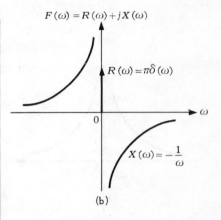

(b)

The above results show that the spectrum of the unit step function contains an impulse at $\omega = 0$. Thus the function $u(t)$ contains a d-c component as expected. Figure 5.5 shows the unit function and its transform and spectrum.

It should be emphasized here that a superficial application of the differentiation theorem (4.91) to

$$\delta(t) = \frac{du(t)}{dt} \tag{5.36}$$

would have resulted in

$$\mathcal{F}[\delta(t)] = j\,\omega\,F(\omega), \tag{5.37}$$

where $F(\omega)$ is the Fourier transform of $u(t)$.

Hence with (5.3),

$$1 = j\,\omega\,F(\omega). \tag{5.38}$$

Therefore,

$$F(\omega) = \frac{1}{j\,\omega}, \tag{5.39}$$

a result which is not in agreement with (5.35).

In general, if

$$\omega\,F_1(\omega) = \omega\,F_2(\omega), \tag{5.40}$$

it does not follow that

$$F_1(\omega) = F_2(\omega). \tag{5.41}$$

Instead, the correct conclusion is

$$F_1(\omega) = F_2(\omega) + k\,\delta(\omega), \tag{5.42}$$

where k is a constant, because $\omega\delta(\omega) = 0$, as one notes from the property (2.75) of the δ-function.

Therefore, from (5.38), the correct conclusion is not (5.39) but

$$F(\omega) = \frac{1}{j\,\omega} + k\,\delta(\omega). \tag{5.43}$$

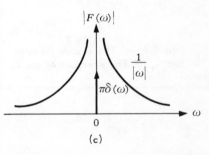

(c)

Fig. 5.5 (a) The unit step function. (b) The Fourier transform of the unit step function. (c) The spectrum of of the unit step function.

PROBLEM 5.10 Prove that the Fourier transform of the unit step function given by (5.39), i.e., $\mathcal{F}[u(t)] = 1/j\omega$, is incorrect.

Solution: We note that $1/j\omega = -j/\omega$ is a pure imaginary function of ω. Then according to the result of Prob. 4.9, it has been proved that if the Fourier transform of a real function $f(t)$ is pure imaginary, then $f(t)$ is an odd function of t. But $u(t)$ is not an odd function of t, and therefore $1/j\omega$ can not be its Fourier transform.

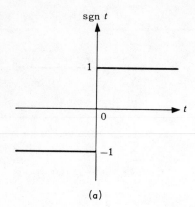

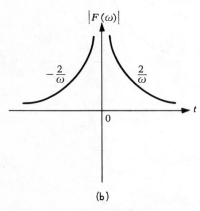

Fig. 5.6 (a) The signum function
sgn t. (b) The spectrum of sgn t.

PROBLEM 5.11   Prove that

$$\mathcal{F}^{-1}\left[\frac{1}{j\omega}\right] = \frac{1}{2}\,\text{sgn}\ t, \tag{5.44}$$

where sgn t (read as *signum t*) is defined as

$$\text{sgn}\ t = \begin{cases} 1 & \text{for } t < 0 \\ -1 & \text{for } t > 0 \ . \end{cases} \tag{5.45}$$

Solution: Let $f(t) = \text{sgn}\ t$ and $\mathcal{F}[\text{sgn}\ t] = F(\omega)$. Since sgn t is an odd function of t [Fig. 5.6(a)], according to the result of Prob. 4.9, $F(\omega)$ will be pure imaginary and consequently is an odd function of ω.

Now from (2.94),

$$f'(t) = 2\,\delta(t). \tag{5.46}$$

Then from (4.91),

$$\mathcal{F}[f'(t)] = j\omega\,F(\omega) = \mathcal{F}[2\,\delta(t)] = 2. \tag{5.47}$$

Therefore,

$$F(\omega) = \frac{2}{j\omega} + k\,\delta(\omega), \tag{5.48}$$

where k is an arbitrary constant. Since $F(\omega)$ must be pure imaginary and odd, $k = 0$. Hence,

$$F(\omega) = \mathcal{F}[\text{sgn}\ t] = \frac{2}{j\omega}. \tag{5.49}$$

From this, we conclude that

$$\mathcal{F}^{-1}\left[\frac{1}{j\omega}\right] = \frac{1}{2}\,\text{sgn}\ t.$$

Figure 5.6 shows the signum function sgn t and its spectrum.

Alternate Solution: From (5.35),

$$\mathcal{F}[u(t)] = \pi\,\delta(\omega) + \frac{1}{j\omega}.$$

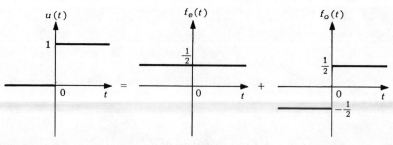

Fig. 5.7 The unit step function and its even and odd components.

Now we note that $u(t)$ may be expressed as (Fig. 5.7)

$$u(t) = f_e(t) + f_0(t), \tag{5.50}$$

where $f_e(t)$ and $f_0(t)$ are the even and odd components of $u(t)$, respectively. From (2.15) and (2.16),

$$f_e(t) = \frac{1}{2}[u(t) + u(-t)] = \frac{1}{2}, \tag{5.51}$$

$$f_0(t) = \frac{1}{2}[u(t) - u(-t)] = \frac{1}{2} \operatorname{sgn} t = \begin{cases} \dfrac{1}{2} & t > 0 \\[2ex] -\dfrac{1}{2} & t < 0 \,. \end{cases} \tag{5.52}$$

Hence from (4.42) and (4.43), we conclude that

$$\mathcal{F}\left[\frac{1}{2}\right] = \pi \, \delta(\omega), \tag{5.53}$$

$$\mathcal{F}\left[\frac{1}{2} \operatorname{sgn} t\right] = \frac{1}{j\omega}. \tag{5.54}$$

Therefore,

$$\mathcal{F}^{-1}\left[\frac{1}{j\omega}\right] = \frac{1}{2} \operatorname{sgn} t.$$

PROBLEM 5.12 In Prob. 4.25, it was shown that if $\mathcal{F}[f(t)] = F(\omega)$, then

$$\mathcal{F}\left[\int_{-\infty}^{t} f(x)\,dx\right] = \frac{1}{j\omega} F(\omega),$$

provided that

$$\int_{-\infty}^{\infty} f(t)\,dt = F(0) = 0\,.$$

Show that if

$$\int_{-\infty}^{\infty} f(t)\,dt = F(0) \neq 0,$$

then

$$\mathcal{F}\left[\int_{-\infty}^{t} f(x)\,dx\right] = \frac{1}{j\omega} F(\omega) + \pi F(0)\,\delta(\omega)\,. \tag{5.55}$$

Solution: Let

$$g(t) = \int_{-\infty}^{t} f(x)\,dx\,.$$

The above integral can be expressed as a convolution of $f(t)$ with the unit step function $u(t)$; i.e.,

$$f(t) * u(t) = \int_{-\infty}^{\infty} f(x)\,u(t-x)\,dx = \int_{-\infty}^{t} f(x)\,dx = g(t) \tag{5.56}$$

since $u(t-x) = 0$ for $x > t$.

Therefore, from the time convolution theorem (4.122) and (5.35),

$$\mathcal{F}[g(t)] = \mathcal{F}\left[\int_{-\infty}^{t} f(x)\,dx\right] = \mathcal{F}[f(t)]\,\mathcal{F}[u(t)]$$

$$= F(\omega)\left[\pi\,\delta(\omega) + \frac{1}{j\omega}\right]$$

$$= \frac{1}{j\omega} F(\omega) + \pi F(\omega)\,\delta(\omega)\,. \tag{5.57}$$

From (2.74),

$$F(\omega)\,\delta(\omega) = F(0)\,\delta(\omega).$$

Hence,

$$\mathcal{F}\left[\int_{-\infty}^{t} f(x)\,dx\right] = \frac{1}{j\omega}F(\omega) + \pi F(0)\,\delta(\omega).$$

5.5 The Fourier Transform of a Periodic Function

In Chap. 4, we developed the Fourier integral as a limiting case of the Fourier series by letting the period of a periodic function become infinite. In this section, we shall show that the Fourier series can be formally derived as a special case of the Fourier integral.

It should be noted that for any periodic function $f(t)$,

$$\int_{-\infty}^{\infty} |f(t)|\,dt = \infty;$$

i.e., it does not satisfy the condition of absolute integrability of (4.17). But its Fourier transform does exist in the sense of a generalized function. This has been demonstrated in finding the Fourier transform of $\cos \omega_0 t$ and $\sin \omega_0 t$.

PROBLEM 5.13 Find the Fourier transform of a periodic function $f(t)$.

Solution: We can express a periodic function $f(t)$ with period T as

$$f(t) = \sum_{n=-\infty}^{\infty} c_n e^{jn\omega_0 t}, \quad \omega_0 = \frac{2\pi}{T}.$$

Taking the Fourier transform of both sides,

$$\mathcal{F}[f(t)] = F(\omega) = \mathcal{F}\left[\sum_{n=-\infty}^{\infty} c_n e^{jn\omega_0 t}\right] = \sum_{n=-\infty}^{\infty} c_n \mathcal{F}[e^{jn\omega_0 t}]. \tag{5.58}$$

Since from (5.21),

$$\mathcal{F}[e^{jn\omega_0 t}] = 2\pi\,\delta(\omega - n\omega_0), \tag{5.59}$$

the Fourier transform of $f(t)$ is

$$F(\omega) = 2\pi \sum_{n=-\infty}^{\infty} c_n\,\delta(\omega - n\omega_0). \tag{5.60}$$

Equation (5.60) states that the Fourier transform of a periodic function consists of a sequence of equidistant impulses located at the harmonic frequencies of the function.

PROBLEM 5.14 Prove that a sequence of equidistance pulses

$$F(\omega) = \sum_{n=-\infty}^{\infty} A_n\,\delta(\omega - n\omega_0), \quad \omega_0 = \frac{2\pi}{T}, \tag{5.61}$$

is the Fourier transform of a periodic function $f(t)$ with period T.

Solution: The periodic function is

$$f(t) = \mathcal{F}^{-1}[F(\omega)] = \mathcal{F}^{-1}\left[\sum_{n=-\infty}^{\infty} A_n \delta(\omega - n\omega_0)\right]$$

$$= \sum_{n=-\infty}^{\infty} A_n \mathcal{F}^{-1}[\delta(\omega - n\omega_0)]. \tag{5.62}$$

From (5.59),

$$\mathcal{F}^{-1}[\delta(\omega - n\omega_0)] = \frac{1}{2\pi} e^{jn\omega_0 t}. \tag{5.63}$$

Hence,

$$f(t) = \sum_{n=-\infty}^{\infty} \frac{A_n}{2\pi} e^{jn\omega_0 t}. \tag{5.64}$$

Since $e^{jn\omega_0(t + 2\pi/\omega_0)} = e^{jn\omega_0 t}$,

$$f\left[t + \left(\frac{2\pi}{\omega_0}\right)\right] = f(t + T) = f(t);$$

i.e., $f(t)$ is a periodic function with period $T = 2\pi/\omega_0$.

PROBLEM 5.15 Find the Fourier transform of the unit impulse train function $\delta_T(t)$, where $\delta_T(t)$ is defined by

$$\delta_T(t) = \cdots + \delta(t + 2T) + \delta(t + T) + \delta(t) + \delta(t - T) + \delta(t - 2T) + \cdots$$

$$= \sum_{n=-\infty}^{\infty} \delta(t - nT).$$

Solution: Since $\delta_T(t)$ is a periodic function with period T and from the result (3.61) of Prob. 3.10, the Fourier series for the function $\delta_T(t)$ is given by

$$\delta_T(t) = \frac{1}{T} \sum_{n=-\infty}^{\infty} e^{jn\omega_0 t}, \tag{5.65}$$

where $\omega_0 = 2\pi/T$. Therefore,

$$\mathcal{F}[\delta_T(t)] = \frac{1}{T} \sum_{n=-\infty}^{\infty} \mathcal{F}[e^{jn\omega_0 t}].$$

From (5.59),

$$\mathcal{F}[\delta_T(t)] = \frac{2\pi}{T} \sum_{n=-\infty}^{\infty} \delta(\omega - n\omega_0)$$

$$= \omega_0 \sum_{n=-\infty}^{\infty} \delta(\omega - n\omega_0)$$

$$= \omega_0 \delta_{\omega_0}(\omega), \tag{5.66}$$

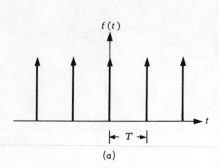

(a)

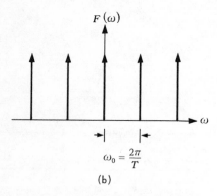

$$\omega_0 = \frac{2\pi}{T}$$

(b)

Fig. 5.8 (a) The impulse train function. (b) The Fourier transform of the impulse train function.

or

$$\mathscr{F}\left[\sum_{n=-\infty}^{\infty}\delta(t-nT)\right] = \omega_0\sum_{n=-\infty}^{\infty}\delta(\omega-n\omega_0). \qquad (5.67)$$

Equation (5.67) states that the Fourier transform of a unit impulse train is also a similar impulse train. Therefore, we may say that the impulse train function is its own transform (Fig. 5.8).

PROBLEM 5.16 Show that the complex coefficients c_n of the Fourier series expansion of a periodic function $f(t)$ with period T equal the values of the Fourier transform $F_0(\omega)$ of the function $f_0(t)$ at $\omega = n\omega_0 = n2\pi/T$ multiplied by $1/T$, where $f_0(t)$ is defined by

$$f_0(t) = \begin{cases} f(t), & |t| < \frac{1}{2}T \\[2mm] 0, & |t| > \frac{1}{2}T. \end{cases} \qquad (5.68)$$

Solution: The periodic function $f(t)$ with period T can be written as

$$f(t) = \sum_{n=-\infty}^{\infty} c_n e^{jn\omega_0 t}, \qquad \omega_0 = \frac{2\pi}{T},$$

where $c_n = \dfrac{1}{T}\displaystyle\int_{-T/2}^{T/2} f(t)\,e^{-jn\omega_0 t}\,dt.$ Now,

$$F_0(\omega) = \mathscr{F}[f_0(t)]$$

$$= \int_{-\infty}^{\infty} f_0(t)\,e^{-j\omega t}\,dt$$

$$= \int_{-T/2}^{T/2} f(t)\,e^{-j\omega t}\,dt. \qquad (5.69)$$

Since

$$F_0(n\omega_0) = \int_{-T/2}^{T/2} f(t)\,e^{-jn\omega_0 t}\,dt, \qquad (5.70)$$

we conclude that

$$c_n = \frac{1}{T}\,F_0(n\omega_0). \qquad (5.71)$$

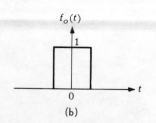

(a)

$f_0(t)$

1

0

(b)

Fig. 5.9 (a) A train of rectangular pulses. (b) A single rectangular pulse.

PROBLEM 5.17 Using the result of Prob. 5.16, find the complex Fourier-series coefficients of a train of rectangular pulses of width d with period T as shown in Fig. 5.9(a).

Solution: Let

$$f(t) = \sum_{n=-\infty}^{\infty} c_n e^{jn\omega_0 t}, \qquad \omega_0 = \frac{2\pi}{T}. \qquad (5.72)$$

Then from Fig. 5.9(b),

$$f_0(t) = p_d(t). \qquad (5.73)$$

Hence, from (4.45),

$$F_0(\omega) = \mathcal{F}[f_0(t)] = \mathcal{F}[p_d(t)] = \frac{2}{\omega} \sin\left(\frac{\omega d}{2}\right)$$

$$= d \frac{\sin\left(\dfrac{\omega d}{2}\right)}{\left(\dfrac{\omega d}{2}\right)}. \qquad (5.74)$$

Therefore, from (5.71), the Fourier-series coefficients c_n of $f(t)$ are given by

$$c_n = \frac{1}{T} F_0(n\omega_0) = \frac{d}{T} \frac{\sin\left(\dfrac{n\omega_0 d}{2}\right)}{\left(\dfrac{n\omega_0 d}{2}\right)}, \qquad (5.75)$$

which is exactly the same as (3.47) except for the factor A of the pulse height.

PROBLEM 5.18 Find the Fourier transform of a train of rectangular pulses of width d with period T as shown in Fig. 5.9(a).

Solution: From the result of Prob. 5.17, the Fourier series for this function is given by

$$f(t) = \sum_{n=-\infty}^{\infty} c_n e^{jn\omega_0 t}, \quad \omega_0 = \frac{2\pi}{T},$$

where

$$c_n = \frac{d}{T} \frac{\sin\left(\dfrac{n\omega_0 d}{2}\right)}{\left(\dfrac{n\omega_0 d}{2}\right)} = \frac{d}{T} \frac{\sin\left(\dfrac{n\pi d}{T}\right)}{\left(\dfrac{n\pi d}{T}\right)}$$

$$= \frac{d}{T} Sa\left(\frac{n\pi d}{T}\right). \qquad (5.76)$$

From (5.60), it follows that the Fourier transform of this function is given by

$$\mathcal{F}[f(t)] = F(\omega) = \frac{2\pi d}{T} \sum_{n=-\infty}^{\infty} Sa\left(\frac{n\pi d}{T}\right) \delta(\omega - n\omega_0). \qquad (5.77)$$

Equation (5.77) indicates that the Fourier transform of a rectangular pulse train consists of impulses located at $\omega = 0,\ \pm\omega_0,\ \pm 2\omega_0,\ \cdots$, etc. The strength of impulse located at $\omega = n\omega_0$ is given by $(2\pi d/T)Sa(n\pi d/T)$. The spectrum is shown in Fig. 5.10 ($d/T = 1/5$ case).

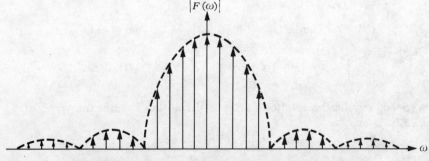

Fig. 5.10 The spectrum of a train of rectangular impulses.

5.6 The Fourier Transforms
of Generalized Functions

In this section, we shall define the Fourier transforms of generalized functions and of certain ordinary functions for which the usual transform definition is meaningless. This will be done with the use of *Parseval's equation*.

PROBLEM 5.19 Let $\mathcal{F}[f(t)] = F(\omega)$ and $\mathcal{F}[g(t)] = G(\omega)$. Establish *Parseval's equation:*

$$\int_{-\infty}^{\infty} f(x) G(x) \, dx = \int_{-\infty}^{\infty} F(x) g(x) \, dx. \tag{5.78}$$

Solution: From the definition of the Fourier transform,

$$F(y) = \int_{-\infty}^{\infty} f(x) e^{-jxy} \, dx, \tag{5.79}$$

$$G(x) = \int_{-\infty}^{\infty} g(y) e^{-jxy} \, dy. \tag{5.80}$$

Then,

$$\int_{-\infty}^{\infty} f(x) G(x) \, dx = \int_{-\infty}^{\infty} f(x) \left[\int_{-\infty}^{\infty} g(y) e^{-jxy} \, dy \right] dx. \tag{5.81}$$

Interchanging the order of integration,

$$\int_{-\infty}^{\infty} f(x) G(x) \, dx = \int_{-\infty}^{\infty} g(y) \left[\int_{-\infty}^{\infty} f(x) e^{-jxy} \, dx \right] dy$$

$$= \int_{-\infty}^{\infty} g(y) F(y) \, dy,$$

and because we can change the dummy variable's symbol,

$$\int_{-\infty}^{\infty} f(x) G(x) \, dx = \int_{-\infty}^{\infty} F(x) g(x) \, dx. \tag{5.82}$$

It is obvious that from (5.78),

$$\int_{-\infty}^{\infty} f(\omega) \mathcal{F}[g(t)] \, d\omega = \int_{-\infty}^{\infty} \mathcal{F}[f(t)] g(\omega) \, d\omega. \tag{5.83}$$

Since $f(t) = \mathcal{F}^{-1}[F(\omega)]$ and $g(t) = \mathcal{F}^{-1}[G(\omega)]$, (5.82) can also be written as

$$\int_{-\infty}^{\infty} \mathcal{F}^{-1}[F(\omega)] G(t) \, dt = \int_{-\infty}^{\infty} F(t) \mathcal{F}^{-1}[G(\omega)] \, dt. \tag{5.84}$$

We may thus extend the relation (5.82) to define the Fourier transform of a generalized function.

Let $\phi(t)$ be a testing function as defined in Sec. 2.4. Then,

$$\mathcal{F}[\phi(t)] = \Phi(\omega)$$

certainly exists, and the Fourier transform $F(\omega)$ of a generalized function $f(t)$ is defined by the relationship

$$\int_{-\infty}^{\infty} F(x)\,\phi(x)\,dx = \int_{-\infty}^{\infty} f(x)\,\Phi(x)\,dx. \tag{5.85}$$

PROBLEM 5.20 Using the definition (5.85), show that

$$\mathcal{F}[\delta(t)] = 1.$$

Solution: From (5.85),

$$\int_{-\infty}^{\infty} \delta(t)\,\Phi(t)\,dt = \int_{-\infty}^{\infty} \mathcal{F}[\delta(t)]\,\phi(\omega)\,d\omega. \tag{5.86}$$

Now, from the definition (2.67) of the δ-function,

$$\int_{-\infty}^{\infty} \delta(t)\,\Phi(t)\,dt = \Phi(t)\big|_{t=0} = \Phi(\omega)\big|_{\omega=0} = \Phi(0).$$

But

$$\Phi(0) = \left[\int_{-\infty}^{\infty} \phi(t)\,e^{-j\omega t}\,dt\right]_{\omega=0},$$

and since in the above equation the integration is with respect to t,

$$\Phi(0) = \int_{-\infty}^{\infty} \phi(t)\,dt = \int_{-\infty}^{\infty} \phi(\omega)\,d\omega. \tag{5.87}$$

Comparing (5.87) with (5.86),

$$\mathcal{F}[\delta(t)] = 1.$$

PROBLEM 5.21 Using the relation (5.85), find the Fourier transform of $\delta(t-\tau)$.

Solution: We can write

$$\int_{-\infty}^{\infty} \delta(t-\tau)\,\Phi(t)\,dt = \int_{-\infty}^{\infty} \mathcal{F}[\delta(t-\tau)]\,\phi(\omega)\,d\omega. \tag{5.88}$$

From (2.68),

$$\int_{-\infty}^{\infty} \delta(t-\tau)\,\Phi(t)\,dt = \Phi(\tau) = \Phi(t)\big|_{t=\tau} = \Phi(\omega)\big|_{\omega=\tau}$$

$$= \left[\int_{-\infty}^{\infty} \phi(t)\,e^{-j\omega t}\,dt\right]_{\omega=\tau}$$

$$= \int_{-\infty}^{\infty} \phi(x)\,e^{-j\tau x}\,dx.$$

Since the symbol from the dummy variable can be changed at will,

$$\int_{-\infty}^{\infty} \delta(t-\tau)\,\Phi(t)\,dt = \int_{-\infty}^{\infty} \phi(\omega)\,e^{-j\tau\omega}\,d\omega. \tag{5.89}$$

Comparing (5.88) with (5.89),

$$\mathcal{F}[\delta(t-\tau)] = e^{-j\omega\tau}.$$

This is the same result (5.8) obtained in Prob. 5.4.

PROBLEM 5.22   Using the relation (5.85), show that

$$\mathcal{F}[f'(t)] = j\omega F(\omega),$$

$$\mathcal{F}[f^{(k)}(t)] = (j\omega)^k F(\omega),$$

where $F(\omega) = \mathcal{F}[f(t)]$.

Solution: From (5.85),

$$\int_{-\infty}^{\infty} \mathcal{F}[f'(t)]\,\phi(\omega)\,d\omega = \int_{-\infty}^{\infty} f'(\omega)\,\Phi(\omega)\,d\omega. \qquad (5.90)$$

Now from the definition of the derivative of a generalized function (2.82),

$$\int_{-\infty}^{\infty} f'(\omega)\,\Phi(\omega)\,d\omega = -\int_{-\infty}^{\infty} f(\omega)\,\Phi'(\omega)\,d\omega. \qquad (5.91)$$

Since

$$\Phi' = \frac{d\Phi(\omega)}{d\omega} = \frac{d}{d\omega}\int_{-\infty}^{\infty} \phi(t)\,e^{-j\omega t}\,dt$$

$$= \int_{-\infty}^{\infty} \phi(t)\,\frac{\partial}{\partial\omega}(e^{-j\omega t})\,dt$$

$$= \int_{-\infty}^{\infty} -jt\,\phi(t)\,e^{-j\omega t}\,dt$$

$$= -\int_{-\infty}^{\infty} [jt\,\phi(t)]\,e^{-j\omega t}\,dt$$

$$= -\mathcal{F}[jt\,\phi(t)],$$

we have

$$\int_{-\infty}^{\infty} f'(\omega)\,\Phi(\omega)\,d\omega = -\int_{-\infty}^{\infty} f(\omega)\,\Phi'(\omega)\,d\omega$$

$$= +\int_{-\infty}^{\infty} f(\omega)\,\mathcal{F}[jt\,\phi(t)]\,d\omega. \qquad (5.92)$$

Again using (5.85),

$$\int_{-\infty}^{\infty} f(\omega)\,\mathcal{F}[jt\,\phi(t)]\,d\omega = \int_{-\infty}^{\infty} j\omega\,\phi(\omega)\,F(\omega)\,d\omega. \qquad (5.93)$$

Comparing (5.93) with (5.90),

$$\mathcal{F}[f'(t)] = j\omega F(\omega). \qquad (5.94)$$

By repetition of (5.94),

$$\mathcal{F}[f^{(k)}(t)] = (j\omega)^k F(\omega). \qquad (5.95)$$

PROBLEM 5.23   Find the Fourier transforms of $\delta'(t)$ and $\delta^{(k)}(t)$.

Solution: Since $\mathcal{F}[\delta(t)] = 1$ from (5.94) and (5.95),

$$\mathcal{F}[\delta'(t)] = j\omega, \qquad (5.96)$$

$$\mathcal{F}[\delta^{(k)}(t)] = (j\omega)^k. \qquad (5.97)$$

PROBLEM 5.24 Using the relation (5.85), show that

$$\mathcal{F}[(-jt)f(t)] = F'(\omega) = \frac{dF(\omega)}{d\omega},$$

$$\mathcal{F}[(-jt)^k f(t)] = F^{(k)}(\omega) = \frac{d^k F(\omega)}{d\omega^k},$$

where $F(\omega) = \mathcal{F}[f(t)]$.

Solution: From the definition of the derivative of a generalized function (2.82),

$$\int_{-\infty}^{\infty} F'(\omega)\phi(\omega)\,d\omega = -\int_{-\infty}^{\infty} F(\omega)\phi'(\omega)\,d\omega. \tag{5.98}$$

From (5.85),

$$-\int_{-\infty}^{\infty} F(\omega)\phi'(\omega)\,d\omega = -\int_{-\infty}^{\infty} f(\omega)\mathcal{F}[\phi'(t)]\,d\omega. \tag{5.99}$$

Now, integrating by parts,

$$\mathcal{F}[\phi'(t)] = \int_{-\infty}^{\infty} \phi'(t)\,e^{-j\omega t}\,dt$$

$$= \phi(t)\,e^{-j\omega t}\Big|_{-\infty}^{\infty} + j\omega \int_{-\infty}^{\infty} \phi(t)\,e^{-j\omega t}\,dt$$

$$= j\omega \int_{-\infty}^{\infty} \phi(t)\,e^{-j\omega t}\,dt$$

$$= j\omega\,\Phi(\omega)$$

since the testing function $\phi(t)$ vanishes outside some interval $\phi(t) \longrightarrow 0$ as $t \longrightarrow \pm\infty$.

Hence,

$$-\int_{-\infty}^{\infty} f(\omega)\mathcal{F}[\phi'(t)]\,d\omega = -\int_{-\infty}^{\infty} f(\omega)j\omega\,\Phi(\omega)\,d\omega$$

$$= \int_{-\infty}^{\infty} (-j\omega)f(\omega)\Phi(\omega)\,d\omega$$

$$= \int_{-\infty}^{\infty} (-jt)f(t)\Phi(t)\,dt. \tag{5.100}$$

Thus,

$$\int_{-\infty}^{\infty} F'(\omega)\phi(\omega)\,d\omega = \int_{-\infty}^{\infty} (-jt)f(t)\Phi(t)\,dt.$$

Therefore from (5.85),

$$\mathcal{F}[(-jt)f(t)] = F'(\omega) = \frac{dF(\omega)}{d\omega}. \tag{5.101}$$

By repetition of (5.101),

$$\mathcal{F}[(-jt)^k f(t)] = F^{(k)}(\omega) = \frac{d^k F(\omega)}{d\omega^k}. \tag{5.102}$$

PROBLEM 5.25 Find the Fourier transforms of t and t^k.

Solution: From (5.20), $\mathcal{F}[1] = 2\pi\delta(\omega)$. From (5.101),

$$\mathcal{F}[(-jt)] = 2\pi\delta'(\omega). \tag{5.103}$$

Hence,

$$\mathcal{F}[t] = \frac{2\pi}{-j}\delta'(\omega) = j\,2\pi\delta'(\omega), \tag{5.104}$$

where $\delta'(\omega) = \dfrac{d\delta(\omega)}{d\omega}$. Similarly, from (5.102),

$$\mathcal{F}[t^k] = \frac{2\pi}{(-j)^k}\delta^{(k)}(\omega) = 2\pi j^k \delta^{(k)}(\omega), \tag{5.105}$$

where

$$\delta^{(k)}(\omega) = \frac{d^k \delta(\omega)}{d\omega^k}.$$

5.7 Supplementary Problems

PROBLEM 5.26 Evaluate the Fourier transforms of the following functions:
(a) $1 - 3\delta(t) + 2\delta'(t-2)$, (b) $\sin^3 t$, (c) $u(t-1)$.

Answer: (a) $2\pi\delta(\omega) - 3 + 3j\omega e^{-j2\omega}$, (b) $j(\pi/4)[\delta(\omega-3) - 3\delta(\omega-1) + 3\delta(\omega+1) - \delta(\omega+3)]$, (c) $\pi\delta(\omega) - e^{-j\omega}/j\omega$.

PROBLEM 5.27 Show that the unit step function $u(t)$ can be expressed as

$$u(t) = \frac{1}{2} + \frac{1}{\pi}\int_0^\infty \frac{\sin \omega t}{\omega}\,d\omega.$$

[Hint: Use (5.35) and (4.27).]

PROBLEM 5.28 Prove that

(a) $\quad \mathcal{F}[\cos \omega_0 t\, u(t)] = \dfrac{\pi}{2}[\delta(\omega-\omega_0) + \delta(\omega+\omega_0)] + j\dfrac{\omega}{\omega_0^2 - \omega^2}$,

(b) $\quad \mathcal{F}[\sin \omega_0 t\, u(t)] = \dfrac{\omega}{\omega_0^2 - \omega^2} - j\dfrac{\pi}{2}[\delta(\omega-\omega_0) - \delta(\omega+\omega_0)]$.

[Hint: $\cos \omega_0 t\, u(t) = \dfrac{1}{2}\{e^{j\omega_0 t}u(t) + e^{-j\omega_0 t}u(t)\}$ and use the result of Prob. 4.19.]

PROBLEM 5.29 Find the Fourier transform of a finite unit impulse train

$$f(t) = \sum_{n=0}^{k-1}\delta(t - nT).$$

Answer: $e^{-j(k-1)\omega T/2}\dfrac{\sin(k\omega T/2)}{\sin(\omega T/2)}$.

PROBLEM 5.30 If $f(t) = e^{-\alpha t} u(t)$, show that $\mathcal{F}[f'(t)] = j\omega \, \mathcal{F}[f(t)]$.
[Hint: $f'(t) = \delta(t) - \alpha e^{-\alpha t} u(t)$.]

PROBLEM 5.31 Let $f(t)$ be a periodic function with period T. If a function $f_0(t)$ is defined as

$$f_0(t) = \begin{cases} f(t) & \text{for } |t| < T/2 \\ 0 & \text{for } |t| > T/2, \end{cases}$$

show that $f(t)$ can be expressed as

$$f(t) = \sum_{n=-\infty}^{\infty} f_0(t - nT) = f_0(t) * \delta_T(t),$$

where $\delta_T(t) = \sum_{n=-\infty}^{\infty} \delta(t - nT)$.

PROBLEM 5.32 Using the result of Prob. 5.31 and the convolution theorem, show that the Fourier transform of a periodic function $f(t)$ with period T and with the complex Fourier coefficients c_n can be expressed as

$$F(\omega) = \frac{2\pi}{T} \sum_{n=-\infty}^{\infty} F_0(n\omega_0)\, \delta(\omega - n\omega_0) = 2\pi \sum_{n=-\infty}^{\infty} c_n \delta(\omega - n\omega_0),$$

where $F_0(\omega) = \mathcal{F}[f_0(t)]$ and $f_0(t) = \begin{cases} f(t) & \text{for } |t| < t/2 \\ 0 & \text{for } |t| > t/2. \end{cases}$

[Hint: Use the results of Probs. 5.15 and 2.50.]

PROBLEM 5.33 Prove that $\mathcal{F}[1/t] = -\pi j \, \text{sgn} \, \omega = \pi j - 2\pi j u(\omega)$.
[Hint: Apply symmetry property (4.79) to the result (5.44) of Prob. 5.11.]

PROBLEM 5.34 From the result of Prob. 5.33, deduce that, for $n = 1, 2, \cdots$,

$$\mathcal{F}[-1/t^2] = -j\omega \pi j \, \text{sgn} \, \omega = \omega \pi \, \text{sgn} \, \omega,$$

$$\mathcal{F}[2/t^3] = -(j\omega)^2 \, \pi j \, \text{sgn} \, \omega = j\omega^2 \pi \, \text{sgn} \, \omega,$$

$$\vdots \qquad \vdots \qquad \vdots$$

$$\mathcal{F}\left[\frac{1}{t^n}\right] = -\frac{(-j\omega)^{n-1}}{(n-1)!} \, \pi j \, \text{sgn} \, \omega.$$

[Hint: Use the result of Prob. 4.24; that is, $\mathcal{F}[f'(t)] = j\omega F(\omega)$.]

PROBLEM 5.35 Show that $\mathcal{F}[tu(t)] = j\pi \delta'(\omega) - 1/\omega^2$.
[Hint: Use the result of Prob. 5.24.]

PROBLEM 5.36 Show that $\mathcal{F}[|t|] = -2/\omega^2$.
[Hint: Use $|t| = 2tu(t) - t$, (5.104), and the result of Prob. 5.35.]

PROBLEM 5.37 Find the particular solution to $x''(t) + 3x'(t) + 2x(t) = u(t)$ by using the Fourier transform.
[Hint: Take the Fourier transform of both sides of the equation. Find $X(\omega) = \mathcal{F}[x(t)]$ and take the inverse Fourier transform.]

Answer: $\frac{1}{2}(1 - 2e^{-t} + e^{-2t}) u(t)$.

PROBLEM 5.38 Find the particular solution to $x''(t) + 3x'(t) + 2x(t) = 3\delta(t)$ by using the Fourier transform.

Answer: $3(e^{-t} - e^{-2t}) u(t)$.

PROBLEM 5.39 Let $F(\omega)$ be the Fourier transform of $f(t)$ and $f_k(t)$ be defined by

$$f_k(t) = \frac{1}{2\pi} \int_{-k}^{k} F(\omega) e^{j\omega t} d\omega.$$

Show that

$$f_k(t) = \frac{1}{\pi} \int_{-\infty}^{\infty} f(t - x) \frac{\sin kx}{x} dx.$$

PROBLEM 5.40 From the result of Prob. 5.39 show that

$$\delta(t) = \lim_{k \to \infty} \frac{\sin kt}{t}.$$

[Hint: Note that $\lim_{k \to \infty} f_k(t) = f(t)$.]

PROBLEM 5.41 Find the Fourier transform of the shifted unit step function $u(t - t_o)$.

Answer: $\pi \delta(\omega) + \dfrac{e^{-j\omega t_o}}{j\omega}$.

PROBLEM 5.42 Use (5.85) to deduce the time convolution theorem

$$\mathcal{F}[f_1(t) * f_2(t)] = F_1(\omega) F_2(\omega).$$

PROBLEM 5.43 Using (5.85), show that

$$\mathcal{F}[e^{j\omega_0 t}] = 2\pi\delta(\omega - \omega_0).$$

PROBLEM 5.44 The Fourier transform $F(\omega)$ of a generalized function $f(t)$ can be defined by

$$\int_{-\infty}^{\infty} f(t) \phi(t) dt = \frac{1}{2\pi} \int_{-\infty}^{\infty} F(\omega) \Phi(-\omega) d\omega,$$

where $\phi(t)$ is a testing function, and $\mathcal{F}[\phi(t)] = \Phi(\omega)$. Using Parseval's equation

$$\int_{-\infty}^{\infty} f(t) g(t) dt = \frac{1}{2\pi} \int_{-\infty}^{\infty} F(\omega) G(-\omega) d\omega, \qquad [4.133]$$

show that the Fourier transform of the unit impulse function is

$$\mathcal{F}[\delta(t)] = 1.$$

[Hint: $\displaystyle\int_{-\infty}^{\infty} \delta(t) \phi(t) dt = \phi(0) = \frac{1}{2\pi} \int_{-\infty}^{\infty} \Phi(\omega) d\omega = \frac{1}{2\pi} \int_{-\infty}^{\infty} \Phi(-\omega) d\omega$.]

APPLICATIONS TO LINEAR SYSTEMS

CHAPTER 6

6.1 Linear Systems

For every system there is an *input function* (or source function) and an *output function* (or response function). The system is completely characterized if the nature of the dependence of the output on the input is known.

Now suppose that $f_i(t)$ and $f_o(t)$, as shown in Fig. 6.1, are the input and output, respectively, of a linear time-invariant (or constant-parameter) system.

By *linear* we mean that if the input $f_i(t)$ produces the output $f_o(t)$, then the input

$$f_i(t) = a_1 f_{i1}(t) + a_2 f_{i2}(t)$$

produces the output

$$f_o(t) = a_1 f_{o1}(t) + a_2 f_{o2}(t).$$

Hence a linear system can be defined as a system to which the principle of superposition can be applied.

By *time-invariant* (or constant-parameter) we mean that if the input $f_i(t)$ produces the output $f_o(t)$, then the input $f_i(t + t_0)$ produces the output $f_o(t + t_0)$.

Another definition of a linear system is that the input source and output response of the system are related by a *linear differential equation*; i.e.,

$$a_n \frac{d^n f_o(t)}{dt^n} + a_{n-1} \frac{d^{n-1} f_o(t)}{dt^{n-1}} + \cdots + a_1 \frac{d f_o(t)}{dt} + a_0 f_o(t)$$

$$= b_m \frac{d^m f_i(t)}{dt^m} + b_{m-1} \frac{d^{m-1} f_i(t)}{dt^{m-1}} + \cdots + b_1 \frac{d f_i(t)}{dt} + b_0 f_i(t). \quad (6.1)$$

Fig. 6.1 Input and output of a linear system.

6.2 Operational System Functions

If we denote d/dt by the operator p, such that

$$pf(t) = \frac{df(t)}{dt}, \qquad p^n f(t) = \frac{d^n f(t)}{dt^n},$$

then (6.1) can be rewritten as

$$\sum_{n=0}^{n} a_n p^n f_o(t) = \sum_{m=0}^{m} b_m p^m f_i(t) \quad (6.2)$$

or

$$A(p) f_o(t) = B(p) f_i(t), \quad (6.3)$$

where

$$A(p) = a_n p^n + a_{n-1} p^{n-1} + \cdots + a_1 p + a_0,$$

$$B(p) = b_m p^m + b_{m-1} p^{m-1} + \cdots + b_1 p + b_0.$$

In a linear system the coefficients a_n and b_m are *independent* of the output response. In the time-invariant (or constant-parameter) system, the coefficients a_n and b_m are *constants*.

Equation (6.3) can be written symbolically in the form

$$f_o(t) = \frac{B(p)}{A(p)} f_i(t) = H(p) f_i(t), \tag{6.4}$$

where $H(p) = B(p)/A(p)$. It is understood that (6.4) is an operational expression of the differential equation (6.1). The operator $H(p)$, which operates on the source function to produce a response, is termed the *operational system function*. Using the symbol L for $H(p)$, (6.4) can be rewritten as

$$L\{f_i(t)\} = f_o(t). \tag{6.5}$$

The symbol or linear operator L in (6.5) designates the law for determining the response function $f_o(t)$ from a given source function $f_i(t)$. Sometimes, (6.5) is referred to as a transformation L of $f_i(t)$ into $f_o(t)$.

With the notation of (6.5), a *linear time-invariant system* is defined by

$$L\{a_1 f_{i1}(t) + a_2 f_{i2}(t)\} = a_1 L\{f_{i1}(t)\} + a_2 L\{f_{i2}(t)\}, \tag{6.6}$$

$$L\{f_i(t + t_0)\} = f_o(t + t_0), \tag{6.7}$$

where t_0 is an arbitrary constant.

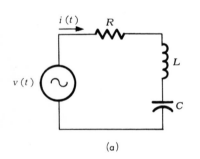

(a)

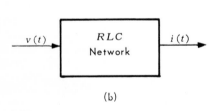

(b)

Fig. 6.2 (a) The circuit of Prob. 6.1.
(b) System representation of the circuit in Fig. 6.2(a).

PROBLEM 6.1 Obtain the operational expression for the current response $i(t)$ to the voltage source $v(t)$ in the circuit of Fig. 6.2(a).

Solution: The source is the applied voltage $v(t)$, and the response is the current $i(t)$, as shown in Fig. 6.2(b). Applying Kirchhoff's law, the differential equation relating $i(t)$ and $v(t)$ can be obtained as

$$R\, i(t) + L\, \frac{di(t)}{dt} + \frac{1}{C} \int_{-\infty}^{t} i(t)\, dt = v(t). \tag{6.8}$$

Differentiating both sides,

$$L\, \frac{d^2 i(t)}{dt^2} + R\, \frac{di(t)}{dt} + \frac{1}{C}\, i(t) = \frac{dv(t)}{dt}, \tag{6.9}$$

where the symbol L stands for inductance and is not an operator.

Using the operator $p = d/dt$, (6.9) can be written as

$$\left(Lp^2 + Rp + \frac{1}{C} \right) i(t) = p\, v(t). \tag{6.10}$$

Hence,

$$i(t) = \frac{p}{Lp^2 + Rp + \dfrac{1}{C}}\, v(t) = H(p)\, v(t), \tag{6.11}$$

where

$$H(p) = \frac{p}{\left(Lp^2 + Rp + \dfrac{1}{C} \right)} = \frac{1}{\left(R + Lp + \dfrac{1}{Cp} \right)} = \frac{1}{Z(p)} = Y(p).$$

In the electrical network of Fig. 6.2(a), $Y(p)$ is called the *operational admittance function*, and $Z(p) = 1/Y(p)$ is called the *operational impedance function*.

PROBLEM 6.2   Consider the simple mechanical system shown in Fig. 6.3(a). Obtain the operational expression for the displacement $x(t)$ of a mass m from the equilibrium position.

Solution: The source is the impressed force $f(t)$, and the response is the displacement $x(t)$ of a mass m from its equilibrium position [Fig. 6.3(b)].

The forces acting on the mass are as follows:
(1) The impressed force $f(t)$.
(2) The inertial reaction $(-m d^2 x/d^2 t)$.
(3) The damping (frictional resistance) force $(-k_d\, dx/dt)$.
(4) The elastic restoring force $(-k_s x)$.

In items (3) and (4) above, k_d and k_s are the frictional coefficient and the spring constant, respectively.

By applying d'Alembert's principle,

$$m\frac{d^2 x(t)}{dt^2} + k_d \frac{dx(t)}{dt} + k_s x(t) = f(t). \tag{6.12}$$

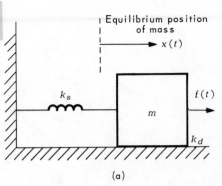

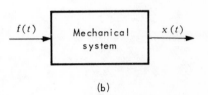

Fig. 6.3 (a) The mechanical system of Prob. 6.2. (b) System representation of the mechanical system in Fig. 6.3(a).

In operator form, (6.12) becomes

$$(mp^2 + k_d p + k_s)\, x(t) = f(t). \tag{6.13}$$

Hence,

$$x(t) = \frac{1}{mp^2 + k_d p + k_s}\, f(t) = H(p)\, f(t), \tag{6.14}$$

where $H(p) = 1/(mp^2 + k_d p + k_s)$.

6.3 Response to Exponential Source Functions and Eigenfunctions– System Functions

The response of linear systems to source functions that are exponential functions of time are of particular importance in the analysis of linear systems.

PROBLEM 6.3   Show that the response of a linear time-invariant system to an exponential function $e^{j\omega t}$ is also an exponential function and proportional to the input; i.e.,

$$L\{e^{j\omega t}\} = k\, e^{j\omega t}. \tag{6.15}$$

Solution: Let $f_o(t)$ be the response to $e^{j\omega t}$. Then,

$$L\{e^{j\omega t}\} = f_o(t). \tag{6.16}$$

Since the system is time-invariant, then from (6.7),

$$L\{e^{j\omega(t + t_0)}\} = f(t + t_0). \tag{6.17}$$

But from (6.6),

$$L\{e^{j\omega(t + t_0)}\} = L\{e^{j\omega t_0} e^{j\omega t}\} = e^{j\omega t_0} \cdot L\{e^{j\omega t}\}. \tag{6.18}$$

Hence,

$$f_o(t + t_0) = e^{j\omega t_0} f_o(t). \tag{6.19}$$

Setting $t = 0$,

$$f_o(t_0) = f_o(0)\, e^{j\omega t_0}. \tag{6.20}$$

Since t_0 is arbitrary, by changing t_0 to t, we can rewrite (6.20) as

$$f_o(t) = f_o(0) \, e^{j\omega t} = k \, e^{j\omega t}.$$

Thus the output is proportional to the input, with $k = f_o(0)$ the proportionality constant. In general, k is complex and depends on ω.

Alternate Solution: Let the input source function in (6.3) be $f_i(t) = e^{j\omega t}$. Then

$$A(p) \, f_o(t) = B(p) \, e^{j\omega t}, \tag{6.21}$$

where $f_o(t)$ is the output response function. Now

$$B(p) = b_m p^m + b_{m-1} p^{m-1} + \cdots + b_1 p + b_0,$$

$$B(p) \, e^{j\omega t} = B(j\omega) \, e^{j\omega t}$$

since

$$p^m \, e^{j\omega t} = \frac{d^m}{dt^m} (e^{j\omega t}) = (j\omega)^m \, e^{j\omega t}.$$

Hence the response $f_o(t)$ is defined by the ordinary linear differential equation

$$A(p) \, f_o(t) = B(j\omega) \, e^{j\omega t}. \tag{6.22}$$

Now the forcing function of (6.22) is $B(j\omega) \, e^{j\omega t}$, an exponential function, and from the theory of differential equations, we can assume that the response $f_o(t)$ also is exponential. Hence, if $f_o(t) = k_1 e^{j\omega t}$, then

$$A(p) \, f_o(t) = A(p) \, [k_1 e^{j\omega t}] = k_1 \, A(p) \, [e^{j\omega t}] = k_1 \, A(j\omega) \, e^{j\omega t} = A(j\omega) \, f_o(t). \tag{6.23}$$

Substituting (6.23) in (6.22),

$$A(j\omega) \, f_o(t) = B(j\omega) \, e^{j\omega t}. \tag{6.24}$$

Hence, if $A(j\omega) \neq 0$,

$$f_o(t) = \frac{B(j\omega)}{A(j\omega)} \, e^{j\omega t} = H(j\omega) \, e^{j\omega t}. \tag{6.25}$$

Figure 6.4 shows a block diagram illustrating the relationship between input and output given by (6.25).

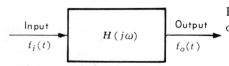

Input $f_i(t)$ — $H(j\omega)$ — Output $f_o(t)$

The input $f_i(t) = e^{j\omega t}$ and the output $f_o(t) = H(j\omega) e^{j\omega t}.$

Fig. 6.4 System function.

Equation (6.25) can be rewritten symbolically as

$$L\{e^{j\omega t}\} = H(j\omega) \, e^{j\omega t}. \tag{6.26}$$

In mathematical language, a function $f(t)$ satisfying the equation

$$L\{f(t)\} = k \, f(t), \tag{6.27}$$

is called an *eigenfunction* (or characteristic function), and the corresponding value of k, an *eigenvalue* (or characteristic value). From (6.26), we can say that the eigenfunction of a linear time-invariant system is an exponential function. The eigenvalue $H(j\omega)$ of the system is defined as the *system function*.

PROBLEM 6.4 Find the response of the system specified by $H(j\omega)$ to a constant K.

Solution: From (6.26) and the linearity of the system,

$$L\{K\} = K \, H(0), \tag{6.28}$$

where $H(0) = H(j\omega)\big|_{\omega=0}.$

PROBLEM 6.5 If the input function of the linear system specified by $H(j\omega)$ is a periodic time function with period T, find the output response of the system.

Solution: Since the input function $f_i(t)$ is periodic,

$$f_i(t) = \sum_{n=-\infty}^{\infty} c_n\, e^{jn\omega_0 t}, \quad \omega_0 = \frac{2\pi}{T}, \tag{6.29}$$

where

$$c_n = \frac{1}{T} \int_{-T/2}^{T/2} f_i(t)\, e^{-jn\omega_0 t}\, dt. \tag{6.30}$$

It follows from (6.26) that

$$f_{on}(t) = H(jn\omega_0)\, c_n\, e^{jn\omega_0 t} \tag{6.31}$$

is the output in response to the input component

$$f_{in}(t) = c_n\, e^{jn\omega_0 t}. \tag{6.32}$$

Since the system is linear, its total response to $f_i(t)$ is the sum of the component outputs $f_{on}(t)$. Thus,

$$f_o(t) = \sum_{n=-\infty}^{\infty} c_n\, H(jn\omega_0)\, e^{jn\omega_0 t}. \tag{6.33}$$

Equation (6.33) indicates that if the input to a linear system is periodic, then the output is also periodic. It must be noted that the response (6.33) is the *steady-state response*.

6.4 Sinusoidal Steady-State Responses

The sinusoidal steady-state response of a linear system can be deduced as the special case of the response to the exponential sources.

PROBLEM 6.6 Show that the steady-state responses of the system specified by $H(j\omega)$ to the input source functions $\cos \omega t$ and $\sin \omega t$ are given by $Re[H(j\omega)e^{j\omega t}]$ and $Im[H(j\omega)e^{j\omega t}]$, respectively, where Re denotes "the real part of" and Im denotes "the imaginary part of."

Solution: Assume that the steady-state response of the system to the input $\cos \omega t$ is $r_c(t)$, and that the steady-state response to $\sin \omega t$ is $r_s(t)$; i.e.,

$$L\{\cos \omega t\} = r_c(t), \tag{6.34}$$

$$L\{\sin \omega t\} = r_s(t). \tag{6.35}$$

It follows from the property of linearity (6.6) that

$$L\{\cos \omega t + j \sin \omega t\} = r_c(t) + j\, r_s(t). \tag{6.36}$$

But since $\cos \omega t + j \sin \omega t = e^{j\omega t}$,

$$L\{e^{j\omega t}\} = r_c(t) + j\, r_s(t). \tag{6.37}$$

From (6.26), it follows that

$$r_c(t) + j\, r_s(t) = H(j\omega)e^{j\omega t}. \tag{6.38}$$

Since $r_c(t)$ and $r_s(t)$ are both real functions of t,

$$r_c(t) = Re[H(j\omega) e^{j\omega t}], \tag{6.39}$$

$$r_s(t) = Im[H(j\omega) e^{j\omega t}]. \tag{6.40}$$

Therefore,

$$L\{\cos \omega t\} = Re[H(j\omega) e^{j\omega t}], \tag{6.41}$$

$$L\{\sin \omega t\} = Im[H(j\omega) e^{j\omega t}]. \tag{6.42}$$

In sinusoidal steady-state analysis, it is customary to use phasor representation for the sinusoidal functions. Thus a cosine function $v(t)$ can be written as

$$v(t) = v_m \cos(\omega t + \beta) = Re[\mathbf{V}_m e^{j\omega t}],$$

where $\mathbf{V}_m = v_m e^{j\beta} = v_m \underline{/\beta}$. The complex quantity $\mathbf{V}_m$ is referred to as the phasor representing $v(t)$.

PROBLEM 6.7 If the system function $H(j\omega)$ is expressed in the phasor form, i.e.,

$$H(j\omega) = |H(j\omega)| e^{j\theta(\omega)} = |H(j\omega)| \underline{/\theta(\omega)},$$

then show that the steady-state responses of the system to inputs $v_m \cos(\omega t + \beta)$ and $v_m \sin(\omega t + \beta)$ are given by, respectively,

$$Re[H(j\omega) \mathbf{V}_m e^{j\omega t}] = v_m|H(j\omega)|\cos(\omega t + \beta + \theta),$$

$$Im[H(j\omega) \mathbf{V}_m e^{j\omega t}] = v_m|H(j\omega)|\sin(\omega t + \beta + \theta).$$

Solution: We proceed as we did in Prob. 6.6. Let

$$L\{v_m \cos(\omega t + \beta)\} = r_c(t), \tag{6.43}$$

$$L\{v_m \sin(\omega t + \beta)\} = r_s(t). \tag{6.44}$$

Then,

$$L\{v_m[\cos(\omega t + \beta) + j \sin(\omega t + \beta)]\} = L\{v_m e^{j(\omega t + \beta)}\}$$

$$= L\{v_m e^{j\beta} e^{j\omega t}\}. \tag{6.45}$$

Let $v_m e^{j\beta} = \mathbf{V}_m$; then from (6.26),

$$L\{\mathbf{V}_m e^{j\omega t}\} = \mathbf{V}_m L\{e^{j\omega t}\} = \mathbf{V}_m H(j\omega) e^{j\omega t}. \tag{6.46}$$

Hence,

$$r_c(t) + j\, r_s(t) = \mathbf{V}_m H(j\omega) e^{j\omega t}. \tag{6.47}$$

Since $\mathbf{V}_m H(j\omega) e^{j\omega t} = v_m|H(j\omega)| e^{j(\omega t + \beta + \theta)}$,

$$r_c(t) = Re[\mathbf{V}_m H(j\omega) e^{j\omega t}] = v_m|H(j\omega)| \cos(\omega t + \beta + \theta), \tag{6.48}$$

$$r(t) = Im[\mathbf{V}_m H(j\omega) e^{j\omega t}] = v_m|H(j\omega)| \sin(\omega t + \beta + \theta). \tag{6.49}$$

Thus,

$$L\{v_m \cos(\omega t + \beta)\} = v_m|H(j\omega)| \cos(\omega t + \beta + \theta), \tag{6.50}$$

$$L\{v_m \sin(\omega t + \beta)\} = v_m|H(j\omega)| \sin(\omega t + \beta + \theta). \tag{6.51}$$

Now, from the above results, if we represent the input $f_i(t)$ by the phasor $\mathbf{V}_m$, then the output $f_o(t)$ can be represented by $\mathbf{V}_m H(j\omega)$. Therefore we can conclude that if the input and output are steady sinusoidal time functions, then the system function $H(j\omega)$ is the ratio of the complex value of the output to that of the input.

PROBLEM 6.8 Find the response $f_o(t)$ of a linear system when the input source $f_i(t)$ is periodic with period T, and is expressed as the Fourier series

$$f_i(t) = C_0 + \sum_{n=1}^{\infty} C_n \cos(n\omega_0 t + \phi_n), \quad \omega_0 = \frac{2\pi}{T}. \tag{6.52}$$

Solution: From the principle of superposition and from the results of Prob. 6.4 and Prob. 6.7, it follows that

$$f_o(t) = L\{f_i(t)\}$$

$$= L\left\{C_0 + \sum_{n=1}^{\infty} C_n \cos(n\omega_0 t + \phi_n)\right\}$$

$$= L\{C_0\} + \sum_{n=1}^{\infty} L\{C_n \cos(n\omega_0 t + \phi_n)\}$$

$$= C_0 H(0) + \sum_{n=1}^{\infty} C_n |H(jn\omega_0)| \cos[n\omega_0 t + \phi_n + \theta(n\omega_0)]. \tag{6.53}$$

6.5 Applications to Electrical Circuits

In this section, we shall apply the ideas developed so far to some of the problems which arise in dealing with electrical circuits.

PROBLEM 6.9 In the series RLC circuit of Fig. 6.5, a voltage source $v(t) = v_m \cos(\omega t + \beta)$ is applied. Find the steady-state response current $i_s(t)$.

Solution: From the result of Prob. 6.1, the response current $i(t)$ is related to the source voltage by

$$i(t) = H(p) v(t) = \frac{1}{Z(p)} [v(t)], \tag{6.54}$$

where $H(p) = 1/Z(p)$ and $Z(p) = R + Lp + \dfrac{1}{Cp}$. Now using phasor representation,

$$v(t) = v_m \cos(\omega t + \beta) = Re[\mathbf{V}_m e^{j\omega t}], \tag{6.55}$$

where $\mathbf{V}_m = v_m e^{j\beta}$.

Then from (6.50) the sinusoidal steady-state response $i_s(t)$ is given by

$$i_s(t) = Re\left[\frac{1}{Z(j\omega)} \mathbf{V}_m e^{j\omega t}\right]. \tag{6.56}$$

Now,

$$Z(j\omega) = R + j\omega L + \frac{1}{j\omega C} = R + j\left(\omega L - \frac{1}{\omega C}\right)$$

$$= |Z(j\omega)| e^{j\theta(\omega)} = |Z(j\omega)| \underline{/\theta(\omega)}, \tag{6.57}$$

where

$$|Z(j\omega)| = \sqrt{R^2 + \left(\omega L - \frac{1}{\omega C}\right)^2}, \qquad \theta(\omega) = \tan^{-1}\left(\frac{\omega L - \dfrac{1}{\omega C}}{R}\right).$$

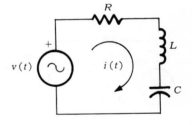

Fig. 6.5 The series RLC circuit of Prob. 6.9.

Then,

$$i_s(t) = \frac{V_m}{|Z(j\omega)|} \cos[\omega t + \beta - \theta(\omega)]. \tag{6.58}$$

Using phasor representation, (6.56) can be rewritten as

$$i_s(t) = \text{Re}[\mathbf{I}_m \, e^{j\omega t}]. \tag{6.59}$$

Then the phasor $\mathbf{I}_m$ representing $i_s(t)$ is related to the phasor $\mathbf{V}_m$ representing $v(t)$ by

$$\mathbf{I}_m = \frac{1}{Z(j\omega)} \, \mathbf{V}_m = Y(j\omega) \, \mathbf{V}_m \tag{6.60}$$

or

$$\frac{\mathbf{V}_m}{\mathbf{I}_m} = Z(j\omega), \quad \frac{\mathbf{I}_m}{\mathbf{V}_m} = Y(j\omega), \tag{6.61}$$

where $Z(j\omega)$ and $Y(j\omega)$ are called the *sinusoidal impedance* and *admittance functions* of the circuit, respectively.

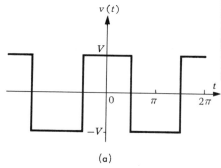

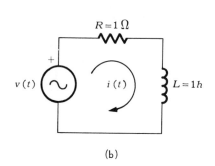

(b)

Fig. 6.6 (a) The waveform of a square-wave voltage source. (b) The series RL circuit of Prob. 6.10.

PROBLEM 6.10 A square-wave voltage source $v(t)$, whose waveform is shown in Fig. 6.6(a), is applied to the series RL circuit of Fig. 6.6(b). Find the steady-state response current $i_s(t)$.

Solution: The Fourier series expansion of the square-wave voltage source $v(t)$ is given by (2.38). With $\omega_0 = 2\pi/T = 1$,

$$v(t) = \frac{4V}{\pi} \left[\cos t - \frac{1}{3} \cos 3t + \frac{1}{5} \cos 5t - \cdots \right]. \tag{6.62}$$

For the RL circuit of Fig. 6.6(b), the impedance function at any radian frequency ω is given by

$$Z(j\omega) = R + j\omega L.$$

Hence for the n-th harmonic, the impedance function is

$$Z(jn\omega_0) = R + jn\omega_0 L.$$

For this problem, $R = 1 \, \Omega$ and $L = 1 \, h$. Hence,

$$Z(jn\omega_0) = Z(jn) = 1 + j \, n = |Z(jn)| \underline{/\theta(n)},$$

where

$$|Z(jn)| = \sqrt{1 + n^2}, \quad \theta(n) = \tan^{-1} n.$$

It follows from the principle of superposition that the steady-state response $i_s(t)$ is given by

$$i_s(t) = \frac{4V}{\pi} \left[\frac{1}{\sqrt{2}} \cos(t - \tan^{-1} 1) - \frac{1}{3\sqrt{10}} \cos(3t - \tan^{-1} 3) \right.$$

$$\left. + \frac{1}{5\sqrt{26}} \cos(5t - \tan^{-1} 5) + \cdots \right]. \tag{6.63}$$

PROBLEM 6.11 The input voltage function to the RC two-port network shown in Fig. 6.7 is the finite Fourier series

$$v_i(t) = 100 \cos t + 10 \cos 3t + \cos 5t.$$

Find the steady-state output response $v_{os}(t)$.

Solution: Since the input source is

$$v_i(t) = R\, i(t) + \frac{1}{C} \int_{-\infty}^{t} i(t)\, dt = \left(R + \frac{1}{pC}\right) i(t), \qquad (6.64)$$

the output response is

$$v_o(t) = \frac{1}{C} \int_{-\infty}^{t} i(t)\, dt = \frac{1}{pC} i(t). \qquad (6.65)$$

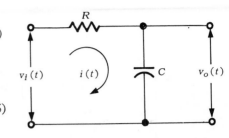

Fig. 6.7 The *RC* two-port network of Prob. 6.11.

Dividing (6.65) by (6.64),

$$\frac{v_o(t)}{v_i(t)} = \frac{\dfrac{1}{pC}}{R + \dfrac{1}{pC}} = \frac{1}{1 + pRC}.$$

Hence the output response $v_o(t)$ and the input source $v_i(t)$ are related by

$$v_o(t) = \frac{\dfrac{1}{pC}}{R + \dfrac{1}{pC}}\, v_i(t) = H(p)\, v_i(t), \qquad (6.66)$$

where

$$H(p) = \frac{\dfrac{1}{pC}}{R + \dfrac{1}{pC}} = \frac{1}{1 + pRC}.$$

Now the phasor ratio $\mathbf{V}_o/\mathbf{V}_i$ at any radian frequency ω is

$$\frac{\mathbf{V}_o}{\mathbf{V}_i} = H(j\omega) = \frac{1}{1 + j\omega RC} = \frac{1}{\sqrt{1 + (\omega RC)^2}} \; \underline{/-\tan^{-1} \omega RC}. \qquad (6.67)$$

Since $\omega_0 = 1$, the phasor ratio of the *n*-th harmonic is

$$\frac{\mathbf{V}_o}{\mathbf{V}_i}\bigg|_n = H(jn\omega_0) = H(jn) = \frac{1}{\sqrt{1 + (nRC)^2}} \; \underline{/-\tan^{-1} nRC}.$$

Hence from the principle of superposition, it follows that the steady-state output response $v_{os}(t)$ is given by

$$v_{os}(t) = \frac{100}{\sqrt{1 + R^2C^2}} \cos(t - \tan^{-1} RC) + \frac{10}{\sqrt{1 + 9R^2C^2}} \cos(3t - \tan^{-1} 3RC)$$

$$+ \frac{1}{\sqrt{1 + 25R^2C^2}} \cos(5t - \tan^{-1} 5RC). \qquad (6.68)$$

In this problem, $H(j\omega)$ of (6.67) is termed the *voltage transfer function.*

6.5a Steady-State Power Calculation

PROBLEM 6.12 At the terminals *a-b* of the network in Fig. 6.8, the voltage $v_{ab}(t)$ is periodic and defined by the Fourier series

$$v_{ab}(t) = V_0 + \sum_{n=1}^{\infty} V_n \cos(n\omega_0 t + \beta_n), \qquad (6.69)$$

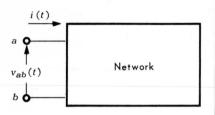

Fig. 6.8 The network of Prob. 6.12.

and the steady-state current $i_s(t)$ entering the a terminal is

$$i_s(t) = I_o + \sum_{n=1}^{\infty} I_n \cos(n\omega_0 t + \alpha_n). \qquad (6.70)$$

Show that the average power input P_{ab} defined by

$$P_{ab} = \frac{1}{T} \int_{-T/2}^{T/2} v_{ab}(t) i_s(t) \, dt \qquad (6.71)$$

is equal to

$$P_{ab} = V_o I_o + \frac{1}{2} \sum_{n=1}^{\infty} V_n I_n \cos(\beta_n - \alpha_n). \qquad (6.72)$$

Solution: By substituting (6.69) and (6.70) into (6.71),

$$P_{ab} = \frac{1}{T} \int_{-T/2}^{T/2} \left[V_o + \sum_{n=1}^{\infty} V_n \cos(n\omega_0 t + \beta_n) \right] \left[I_o + \sum_{k=1}^{\infty} I_k \cos(k\omega_0 t + \alpha_k) \right] dt$$

$$= \frac{1}{T} \int_{-T/2}^{T/2} \left[V_o I_o + V_o \sum_{k=1}^{\infty} I_k \cos(k\omega_0 t + \alpha_k) + I_o \sum_{n=1}^{\infty} V_n \cos(n\omega_0 t + \beta_n) \right.$$

$$\left. + \sum_{n=1}^{\infty} \sum_{k=1}^{\infty} V_n I_k \cos(n\omega_0 t + \beta_n) \cos(k\omega_0 t + \alpha_k) \right] dt$$

$$= V_o I_o \frac{1}{T} \int_{-T/2}^{T/2} dt + V_o \sum_{k=1}^{\infty} I_k \frac{1}{T} \int_{-T/2}^{T/2} \cos(k\omega_0 t + \alpha_k) \, dt$$

$$+ I_o \sum_{n=1}^{\infty} V_n \frac{1}{T} \int_{-T/2}^{T/2} \cos(n\omega_0 t + \beta_n) \, dt$$

$$+ \sum_{n=1}^{\infty} V_n \sum_{k=1}^{\infty} I_k \frac{1}{T} \int_{-T/2}^{T/2} \cos(n\omega_0 t + \beta_n) \cos(k\omega_0 t + \alpha_k) \, dt. \qquad (6.73)$$

Making use of the orthogonality relationships of Sec. 1.3,

$$\int_{-T/2}^{T/2} \cos(n\omega_0 t + \beta_n) \, dt = 0,$$

$$\int_{-T/2}^{T/2} \cos(n\omega_0 t + \beta_n) \cos(k\omega_0 t + \alpha_k) \, dt = \begin{cases} 0, & k \neq n \\ \dfrac{T}{2} \cos(\beta_n - \alpha_n), & k = n. \end{cases}$$

Hence (6.73) can be rewritten as

$$P_{ab} = V_o I_o + \frac{1}{2} \sum_{n=1}^{\infty} V_n I_n \cos(\beta_n - \alpha_n).$$

Denoting the rms values of the n-th harmonic voltage by $V_{eff,n}$ and that of the n-th harmonic current by $I_{eff,n}$,

$$\frac{1}{2} V_n I_n = V_{eff,n} I_{eff,n}. \qquad (6.74)$$

Let

$$\theta_n = \beta_n - \alpha_n. \qquad (6.75)$$

Then θ_n denotes the phase difference between the n-th harmonic voltage and current. Introducing (6.74) and (6.75) into (6.72),

$$P_{ab} = V_o I_o + \sum_{n=1}^{\infty} V_{\text{eff},n} I_{\text{eff},n} \cos \theta_n$$

$$= P_0 + P_1 + P_2 + \cdots = \sum_{n=0}^{\infty} P_n, \qquad (6.76)$$

where P_n is the average power in the n-th harmonic component.

Equation (6.76) shows that the average power delivered by a periodic source to a network is the sum of the average power delivered by individual harmonics. There are no contributions to the average power from the current at one frequency and the voltage at another.

PROBLEM 6.13 For the one-port network of Fig. 6.8, it is known that

$$v_{ab}(t) = 10 + 2 \cos (t + 45°) + \cos (2t + 45°) + \cos (3t - 60°),$$

$$i(t) = 5 + \cos t + 2 \cos (3t + 75°).$$

Determine the average power delivered to the network.

Solution: For V_i, I_i, θ_i, and P_i, $i = 0, 1, 2, 3$,

$$V_o = 10, \quad I_o = 5, \qquad\qquad P_0 = 50,$$

$$V_1 = 2, \quad I_1 = 1, \quad \theta_1 = 45°, \qquad P_1 = \frac{1}{2} 2 \cos 45° = 0.707,$$

$$V_2 = 1, \quad I_2 = 0, \qquad\qquad\qquad P_2 = 0,$$

$$V_3 = 1, \quad I_3 = 2, \quad \theta_3 = -135°, \quad P_3 = \frac{1}{2} 2 \cos (-135°) = -0.707.$$

Hence, the power delivered to the network is

$$P_{ab} = P_0 + P_1 + P_2 + P_3 = 50 + 0.707 + 0 - 0.707 = 50 \text{ w}.$$

6.6 Applications to Mechanical Systems

The method discussed in the preceeding section can be applied equally well to mechanical systems.

PROBLEM 6.14 Consider the mechanical system illustrated in Fig. 6.9 that consists of a spring, a mass, and a damper which is represented by a dashpot. The system is disturbed from its equilibrium position by the application of a force $f(t) = f_o \cos (\omega t + \beta)$. Find the steady-state response displacement $x_s(t)$.

Solution: The response $x(t)$ and the forcing input $f(t)$ are related by the following differential equation of motion:

$$m \frac{d^2 x(t)}{dt^2} + B \frac{dx(t)}{dt} + k x(t) = f(t), \qquad (6.77)$$

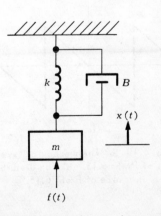

Fig. 6.9 The mechanical system of Prob. 6.14.

where m, B, and k represent mass, damping coefficient, and the spring constant of the system, respectively. Equation (6.77) can be rewritten in operational form as

$$x(t) = \frac{1}{mp^2 + Bp + k} f(t) = H(p) f(t), \qquad (6.78)$$

where

$$H(p) = \frac{1}{(mp^2 + Bp + k)}.$$

Since we are interested in the steady-state response, using phasor notation,

$$f(t) = f_o \cos (\omega t + \beta) = Re\,[\mathbf{F}_o \, e^{j\omega t}],$$

where $\mathbf{F}_o = f_o \, e^{j\beta}$.

Then from (6.50), the steady-state response $x_s(t)$ is given by

$$x_s(t) = Re\,[\mathbf{F}_o H(j\omega)\, e^{j\omega t}]. \qquad (6.79)$$

Now,

$$H(j\omega) = \frac{1}{m(j\omega)^2 + B(j\omega) + k} = \frac{1}{k - m\omega^2 + j\omega B} = |H(j\omega)|\ \underline{/\theta(\omega)},$$

where

$$|H(j\omega)| = \frac{1}{\sqrt{(k - m\omega^2)^2 + \omega^2 B^2}}, \quad \theta(\omega) = -\tan^{-1}\left(\frac{\omega B}{k - m\omega^2}\right).$$

Then,

$$x_s(t) = \frac{f_o}{\sqrt{(k - m\omega^2)^2 + \omega^2 B^2}} \cos\left(\omega t + \beta - \tan^{-1}\frac{\omega B}{k - m\omega^2}\right). \qquad (6.80)$$

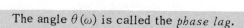

The angle $\theta(\omega)$ is called the *phase lag*.

PROBLEM 6.15 Discuss the steady-state motion of the system shown in Fig. 6.10(a) if the disturbing force $f(t)$ is as shown in Fig. 6.10(b).

Solution: The response $x(t)$, the displacement of the mass m from its position of stable equilibrium, and the forcing input $f(t)$ are related by

$$m \frac{d^2 x(t)}{dt^2} + k\, x(t) = f(t), \qquad (6.81)$$

which can be rewritten as

$$x(t) = \frac{1}{mp^2 + k} f(t) = H(p) f(t), \qquad (6.82)$$

where

$$H(p) = \frac{1}{(mp^2 + k)}.$$

Next, from the result of Prob. 2.15, the Fourier series expansion of $f(t)$ is obtained as

$$f(t) = -\frac{A}{\pi}\left(\sin \omega_0 t + \frac{1}{2} \sin 2\omega_0 t + \frac{1}{3} \sin 3\omega_0 t + \dots\right),$$

where $\omega_0 = 2\pi/T$.

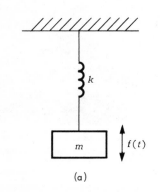

(a)

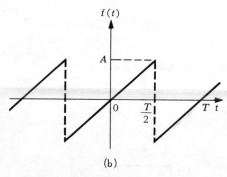

(b)

Fig. 6.10 (a) The mechanical system of Prob. 6.15. (b) The disturbing force of Prob. 6.15.

Since we are concerned only with the forced or steady-state motion of the system, we proceed with phasor representation. Now,

$$H(j\omega) = \frac{1}{m(j\omega)^2 + k} = \frac{1}{k - m\omega^2} = |H(j\omega)| \underline{/\theta(\omega)}$$

and

$$H(jn\omega_0) = \frac{1}{[k - m(n\omega_0)^2]}.$$

Since the phase lag $\theta(\omega)$ is zero, from (6.51),

$$x_s(t) = -\frac{A}{\pi}\left[\frac{\sin \omega_0 t}{k - m\omega_0^2} + \frac{1}{2}\frac{\sin 2\omega_0 t}{k - 4m\omega_0^2} + \frac{1}{3}\frac{\sin 3\omega_0 t}{k - 9m\omega_0^2} + \cdots\right]. \tag{6.83}$$

6.7 Response of a Linear System to a Unit Impulse-System Function

We shall now consider a more general situation in which the input excitation of a system is any given function of time.

We denote the response of a linear system to a unit impulse $\delta(t)$ by $h(t)$. Symbolically this is expressed as

$$L\{\delta(t)\} = h(t). \tag{6.84}$$

If the system is time-invariant (or with constant parameters), then we see from (6.7) that its response to $\delta(t - \tau)$ is given by $h(t - \tau)$; i.e.,

$$L\{\delta(t - \tau)\} = h(t - \tau). \tag{6.85}$$

PROBLEM 6.16 Show that the response $f_o(t)$ of a time-invariant linear system to an arbitrary input $f_i(t)$ can be expressed as the convolution of the input $f_i(t)$ and the unit impulse response $h(t)$ of the system; i.e.,

$$f_o(t) = \int_{-\infty}^{\infty} f_i(\tau) h(t - \tau) d\tau = f_i(t) * h(t) \tag{6.86}$$

$$= \int_{-\infty}^{\infty} f_i(t - \tau) h(\tau) d\tau = h(t) * f_i(t). \tag{6.87}$$

Solution: From the property (2.68) of the δ-function, we can express $f_i(t)$ as

$$f_i(t) = \int_{-\infty}^{\infty} f_i(\tau) \delta(t - \tau) d\tau. \tag{6.88}$$

Then from the linearity (6.6) of the L operator, in view of (6.85),

$$f_o(t) = L\{f_i(t)\} = \int_{-\infty}^{\infty} f_i(\tau) L\{\delta(t - \tau)\} d\tau = \int_{-\infty}^{\infty} f_i(\tau) h(t - \tau) d\tau. \tag{6.89}$$

From the definition (4.105) and property (4.108) of convolution, (6.89) can be expressed as

$$f_o(t) = f_i(t) * h(t) = h(t) * f_i(t)$$

$$= \int_{-\infty}^{\infty} f_i(t - \tau) h(\tau) d\tau.$$

Equation (6.86) or (6.87) indicates a very interesting result. It tells us that the response of a linear system is uniquely determined from the knowledge of the unit impulse response $h(t)$ of the system.

6.7a System Function

The Fourier transform of the unit impulse response of a linear system is called the *system function*:

$$H(\omega) = \mathcal{F}[h(t)] = \int_{-\infty}^{\infty} h(t)\, e^{-j\omega t}\, dt, \tag{6.90}$$

$$h(t) = \mathcal{F}^{-1}[H(\omega)] = \frac{1}{2\pi} \int_{-\infty}^{\infty} H(\omega)\, e^{j\omega t}\, d\omega. \tag{6.91}$$

Equations (6.90) and (6.91) indicate that the unit impulse response and the system function constitute the Fourier transform pair.

PROBLEM 6.17 With $F_i(\omega)$ and $F_o(\omega)$ denoting the Fourier transforms of the input $f_i(t)$ and the output $f_o(t)$ of a linear system, respectively, show that

$$F_o(\omega) = F_i(\omega)\, H(\omega), \tag{6.92}$$

$$f_o(t) = \frac{1}{2\pi} \int_{-\infty}^{\infty} F_i(\omega)\, H(\omega)\, e^{j\omega t}\, d\omega, \tag{6.93}$$

where $H(\omega)$ is the system function defined by (6.90).

Solution: From (6.86),

$$f_o(t) = f_i(t) * h(t).$$

Hence applying the time convolution theorem (4.122),

$$F_o(\omega) = F_i(\omega)\, H(\omega).$$

Applying the Fourier inverse transform formula (4.16),

$$f_o(t) = \mathcal{F}^{-1}[F_o(\omega)] = \frac{1}{2\pi} \int_{-\infty}^{\infty} F_i(\omega)\, H(\omega)\, e^{j\omega t}\, d\omega.$$

PROBLEM 6.18 Verify that the system function $H(\omega)$ defined by (6.90) is exactly the same system function $H(j\omega)$ defined by (6.26).

Solution: If $f_i(t) = e^{j\omega_0 t}$, then from (5.21),

$$F_i(\omega) = \mathcal{F}[f_i(t)] = \mathcal{F}[e^{j\omega_0 t}] = 2\pi\, \delta(\omega - \omega_0). \tag{5.21}$$

Hence,

$$F_i(\omega)\, H(\omega) = 2\pi\, \delta(\omega - \omega_0)\, H(\omega) = 2\pi\, H(\omega_0)\, \delta(\omega - \omega_0), \tag{6.94}$$

in view of the property (2.74) of the δ-function. Then from (6.93),

$$f_o(t) = L\{e^{j\omega_0 t}\} = \frac{1}{2\pi} \int_{-\infty}^{\infty} 2\pi\, H(\omega_0)\, \delta(\omega - \omega_0)\, e^{j\omega t}\, d\omega$$

$$= H(\omega_0) \int_{-\infty}^{\infty} \delta(\omega - \omega_0)\, e^{j\omega t}\, d\omega$$

$$= H(\omega_0)\, e^{j\omega_0 t}. \tag{6.95}$$

Since (6.95) holds for any value of ω_0, we can change ω_0 to ω and obtain

$$f_o(t) = L\{e^{j\omega t}\} = H(\omega)\,e^{j\omega t}. \tag{6.96}$$

From (6.26),

$$f_o(t) = L\{e^{j\omega t}\} = H(j\omega)\,e^{j\omega t}. \tag{[6.26]}$$

Comparing (6.96) and (6.26), we conclude that

$$H(\omega) = H(j\omega).$$

As a matter of fact, in the definition of the Fourier transform of $f(t)$,

$$F(\omega) = \mathcal{F}[f(t)] = \int_{-\infty}^{\infty} f(t)\,e^{-j\omega t}\,dt, \tag{[4.15]}$$

the variable ω always appears with j, and hence the integral can be written as a function of $j\omega$. Thus we may express (4.15) as

$$F(j\omega) = \mathcal{F}[f(t)] = \int_{-\infty}^{\infty} f(t)\,e^{-j\omega t}\,dt,$$

and, consequently,

$$f(t) = \mathcal{F}^{-1}[F(j\omega)] = \frac{1}{2\pi}\int_{-\infty}^{\infty} F(j\omega)\,e^{j\omega t}\,d\omega.$$

Therefore, $F(\omega)$ and $F(j\omega)$ represent the same function $\mathcal{F}[f(t)]$. The distinction is only a matter of notation. Throughout the rest of this book, $F(\omega)$ and $F(j\omega)$ will be used interchangeably. Thus (6.92) can be rewritten as

$$F_o(j\omega) = F_i(j\omega)\,H(j\omega). \tag{6.97}$$

From (6.92) or (6.97),

$$H(j\omega) = \frac{F_o(j\omega)}{F_i(j\omega)} = \frac{\mathcal{F}[f_o(t)]}{\mathcal{F}[f_i(t)]}. \tag{6.98}$$

Equation (6.98) indicates that the system function $H(j\omega)$ is also the ratio of the response transform to the source transform.

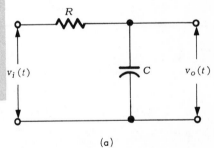

(a)

PROBLEM 6.19 Find the unit impulse response of the RC network shown in Fig. 6.11(a).

Solution: From the result (6.67) of Prob. 6.11, the system function $H(j\omega)$ is given by

$$H(j\omega) = \frac{\dfrac{1}{j\omega C}}{R + \dfrac{1}{j\omega C}} = \frac{1}{1 + j\omega RC} = \frac{1}{RC\left(j\omega + \dfrac{1}{RC}\right)}. \tag{6.99}$$

Therefore, from the result of Prob. 4.11,

$$h(t) = \mathcal{F}^{-1}[H(j\omega)] = \frac{1}{RC}\,\mathcal{F}^{-1}\left[\frac{1}{j\omega + \dfrac{1}{RC}}\right] = \frac{1}{RC}\,e^{-t/RC}\,u(t). \tag{6.100}$$

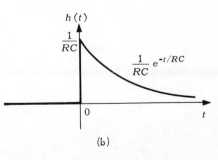

(b)

Fig. 6.11 (a) The RC network of Prob. 6.19. (b) The unit impulse response.

The unit impulse response $h(t)$ is plotted in Fig. 6.11(b).

PROBLEM 6.20 A voltage source $v_i(t) = e^{-t}u(t)$ is applied to the RC network of Fig. 6.11(a). Find the response output voltage $v_o(t)$ when $R = 1/2\,\Omega$ and $C = 1$ f.

Solution: Substituting $R = 1/2 \ \Omega$ and $C = 1$ f in (6.100),

$$h(t) = 2 \ e^{-2t} \ u(t).$$ (6.101)

Hence, from (6.86),

$$v_o(t) = v_i(t) * h(t)$$

$$= \int_{-\infty}^{\infty} v_i(\tau) \ h(t - \tau) \ d\tau$$

$$= \int_{-\infty}^{\infty} e^{-\tau} u(\tau) \ 2e^{-2(t-\tau)} \ u(t - \tau) \ d\tau$$

$$= 2 \ e^{-2t} \int_{-\infty}^{\infty} e^{\tau} u(\tau) \ u(t - \tau) \ d\tau.$$

Since

$$u(\tau) \ u(t - \tau) = \begin{cases} 0 & \text{for } \tau < 0, \ \tau > t \\ 1 & \text{for } 0 < \tau < t, \end{cases}$$

we have

$$v_o(t) = \left(2 \ e^{-2t} \int_0^t e^{\tau} \ d\tau \right) u(t)$$

$$= 2 \ e^{-2t} \ (e^t - 1) \ u(t)$$

$$= 2 \ (e^{-t} - e^{-2t}) \ u(t).$$ (6.102)

The $u(t)$ in (6.102) indicates that there is no response due to the input source before that source is applied.

PROBLEM 6.21 Find the response of the RC network of Fig. 6.11(a) to a unit step function $u(t)$ by convolution.

Solution: From (6.100),

$$h(t) = \frac{1}{RC} \ e^{-t/RC} \ u(t).$$

Hence, from (6.86),

$$v_o(t) = v_i(t) * h(t)$$

$$= \int_{-\infty}^{\infty} v_i(\tau) \ h(t - \tau) \ d\tau$$

$$= \int_{-\infty}^{\infty} u(\tau) \ \frac{1}{RC} \ e^{-(t-\tau)/RC} \ u(t - \tau) \ d\tau$$

$$= \left[\frac{1}{RC} \int_0^t e^{-(t-\tau)/RC} \ d\tau \right] u(t)$$

$$= \left(\frac{1}{RC} \ e^{-t/RC} \int_0^t e^{\tau/RC} \ d\tau \right) u(t)$$

$$= (1 - e^{-t/RC}) \ u(t).$$ (6.103)

6.7b Causal System

A physical passive system has the property that if the input source is zero for $t < t_0$, then the output response is also zero for $t < t_0$; i.e., if

$$f_i(t) = 0 \quad \text{for } t < t_0, \tag{6.104}$$

then

$$f_o(t) = L\{f_i(t)\} = 0 \quad \text{for } t < t_0. \tag{6.105}$$

A system which satisfies (6.104) and (6.105) is called a *causal system*. A function $f(t)$ will be called *causal* if it has zero value for $t < 0$; i.e., $f(t) = 0$ for $t < 0$. It can be shown that all physically realizable systems are causal.

PROBLEM 6.22 Show that the response $f_o(t)$ of a linear causal system to any source $f_i(t)$ is given by

$$f_o(t) = \int_{-\infty}^{t} f_i(\tau)\, h(t - \tau)\, d\tau \tag{6.106}$$

$$= \int_{0}^{\infty} f_i(t - \tau)\, h(\tau)\, d\tau. \tag{6.107}$$

Solution: From (6.104) and (6.105), it follows that the unit impulse response $h(t)$ is causal; i.e.,

$$h(t) = 0 \quad \text{for } t < 0. \tag{6.108}$$

This means that

$$h(\tau) = 0 \quad \text{for } \tau < 0 \tag{6.109}$$

and

$$h(t - \tau) = 0 \quad \text{for } t - \tau < 0 \quad \text{or} \quad -\tau > t. \tag{6.110}$$

Therefore, in view of (6.110), the integrand in (6.86) is zero in the interval $\tau = t$ to $\tau = \infty$. Thus from (6.86),

$$f_o(t) = \int_{-\infty}^{\infty} f_i(\tau)\, h(t - \tau)\, d\tau$$

$$= \int_{-\infty}^{t} f_i(\tau)\, h(t - \tau)\, d\tau.$$

Similarly, from (6.109), the integrand in (6.87) is zero in the interval $\tau = -\infty$ to $\tau = 0$. Thus from (6.87),

$$f_o(t) = \int_{-\infty}^{\infty} f_i(t - \tau)\, h(\tau)\, d\tau$$

$$= \int_{0}^{\infty} f_i(t - \tau)\, h(\tau)\, d\tau.$$

PROBLEM 6.23 If the source function $f_i(t)$ is causal, i.e., if the source $f_i(t)$ is impressed at $t = 0$, then show that the response $f_o(t)$ of a linear causal system is

$$f_o(t) = \int_{0}^{t} f_i(\tau)\, h(t - \tau)\, d\tau. \tag{6.111}$$

Solution: In (6.106), if $f_i(\tau) = 0$ for $\tau < 0$, then the lower limit of the integral may be changed to 0, since in the interval $\tau = -\infty$ to $\tau = 0$, the integrand is zero. Thus,

$$f_o(t) = \int_{-\infty}^{t} f_i(\tau)\, h(t - \tau)\, d\tau = \int_{0}^{t} f_i(\tau)\, h(t - \tau)\, d\tau.$$

6.8 Response of a Linear System to a Unit Step Function— Superposition Integral

Equations (6.86) and (6.87) express the response of a linear system in terms of its unit impulse response. It is also sometimes convenient to express the response in terms of the *unit step response* of the system. The response of a system to a unit step $u(t)$ is denoted by $a(t)$, i.e.,

$$L\{u(t)\} = a(t). \qquad (6.112)$$

PROBLEM 6.24 Show that the unit step response $a(t)$ of a linear system can be expressed as

$$a(t) = \int_{-\infty}^{t} h(\tau)\, d\tau, \qquad (6.113)$$

$$a(\infty) = a(t)\big|_{t=\infty} = H(0), \qquad (6.114)$$

where $H(\omega)$ is the system function of the system, and $h(t)$ its unit impulse response. If the system is causal, show that

$$a(t) = \int_{0}^{t} h(\tau)\, d\tau. \qquad (6.115)$$

Solution: Since $f_i(t) = u(t)$ and $f_o(t) = a(t)$, it follows from (6.87) that

$$a(t) = \int_{-\infty}^{\infty} u(t - \tau)\, h(\tau)\, d\tau. \qquad (6.116)$$

Since

$$u(t - \tau) = \begin{cases} 0 & \text{for } \tau > t \\[2mm] 1 & \text{for } \tau < t, \end{cases}$$

we have

$$a(t) = \int_{-\infty}^{t} h(\tau)\, d\tau.$$

With $t = \infty$,

$$a(\infty) = a(t)\big|_{t=\infty} = \int_{-\infty}^{\infty} h(\tau)\, d\tau.$$

Certainly this integral can be written as

$$a(\infty) = \int_{-\infty}^{\infty} h(\tau)\, e^{-j\omega\tau}\, d\tau\Big|_{\omega=0} = H(\omega)\big|_{\omega=0} = H(0).$$

For a causal system, since $h(\tau) = 0$ for $\tau < 0$, (6.113) becomes

$$a(t) = \int_0^t h(\tau)\, d\tau.$$

PROBLEM 6.25 Using (6.115), rework Prob. 6.21.

Solution: From (6.100),

$$h(t) = \frac{1}{RC} e^{-t/RC}\, u(t).$$
$$[6.100]$$

Substituting (6.100) into (6.115),

$$v_o(t) = a(t) = \int_0^t h(\tau)\, d\tau = \int_0^t \frac{1}{RC} e^{-\tau/RC}\, d\tau$$

$$= \left[\frac{1}{RC} \int_0^t e^{-\tau/RC}\, d\tau \right] u(t)$$

$$= (1 - e^{-t/RC})\, u(t),$$

which is exactly the same as (6.103).

PROBLEM 6.26 Show that the Fourier transform of $a(t)$ is given by

$$A(\omega) = \mathcal{F}[a(t)] = \pi H(0)\, \delta(\omega) + \frac{1}{j\omega} H(\omega),$$
$$(6.117)$$

where $H(\omega)$ is the system function of the system.

Solution: From (5.35),

$$\mathcal{F}[f_i(t)] = \mathcal{F}[u(t)] = \pi \delta(\omega) + \frac{1}{j\omega}.$$
$$[5.35]$$

Now if $\mathcal{F}[f_o(t)] = \mathcal{F}[a(t)] = A(\omega)$, then from (6.92),

$$A(\omega) = \left[\pi \delta(\omega) + \frac{1}{j\omega} \right] H(\omega)$$

$$= \pi \delta(\omega) H(\omega) + \frac{1}{j\omega} H(\omega)$$

$$= \pi H(0)\, \delta(\omega) + \frac{1}{j\omega} H(\omega),$$

in view of a property of the δ-function (2.74).

Alternate Solution: Since, from (6.113),

$$a(t) = \int_{-\infty}^t h(\tau)\, d\tau,$$

it follows from the result (5.55) of Prob. 5.12 that

$$A(\omega) = \frac{1}{j\omega} H(\omega) + \pi H(0)\, \delta(\omega).$$

PROBLEM 6.27 If $a(t)$ is the unit step response of a linear system with the system function $H(\omega)$, show that the response $f_o(t)$ of the system to any source $f_i(t)$ is given by

$$f_o(t) = f_i(-\infty) H(0) + \int_{-\infty}^{\infty} f_i'(\tau) a(t-\tau) d\tau, \tag{6.118}$$

where $f_i'(\tau) = df_i(\tau)/d\tau$.

Solution: Any input source $f_i(t)$ can be written in the form

$$f_i(t) = f_i(-\infty) + \int_{-\infty}^{t} f_i'(\tau) d\tau$$

$$= f_i(-\infty) + \int_{-\infty}^{\infty} f_i'(\tau) u(t-\tau) d\tau \tag{6.119}$$

since

$$u(t-\tau) = \begin{cases} 0 & \text{for } t < \tau \\ 1 & \text{for } t > \tau. \end{cases}$$

Then from (6.28) and (6.112),

$$L\{K\} = K H(0) \qquad \text{and} \qquad L\{u(t)\} = a(t) \longrightarrow L\{u(t-\tau)\} = a(t-\tau).$$

Thus,

$$f_o(t) = L\{f_i(t)\} = L\{f(-\infty)] + \int_{-\infty}^{\infty} f_i'(\tau) L\{u(t-\tau)\} d\tau$$

$$= f(-\infty) H(0) + \int_{-\infty}^{\infty} f_i'(\tau) a(t-\tau) d\tau.$$

PROBLEM 6.28 For a linear causal system, the input source $f_i(t) = 0$ for $t < 0$ has a jump of value $f_i(0+)$ at $t = 0$, and is continuous for $t > 0$ as shown in Fig. 6.12. Show that the output response $f_o(t)$ of the system is given by the *superposition*, or *Duhamel's, integral*

$$f_o(t) = f_i(0+) a(t) + \int_{0+}^{t} f_i'(\tau) a(t-\tau) d\tau. \tag{6.120}$$

Solution: Since $f_i(-\infty) = 0$ from (6.119),

$$f_o(t) = \int_{-\infty}^{\infty} f_i'(\tau) a(t-\tau) d\tau. \tag{6.121}$$

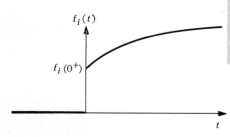

Fig. 6.12 The input source function $f_i(t)$ of Prob. 6.27.

Since $f_i(t)$ has a jump value of $f_i(0+)$ at $t = 0$ from the result (2.94) of Prob. 2.28,

$$f_i'(t) = f_i(0+) \delta(t) + f_{i+}'(t), \tag{6.122}$$

where $f_{i+}'(t) = f_i'(t) u(t)$, i.e., the derivative of $f_i(t)$ for $t > 0$. Substituting (6.122) into (6.121),

$$f_o(t) = \int_{-\infty}^{\infty} [f_i(0+) \delta(\tau) + f_i'(\tau) u(\tau)] a(t-\tau) d\tau$$

$$= f_i(0+) \int_{-\infty}^{\infty} \delta(\tau) a(t-\tau) d\tau + \int_{0+}^{\infty} f_i'(\tau) a(t-\tau) d\tau$$

$$= f_i(0+) a(t) + \int_{0+}^{t} f_i'(\tau) a(t-\tau) d\tau$$

since $a(t-\tau) = 0$ for $\tau > t$ in the causal system.

Equation (6.120) expresses the response of a causal system in terms of its unit step response $a(t)$.

PROBLEM 6.29 Explain that the superposition integral (6.120) actually expresses the response of a system as a continuous sum of the responses to the step components of $f_i(t)$.

Solution: An input source $f_i(t)$ can be approximated by a sum of a large number of infinitesimal step functions as shown in Fig. 6.13. An infinitesimal step function located at τ can be expressed as

$$\frac{df_i(\tau)}{d\tau}\, \Delta\tau\, u(t-\tau) = f_i'(\tau)\, \Delta\tau\, u(t-\tau). \tag{6.123}$$

Now we see from Fig. 6.13 that $f_i(t)$ can be expressed as

$$f_i(t) = f_i(0+)\, u(t) + \lim_{\Delta\tau\to 0} \sum_{\tau=0}^{t} f_i'(\tau)\, \Delta\tau\, u(t-\tau). \tag{6.124}$$

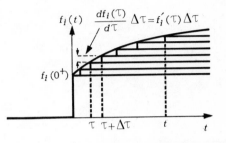

Fig. 6.13 The input source function $f_i(t)$ approximated as a sum of step functions.

Since the response of the system to a unit step function $u(t)$ is $a(t)$, the response due to an infinitesimal step function (6.123) is given by

$$f_i'(\tau)\, \Delta\tau\, a(t-\tau).$$

Hence the response $f_o(t)$ of the system to the source $f_i(t)$ will be expressed as a continuous sum of the responses to the step components of $f_i(t)$, i.e.,

$$f_o(t) = f_i(0+)\, a(t) + \lim_{\Delta\tau\to 0} \sum_{\tau=0}^{t} f_i'(\tau)\, \Delta\tau\, a(t-\tau) \tag{6.125}$$

$$= f_i(0+)\, a(t) + \int_{0+}^{t} f_i'(\tau)\, a(t-\tau)\, d\tau.$$

PROBLEM 6.30 Using the superposition integral (6.120), rework Prob. 6.20.

Solution: Refer to Fig. 6.14. Let $v_i(t) = e^{-t} u(t)$. Thus,

$$v_i(0+) = 1, \qquad v_i'(t) = -e^{-t} \quad \text{for} \quad t > 0.$$

From the result (6.103) of Prob. 6.21, the unit step response $a(t)$ is obtained as

$$a(t) = (1 - e^{-2t})\, u(t).$$

Hence using (6.120),

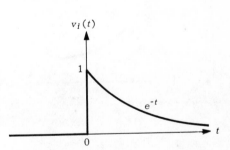

Fig. 6.14 The voltage source of Prob. 6.30.

$$v_o(t) = v_i(0+)\, a(t) + \int_{0+}^{t} v_i'(\tau)\, a(t-\tau)\, d\tau$$

$$= (1 - e^{-2t})\, u(t) + \int_{0+}^{t} -e^{-\tau}[1 - e^{-2(t-\tau)}\, u(t-\tau)]\, d\tau$$

$$= (1 - e^{-2t})\, u(t) - \left[\int_{0}^{t} e^{-\tau}\, d\tau - e^{-2t} \int_{0}^{t} e^{\tau}\, d\tau \right] u(t)$$

$$= (1 - e^{-2t})\, u(t) + (e^{-t} - 1)\, u(t) + e^{-2t}(e^{t} - 1)\, u(t)$$

$$= 2(e^{-t} - e^{-2t})\, u(t),$$

which is (6.102).

6.9 Distortionless Transmission

For distortionless transmission, we require the response waveform to be an exact replica of the input source waveform. However, the amplitude of the response may differ from that of the input.

PROBLEM 6.31   Suppose the system function $H(j\omega)$ of a linear system is given by

$$H(j\omega) = K\, e^{-j\omega t_0}, \qquad (6.126)$$

where K and t_0 are positive constants. Find the response $f_o(t)$ of the system to an input source $f_i(t)$.

Solution: Let

$$\mathcal{F}[f_i(t)] = F_i(j\omega), \qquad \mathcal{F}[f_o(t)] = F_o(j\omega).$$

From (6.92), $F_i(j\omega)$ and $F_o(j\omega)$ are related by

$$F_o(j\omega) = F_i(j\omega)\, H(j\omega)$$
$$= K\, F_i(j\omega)\, e^{-j\omega t_0}. \qquad (6.127)$$

Hence,

$$f_o(t) = \mathcal{F}^{-1}[F_o(j\omega)]$$

$$= \frac{K}{2\pi} \int_{-\infty}^{\infty} [F_i(j\omega)\, e^{-j\omega t_0}]\, e^{j\omega t}\, d\omega$$

$$= \frac{K}{2\pi} \int_{-\infty}^{\infty} F_i(j\omega)\, e^{j\omega(t - t_0)}\, d\omega.$$

In view of the fact that

$$f_i(t) = \mathcal{F}^{-1}[F_i(j\omega)] = \frac{1}{2\pi} \int_{-\infty}^{\infty} F_i(j\omega)\, e^{j\omega t}\, d\omega,$$

$f_o(t)$ can be written as

$$f_o(t) = K\, f_i(t - t_0). \qquad (6.128)$$

Equation (6.128) shows that the output response is a delayed replica of the input function, with the magnitude of the response changed by the constant factor K. This is illustrated in Fig. 6.15.

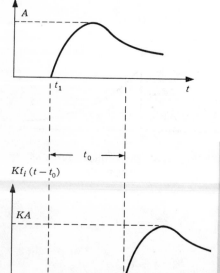

Fig. 6.15 The input function of Prob. 6.31 and its delayed replica.

In general,

$$H(j\omega) = |H(j\omega)|\, e^{j\theta(\omega)},$$

where $|H(j\omega)|$ is referred to as the *amplitude response* of the system, and $\theta(\omega)$, the *phase response*. From the result of Prob. 6.30, we conclude that the system function which yields distortionless transmission has a constant amplitude and a linear phase response, i.e.,

$$|H(j\omega)| = K_1, \quad \text{a constant (independent of } \omega\text{),}$$
$$\theta(\omega) = \omega K_2, \text{ a linear function of } \omega, \qquad (6.129)$$

where K_1 and K_2 are arbitrary constants.

PROBLEM 6.32   Find the unit impulse response $h(t)$ of the distortionless transmission system.

Solution: From the definition of a system function (6.91),

$$h(t) = \mathcal{F}^{-1}[H(j\omega)] = \frac{1}{2\pi} \int_{-\infty}^{\infty} H(j\omega)\, e^{j\omega t}\, d\omega.$$

Now substituting $H(j\omega)$ of the distortionless transmission system (6.126) into the above expression,

$$h(t) = \frac{1}{2\pi} \int_{-\infty}^{\infty} K\, e^{-j\omega t_0}\, e^{j\omega t}\, d\omega$$

$$= K\, \frac{1}{2\pi} \int_{-\infty}^{\infty} e^{j\omega(t-t_0)}\, d\omega$$

$$= K\, \delta(t - t_0) \tag{6.130}$$

with the use of identity (5.6).

PROBLEM 6.33 Consider a transmission line. The so-called propagation constant $\gamma(\omega)$ under sinusoidal steady-state conditions for any transmission line, is defined as

$$\gamma(\omega) = \sqrt{(R + j\omega L)(G + j\omega C)},$$

where R is the series resistance, L is the series inductance, G is the shunt conductance, and C is the shunt capacitance per unit length of the line. Show that the condition for the line to be distortionless is given by

$$\frac{L}{R} = \frac{C}{G}. \tag{6.131}$$

Solution: If $v(x, t)$ is the voltage at a point distant x from the input at time t, then for a sinusoidal input of frequency ω, it may be expressed as

$$v(x, t) = \text{Re}\,[\mathbf{V}_m\, e^{j\omega t - \gamma(\omega)x}], \tag{6.132}$$

where $\mathbf{V}_m$ is the complex amplitude of the voltage at the input, and $\gamma(\omega)$ is the propagation constant.

Then the input voltage is given by $v_i(t) = v(0, t)$, and the output voltage $v_o(t) = v(l, t)$, where l is the length of the transmission line. Thus, using the phasor representation,

$$v_i(t) = \text{Re}[\mathbf{V}_m\, e^{j\omega t}]$$

and

$$v_o(t) = \text{Re}[\mathbf{V}_m e^{j\omega t - \gamma(\omega)l}] = \text{Re}[\mathbf{V}_m e^{-\gamma(\omega)l} e^{j\omega t}].$$

Hence the system function $H(j\omega)$ for the transmission line is given by

$$H(j\omega) = \frac{\mathbf{V}_m\, e^{-\gamma(\omega)l}}{\mathbf{V}_m} = e^{-\gamma(\omega)l}. \tag{6.133}$$

If $\gamma(\omega) = \sqrt{(R + j\omega L)(G + j\omega C)} = \alpha(\omega) + j\beta(\omega)$, then

$$H(j\omega) = e^{-\gamma(\omega)l} = e^{-[\alpha(\omega) + j\beta(\omega)]l}$$

$$= e^{-\alpha(\omega)l}\, e^{-j\beta(\omega)l}$$

$$= |H(j\omega)|\, e^{j\theta(\omega)}, \tag{6.134}$$

where

$$|H(j\omega)| = e^{-\alpha(\omega)l}, \qquad \theta(\omega) = -\beta(\omega)l.$$

Now, from the conditions for distortionless transmission (6.129), we conclude that $\alpha(\omega)$ must be a constant and independent of ω, and $\beta(\omega)$ must be a linear function of ω; i.e.,

$$\alpha(\omega) = K_1, \qquad \beta(\omega) = K_2\omega.$$

Then $\gamma(\omega)$ may be rewritten as

$$\gamma(\omega) = \sqrt{(R + j\omega L)(G + j\omega C)}$$

$$= \sqrt{RG\left(1 + \frac{j\omega L}{R}\right)\left(1 + \frac{j\omega C}{G}\right)}$$

$$= \alpha(\omega) + j\beta(\omega)$$

$$= K_1 + jK_2\omega. \tag{6.135}$$

It is obvious that (6.135) will be satisfied if

$$\frac{L}{R} = \frac{C}{G}.$$

Then, the propagation constant is given by

$$\gamma(\omega) = \sqrt{RG\left(1 + \frac{j\omega L}{R}\right)^2} = \sqrt{RG} + j\omega L\sqrt{\frac{G}{R}} = \alpha(\omega) + j\beta(\omega).$$

Hence,

$$\alpha(\omega) = \sqrt{RG} = K_1, \quad \beta(\omega) = \omega L\sqrt{\frac{G}{R}} = \omega L\sqrt{\frac{C}{L}} = \omega\sqrt{LC} = \omega K_2.$$

Thus when (6.131) holds, we have the distortionless line.

6.10 Ideal Filters

Equation (6.97) shows that the frequency spectrum of the response $F_o(j\omega)$ is related to the source frequency spectrum $F_i(j\omega)$ through the system function $H(j\omega)$ by

$$F_o(j\omega) = F_i(j\omega)\,H(j\omega). \tag{6.97}$$

This is illustrated in Fig. 6.16.

It is seen that $H(j\omega)$ acts as a weighting function for different frequency components in the input. In this sense, the relation (6.97) indicates the filter characteristic of the linear system. If this weighting characteristic or filtering characteristic is the main concern, then the system is often referred to as the *filter*.

The so-called *ideal low-pass filter* is defined as a system for which the system function $H(j\omega)$ is given by

$$H(j\omega) = \begin{cases} e^{-j\omega t_0} & \text{for } |\omega| < \omega_c \\ 0 & \text{for } |\omega| > \omega_c, \end{cases} \tag{6.136}$$

where ω_c is referred to as the *cut-off frequency*.

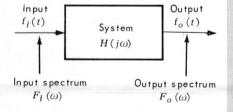

Input
$f_i(t)$

System
$H(j\omega)$

Output
$f_o(t)$

Input spectrum
$F_I(\omega)$

Output spectrum
$F_o(\omega)$

Fig. 6.16 Illustration of (6.97).

PROBLEM 6.34 Find the unit impulse response $h(t)$ of an ideal low-pass filter, and discuss the result.

Solution: Figure 6.17(a) shows the characteristics of an ideal low-pass filter. From (6.91), the unit impulse response $h(t)$ is obtained by

$$h(t) = \mathcal{F}^{-1}\left[H(j\omega)\right]$$

$$= \frac{1}{2\pi} \int_{-\infty}^{\infty} H(j\omega)\, e^{j\omega t}\, d\omega$$

$$= \frac{1}{2\pi} \int_{-\omega_c}^{\omega_c} e^{j\,\omega(t - t_0)}\, d\omega$$

$$= \frac{1}{\pi(t - t_0)\,2j}\, e^{j\,\omega(t - t_0)}\,\Big|_{-\omega_c}^{\omega_c}$$

$$= \frac{\omega_c}{\pi}\, \frac{\sin\,\omega_c(t - t_0)}{\omega_c(t - t_0)}. \tag{6.137}$$

The result (6.137) is plotted in Fig. 6.17(b), from which we draw the following conclusions:

(1) The applied input is distorted by the system due to the fact that the filter transmits only a limited range of frequencies.

(2) The peak value of the response ω_c/π is proportional to the cut-off frequency ω_c. The width of the main pulse is $2\pi/\omega_c$. We may refer to this quantity as the effective output pulse duration T_d. It is noted that as $\omega_c \longrightarrow \infty$ (i.e., when the filter becomes all-pass), $T_d \longrightarrow 0$ and the output response peak $\longrightarrow \infty$; in other words, the response approaches an impulse as it should.

(3) We also note that the response is not zero before $t = 0$, i.e., before the input is impressed. This is characteristic of a physically nonrealizable system. Ideal filters are not physically realizable and hence are not necessarily causal systems.

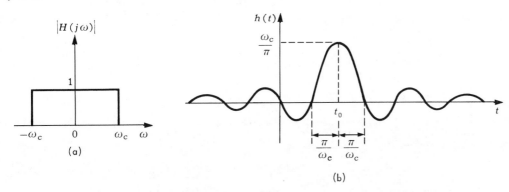

Fig. 6.17 (a) Frequency characteristics of an ideal low-pass filter. (b) The unit impulse response of an ideal low-pass filter.

The *sine-integral function* (of the upper limit y) is

$$Si(y) = \int_0^y \frac{\sin x}{x}\, dx = \int_0^y Sa(x)\, dx.$$

PROBLEM 6.35 (a) Evaluate the sine-integral function. (b) Find the unit step response $a(t)$ of an ideal low-pass filter and discuss the result.

Solution: (a) Since $Sa(x) = \dfrac{\sin x}{x}$ is an even function,

$$Si(-y) = -Si(y).$$

From the definition, when $y = 0$,

$$Si\,(0) = 0.$$

Since

$$\int_{-\infty}^{\infty} \frac{\sin x}{x}\,dx = 2\int_{0}^{\infty} \frac{\sin x}{x}\,dx = \pi,$$

we have

$$Si\,(\infty) = \frac{\pi}{2} \qquad \text{and} \qquad Si\,(-\infty) = -\frac{\pi}{2}.$$

A sketch of $Si\,(y)$ is shown in Fig. 6.18.

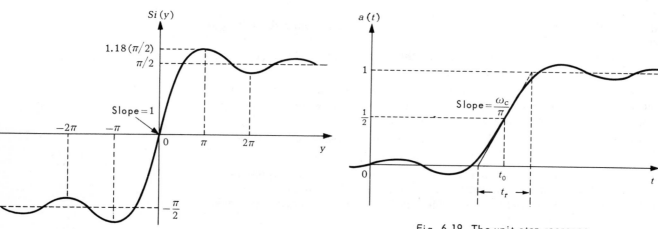

Fig. 6.18 The sine-integral function.

Fig. 6.19 The unit step response
of an ideal low-pass filter.

(b) From (6.113), the unit step response $a(t)$ can be obtained from the unit impulse response $h(t)$; i.e.,

$$a(t) = \int_{-\infty}^{t} h(\tau)\,d\tau \qquad\qquad [6.113]$$

$$= \frac{1}{\pi}\int_{-\infty}^{t} \frac{\sin \omega_c(\tau - t_0)}{(\tau - t_0)}\,d\tau. \qquad\qquad (6.138)$$

In the above integral (6.138), by changing the variable $\omega_c(\tau - t_0)$ to x,

$$a(t) = \frac{1}{\pi}\int_{-\infty}^{\omega_c\,(t-t_0)} \frac{\sin x}{x}\,dx = \frac{1}{\pi}\int_{-\infty}^{0} \frac{\sin x}{x}\,dx + \frac{1}{\pi}\int_{0}^{\omega_c\,(t-t_0)} \frac{\sin x}{x}\,dx$$

$$= \frac{1}{\pi}\int_{0}^{\infty} \frac{\sin x}{x}\,dx + \frac{1}{\pi}\int_{0}^{\omega_c\,(t-t_0)} \frac{\sin x}{x}\,dx. \quad (6.139)$$

Using the sine-integral function, (6.139) can be rewritten as

$$a(t) = \frac{1}{2} + \frac{1}{\pi}\,Si[\omega_c(t - t_0)]. \qquad\qquad (6.140)$$

A sketch of the unit step response $a(t)$ is shown in Fig. 6.19.

From the above result, we can see the following:

(1) We again observe the distortion due to the limited passband of the filter.

(2) We again note that the response is not zero before $t = 0$.

(3) Using $Si(\pm\infty) = \pm\pi/2$, we observe that as $\omega_c \longrightarrow \infty$,

$$a(t) = \frac{1}{2} - \frac{1}{2} = 0 \quad \text{for } t < t_0$$

$$= \frac{1}{2} + \frac{1}{2} = 1 \quad \text{for } t > t_0,$$

and the response becomes the delayed unit step $u(t - t_0)$ as it should.

(4) The input, a unit step, has an abrupt rise, while the response shows a gradual rise.

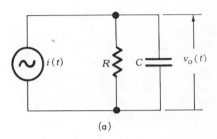

(a)

If we define the so-called *rise time* or build-up time of the response $a(t)$ as the interval t_r between the intercepts of the tangent at $t = t_0$ with the lines $a(t) = 0$ and $a(\infty) = 1$, then evidently from Fig. 6.19,

$$\left. \frac{da(t)}{dt} \right|_{t=t_0} = \frac{1}{t_r} = \frac{\omega_c}{\pi}.$$

Hence,

$$t_r = \frac{\pi}{\omega_c} \tag{6.141}$$

or

$$\omega_c t_r = \pi. \tag{6.142}$$

The rise time (or build-up time) t_r is given by (6.141), and it is inversely proportional to the filter bandwidth. Equation (6.142) indicates that

$$(\text{bandwidth}) \times (\text{rise time}) = \text{constant}.$$

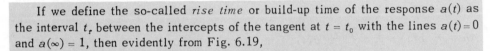

(b)

Fig. 6.20 (a) The circuit of Prob. 6.36. (b) The waveshape of the input current of Prob. 6.36.

6.11 Supplementary Problems

PROBLEM 6.36 Find the steady-state output voltage of the circuit in Fig. 6.20(a) when the input current has the waveshape shown in Fig. 6.20(b). Let $R = 1\,\Omega$ and $C = 1\,\text{f}$.

Answer: $v_{os}(t) = \frac{1}{2} + \frac{2}{\pi}\left[\frac{1}{\sqrt{1 + \pi^2}} \sin(\pi t - \tan^{-1}\pi) \right.$

$$\left. + \frac{1}{3\sqrt{1 + 9\pi^2}} \sin(3\pi t - \tan^{-1}3\pi) + \cdots \right].$$

PROBLEM 6.37 Calculate the power delivered to the circuit of Prob. 6.36 and the rms values of $i(t)$ and $v_0(t)$.

Answer: $P = 0.2689$ watts, $I_{rms} = 0.707$, and $V_{orms} = 0.519$.

PROBLEM 6.38 The input current for the RLC circuit in Fig. 6.21(a) has the waveshape shown in Fig. 6.21(b). The inductance is $L = 10$ mh and the output voltage is a 300-Hz sine wave. If the peak value of the other frequencies in the output voltage is less than $1/20$ of the peak value of the 300-Hz component, find the values of C and R.

Answer: $C = 28.2\ \mu\text{f}$, $R = 590\ \Omega$.

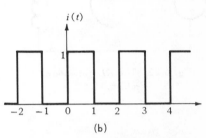

(a)

(b)

Fig. 6.21 (a) The RLC circuit of Prob. 6.38. (b) The waveshape of the circuit of Fig. 6.21 (a).

PROBLEM 6.39 Discuss the steady-state motion of the mechanical system shown in Fig. 6.10 if the disturbing force $f(t)$ is a full-rectified sine wave $f(t) = |A \sin \omega_0 t|$.

Answer: $x_s(t) = \dfrac{2A}{k\pi} - \dfrac{4A}{\pi} \left[\dfrac{1}{3} \dfrac{\cos 2\omega_0 t}{(k - m\omega_0^2)} + \dfrac{1}{15} \dfrac{\cos 4\omega_0 t}{(k - 4m\omega_0^2)} + \cdots \right]$.

PROBLEM 6.40 When the rectangular pulse $f_i(t) = u(t) - u(t-1)$ is applied to a certain linear system, the response is $f_0(t) = \frac{1}{2}[u(t-2) - u(t-4)]$. Find (a) the system function $H(j\omega)$, and (b) the unit impulse response $h(t)$.

Answer: (a) $H(j\omega) = \dfrac{1}{2}(e^{-j2\omega} + e^{-j3\omega})$, (b) $h(t) = \dfrac{1}{2}[\delta(t-2) + \delta(t-3)]$.

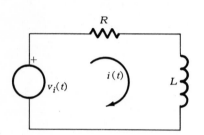

PROBLEM 6.41 Find the unit impulse response for the current of the RL network of Fig. 6.22.

Answer: $h(t) = \dfrac{1}{L} e^{-(R/L)t} u(t)$.

Fig. 6.22. The RL network of Prob. 6.41.

PROBLEM 6.42 A voltage source $v_i(t) = 2e^{-t} u(t)$ is applied to the RL network of Fig. 6.23. Find the response $i(t)$, where $R = 2\ \Omega$ and $L = 1$ h.

Answer: $2(e^{-t} - e^{-2t})\, u(t)$.

PROBLEM 6.43 The unit impulse response of a linear system is $e^{-t} \cos t\, u(t)$. Find the response due to a unit step function $u(t)$ by convolution.

Answer: $\dfrac{1}{2}[e^{-t}(\sin t - \cos t) + 1]\, u(t)$.

PROBLEM 6.44 If the unit impulse response of a linear system is $h(t) = t e^{-t} u(t)$ and the input is $f_i(t) = e^{-t} u(t)$, find the output frequency spectrum.

Answer: $1/(1 + j\omega)^3$.

PROBLEM 6.45 Show that if the input to a linear system is differentiated, then the response is also differentiated.
[Hint: Show that $f_i'(t) * h(t) = [f_i(t) * h(t)]' = f_0'(t)$.]

PROBLEM 6.46 Show that if $\displaystyle\int_{-\infty}^{\infty} |h(t)|\, dt < \infty$, where $h(t)$ is the unit impulse response of a linear system, then the response of the system to any bounded input is bounded.
[Hint: Make use of $|f_0(t)| = |f_i(t) * h(t)|$.]

PROBLEM 6.47 If $H(\omega) = R(\omega) + j X(\omega)$ is the system function of a linear system, show that the response of the system to an input of $f_i(t) = \cos \omega_0 t\, u(t)$ can be expressed as

$$f_0(t) = R(\omega)\cos \omega_0 t + \frac{2}{\pi}\int_0^{\infty} \frac{\omega X(\omega)}{\omega^2 - \omega_0^2}\cos \omega t\, d\omega$$

$$= -X(\omega_0)\sin \omega_0 t + \frac{2}{\pi}\int_0^{\infty} \frac{\omega R(\omega)}{\omega^2 - \omega_0^2}\sin \omega t\, d\omega.$$

[Hint: Use the result of Prob. 5.28.]

PROBLEM 6.48 Find the unit impulse response $h(t)$ of a linear system whose system function is

$$H(\omega) = \begin{cases} e^{-j\theta_0} & \text{for} \quad \omega > 0 \\ e^{j\theta_0} & \text{for} \quad \omega < 0. \end{cases}$$

[Hint: Note that $H(\omega) = \cos \theta_0 - j \sin \theta_0 \, \text{sgn } \omega$, and use the result of Prob. 5.33.]

Answer: $h(t) = \cos \theta_0 \, \delta(t) + \dfrac{\sin \theta_0}{\pi t}$.

PROBLEM 6.49 The system of Prob. 6.48 is called a *phase shifter*. Show that the response of the system of Prob. 6.48 to $\cos \omega_c t$ is $\cos (\omega_c t - \theta_0)$.

PROBLEM 6.50 Show that if the input signal to a linear system, whose system function $H(j\omega)$ is defined by

$$H(j\omega) = -j \, \text{sgn } \omega = \begin{cases} -j & \text{for} \quad \omega > 0 \\ +j & \text{for} \quad \omega < 0, \end{cases}$$

is a real time function, then the output of this system is also a real time function. [Hint: Make use of Prob. 4.7.]

PROBLEM 6.51 Find the output $\hat{m}(t)$ if the input $m(t)$ is (a) $\cos \omega_c t$ and (b) $1/(1 + t^2)$ for the system of Prob. 6.50 which is a $-\pi/2$- (or $-90°$) phase shifter since the system function can be rewritten as

$$H(j\omega) = -j \, \text{sgn } \omega = \begin{cases} e^{-j\pi/2} & \text{for} \quad \omega > 0 \\ e^{j\pi/2} & \text{for} \quad \omega < 0. \end{cases}$$

Answer: (a) $\sin \omega_c t$, (b) $t/(1 + t^2)$.

PROBLEM 6.52 Let a system be formed by a cascade connection of the two identical phase shifters of Prob. 6.51. Show that the output of this system is $-m(t)$ when the input is $m(t)$.

PROBLEM 6.53 The input to an ideal low-pass filter, whose system function is

$$H(j\omega) = \begin{cases} e^{-j\omega t_0} & \text{for} \quad |\omega| < \omega_c \\ 0 & \text{for} \quad |\omega| > \omega_c, \end{cases}$$

is a train of impulses

$$f_i(t) = T f(t) \, \delta_T(t) = T f(t) \sum_{n=-\infty}^{\infty} \delta(t - nT)$$

whose envelope $f(t)$ has a band-limited spectrum $|F(\omega)| = 0$ for $|\omega| > \omega_c$. Show that if $T < \pi/\omega_c$, then the response of the filter is $f_0(t) = f(t - t_0)$.

PROBLEM 6.54 Find the unit impulse response $h(t)$ of the *ideal high-pass filter* whose system function $H(j\omega)$ is

$$H(j\omega) = \begin{cases} 0 & \text{for } |\omega| < \omega_c \\ e^{-j\omega t_0} & \text{for } |\omega| > \omega_c. \end{cases}$$

[Hint: Use the result of Prob. 6.34, and note that $H(j\omega) = e^{-j\omega t_0} - H_l(j\omega)$, where $H_l(j\omega)$ is the system function of an ideal low-pass filter.]

Answer: $h(t) = \delta(t - t_0) - \dfrac{\omega_c}{\pi} \dfrac{\sin \omega_c (t - t_0)}{\omega_c (t - t_0)}$.

PROBLEM 6.55 Find the unit step response $a(t)$ of an ideal high-pass filter. [Hint: Use the result of Prob. 6.35.]

Answer: $a(t) = u(t - t_0) - \left\{ \dfrac{1}{2} + \dfrac{1}{\pi} \sin \left[\omega_c (t - t_0) \right] \right\}$.

PROBLEM 6.56 A *Gaussian filter* is a linear system whose system function is

$$H(\omega) = e^{-a\omega^2} e^{-j\omega t_0}.$$

Find its unit impulse response.

Answer: $h(t) = \dfrac{1}{2\sqrt{\pi a}} e^{-(t - t_0)^2/4a}$.

PROBLEM 6.57 If $H(\omega) = R(\omega) + jX(\omega)$ is the system function of a linear causal system, then show that the unit impulse response $h(t)$ of the system can be expressed as a function of either $R(\omega)$ or $X(\omega)$; i.e.,

$$h(t) = \frac{2}{\pi} \int_0^\infty R(\omega) \cos \omega t \, d\omega = -\frac{2}{\pi} \int_0^\infty X(\omega) \sin \omega t \, d\omega .$$

[Hint: $h(t) = 0$ for $t < 0$; hence $h(t)$ can be expressed as $h(t) = 2h_e(t) = 2h_o(t)$ for $t > 0$, where $h_e(t)$ and $h_o(t)$ are the even and odd components of $h(t)$, respectively.]

PROBLEM 6.58 Show that if $H(\omega) = R(\omega) + jX(\omega)$ is the system function of a linear causal system, then (a) the Fourier transform of the unit step response $a(t)$ of the system is given by

$$\mathcal{F}[a(t)] = \pi R(0) \delta(\omega) + \frac{X(\omega)}{\omega} - j \frac{R(\omega)}{\omega} ,$$

(b) the unit step response $a(t)$ can be expressed as

$$a(t) = \frac{2}{\pi} \int_0^\infty \frac{R(\omega)}{\omega} \sin \omega t \, d\omega = R(0) + \frac{2}{\pi} \int_0^\infty \frac{X(\omega)}{\omega} \cos \omega t \, d\omega .$$

7

APPLICATIONS TO
COMMUNICATION THEORY

7.1 Sampling Theory

The *uniform sampling theorem in the time domain* states that if a time function $f(t)$ contains no frequency components higher than f_M cycles per second, then $f(t)$ can be completely determined by its values at uniform intervals less than $1/(2 f_M)$ seconds apart.

PROBLEM 7.1 Prove the uniform sampling theorem in the time domain.

Solution: The sampling theorem can be proved with the help of the frequency convolution theorem (4.125); i.e.,

$$\mathcal{F}[f_1(t) f_2(t)] = \frac{1}{2\pi} [F_1(\omega) * F_2(\omega)], \qquad [4.125]$$

where $F_1(\omega) = \mathcal{F}[f_1(t)]$ and $F_2(\omega) = \mathcal{F}[f_2(t)]$.

Since $f(t)$ has no spectral components above f_M cycles per second, $f(t)$ is a *band-limited function,* as shown in Fig. 7.1(a), and this means that

$$F(\omega) = \mathcal{F}[f(t)] = 0 \quad \text{for} \ |\omega| > \omega_M = 2\pi f_M \qquad (7.1)$$

[see Fig. 7.1(b)].

Now consider a sampled function $f_s(t)$ defined by the product of the function $f(t)$ and a periodic unit impulse train function $\delta_T(t)$ [see Fig. 7.1(c)]:

$$f_s(t) = f(t) \delta_T(t). \qquad (7.2)$$

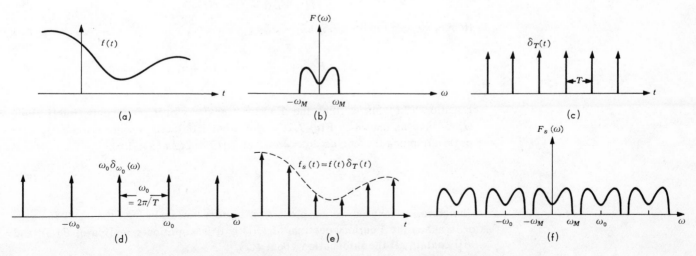

Fig. 7.1 (a) The band-limited time function $f(t)$. (b) The spectrum of $f(t)$. (c) The unit impulse train function. (d) The spectrum of the unit impulse train function. (e) The sampled function $f_s(t)$. (f) The spectrum of $f_s(t)$.

Recalling the definition (2.104) of $\delta_T(t)$ and its properties,

$$f_s(t) = f(t) \sum_{n=-\infty}^{\infty} \delta(t - nT)$$

$$= \sum_{n=-\infty}^{\infty} f(t) \delta(t - nT)$$

$$= \sum_{n=-\infty}^{\infty} f(nT) \delta(t - nT). \tag{7.3}$$

[See Fig. 7.1(d).] Equation (7.3) shows that the function $f_s(t)$ is a sequence of impulses located at regular intervals of T seconds, and having strength equal to the values of $f(t)$ at the sampling instants [Fig. 7.1(e)].

From the result of Prob. 5.15,

$$\mathcal{F}[\delta_T(t)] = \omega_0 \, \delta_{\omega_0}(\omega) = \omega_0 \sum_{n=-\infty}^{\infty} \delta(\omega - n\omega_0). \tag{5.66}$$

Now according to the frequency convolution theorem (4.125),

$$\mathcal{F}[f_s(t)] = F_s(\omega) = \frac{1}{2\pi} [F(\omega) * \omega_0 \, \delta_{\omega_0}(\omega)]. \tag{7.4}$$

Substituting $\omega_0 = 2\pi/T$,

$$F_s(\omega) = \frac{1}{T} [F(\omega) * \delta_{\omega_0}(\omega)]$$

$$= \frac{1}{T} \left[F(\omega) * \sum_{n=-\infty}^{\infty} \delta(\omega - n\omega_0) \right]$$

$$= \frac{1}{T} \sum_{n=-\infty}^{\infty} F(\omega) * \delta(\omega - n\omega_0). \tag{7.5}$$

It was shown in Chap. 4 that

$$f(t) * \delta(t) = f(t), \tag{4.119}$$

$$f(t) * \delta(t - T) = f(t - T). \tag{4.120}$$

Hence, we can rewrite (7.5) as

$$F_s(\omega) = \frac{1}{T} \sum_{n=-\infty}^{\infty} F(\omega - n\omega_0). \tag{7.6}$$

Equation (7.6) shows that the Fourier transform of $f_s(t)$ repeats itself every ω_0 rad/sec as shown in Fig. 7.1(f). Note that $F(\omega)$ will repeat periodically without overlapping as long as $\omega_0 > 2\omega_M$, or $2\pi/T > 2(2\pi f_M)$; i.e.,

$$T < \frac{1}{2f_M}. \tag{7.7}$$

Therefore, as long as we sample $f(t)$ at uniform intervals less than $1/(2f_M)$ seconds apart, the Fourier spectrum of $f_s(t)$ will be a periodic replica of $F(\omega)$, and will contain all the information about $f(t)$.

Let us investigate the above result by arriving at the same conclusions through a different approach. The Fourier spectrum $F(\omega)$ of a band-limited function $f(t)$ is shown in Fig. 7.1(b). Imagine that the spectrum $F(\omega)$ is that portion of the periodic spectrum $F_s(\omega)$ [Fig. 7.1(f)] between $-1/2\,\omega_0$ and $1/2\,\omega_0$, where $\omega_0 = 2\pi/T$ and $\omega_0 > 2\,\omega_M$. Since $F_s(\omega)$ is a periodic function of ω with period ω_0, it can be expanded into the Fourier series

$$F_s(\omega) = \sum_{n=-\infty}^{\infty} c_n\, e^{jn2\pi\omega/\omega_0}, \qquad (7.8)$$

where, by definition,

$$c_n = \frac{1}{\omega_0} \int_{-\omega_0/2}^{\omega_0/2} F_s(\omega)\, e^{-jn2\pi\omega/\omega_0}\, d\omega. \qquad (7.9)$$

Since $F_s(\omega) = F(\omega)$ for $-\omega_M < \omega < \omega_M$, and $(1/2)\omega_0 > \omega_M$, (7.9) can be rewritten as

$$c_n = \frac{1}{\omega_0} \int_{-\omega_M}^{\omega_M} F(\omega)\, e^{-jn2\pi\omega/\omega_0}\, d\omega. \qquad (7.10)$$

Now,

$$f(t) = \mathcal{F}^{-1}[F(\omega)] = \frac{1}{2\pi} \int_{-\infty}^{\infty} F(\omega)\, e^{j\omega t}\, d\omega. \qquad (7.11)$$

Since $f(t)$ is band-limited, i.e., $F(\omega) = 0$ for $|\omega| > \omega_M$, (7.11) becomes

$$f(t) = \frac{1}{2\pi} \int_{-\omega_M}^{\omega_M} F(\omega)\, e^{j\omega t}\, d\omega. \qquad (7.12)$$

Designating the sampling points to be at $t = -nT = -n\,2\pi/\omega_0$, from (7.12),

$$f(-nT) = f\left(-\frac{n\,2\pi}{\omega_0}\right) = \frac{1}{2\pi} \int_{-\omega_M}^{\omega_M} F(\omega)\, e^{-jn2\pi\omega/\omega_0}\, d\omega. \qquad (7.13)$$

Comparing (7.13) with (7.10),

$$c_n = \frac{2\pi}{\omega_0}\, f\left(-\frac{n\,2\pi}{\omega_0}\right) = T\, f(-nT). \qquad (7.14)$$

Equation (7.14) indicates that c_n can be uniquely found from the value of the function at the sample points. But knowing c_n, we can in turn find $F_s(\omega)$ from (7.8) and consequently $F(\omega)$. Knowing $F(\omega)$, we find $f(t)$ for all possible time by (7.11).

Now from the assumption $\omega_0 > 2\,\omega_M$,

$$\frac{2\pi}{T} > 4\pi\, f_M,$$

$$T < \frac{1}{2\, f_M}. \qquad (7.15)$$

This completes the proof.

The maximum interval of sampling $T = 1/(2 f_M)$ is sometimes called the *Nyquist interval*.

In the above we have demonstrated that $f(t)$ may be reproduced completely from a knowledge of $f(t)$ only at the uniform periodic sampling intervals. We shall next show how $f(t)$ can be reconstructed from the samples.

PROBLEM 7.2 Consider a band-limited signal $f(t)$ sampled at the minimum required rate ($2 f_M$ samples per second). [See Fig. 7.2(a-b).] Show that the signal $f(t)$ can be expressed as

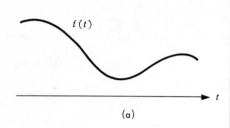

(a)

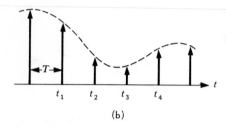

(b)

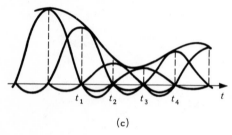

(c)

Fig. 7.2 (a) The band-limited time function $f(t)$. (b) The sampled function. (c) Reconstruction of a waveform.

$$f(t) = \sum_{n=-\infty}^{\infty} f(nT) \frac{\sin \omega_M(t - nT)}{\omega_M(t - nT)} \qquad (7.16)$$

or

$$f(t) = \sum_{n=-\infty}^{\infty} f\left(\frac{n\pi}{\omega_M}\right) \frac{\sin (\omega_M t - n\pi)}{\omega_M t - n\pi}, \qquad (7.17)$$

where $\omega_M = 2\pi f_M$ and $T = 1/(2 f_M) =$ the sampling interval.

Solution: Since $T = 1/(2 f_M)$, $\omega_0 = 2\pi/T = 4\pi f_M = 2\omega_M$. Hence (7.8) becomes

$$F_s(\omega) = \sum_{n=-\infty}^{\infty} c_n e^{jn2\pi\omega/2\omega_M} = \sum_{n=-\infty}^{\infty} c_n e^{jnT\omega}. \qquad (7.18)$$

From (7.14),

$$c_n = T f(-nT) = \frac{\pi}{\omega_M} f(-nT). \qquad (7.19)$$

Substituting (7.19) into (7.18),

$$F_s(\omega) = \sum_{n=-\infty}^{\infty} \frac{\pi}{\omega_M} f(-nT) e^{jnT\omega}. \qquad (7.20)$$

Since $F_s(\omega) = F(\omega)$ for $-\omega_M < \omega < \omega_M$, substituting (7.20) into (7.12),

$$f(t) = \frac{1}{2\pi} \int_{-\omega_M}^{\omega_M} \left[\sum_{n=-\infty}^{\infty} \frac{\pi}{\omega_M} f(-nT) e^{jnT\omega} \right] e^{j\omega t} d\omega. \qquad (7.21)$$

Interchanging the order of integration and summation,

$$f(t) = \sum_{n=-\infty}^{\infty} \left[f(-nT) \int_{-\omega_M}^{\omega_M} \frac{1}{2\omega_M} e^{j\omega(t+nT)} d\omega \right] = \sum_{n=-\infty}^{\infty} f(-nT) \frac{\sin \omega_M(t + nT)}{\omega_M(t + nT)}$$

$$= \sum_{n=-\infty}^{\infty} f(nT) \frac{\sin \omega_M(t - nT)}{\omega_M(t - nT)}.$$

In the last equation, $(-n)$ was replaced by n because all positive and negative values of n are included in the summation. Since $T = \pi/\omega_M$, (7.16) also can be written as

$$f(t) = \sum_{n=-\infty}^{\infty} f\left(\frac{n\pi}{\omega_M}\right) \frac{\sin (\omega_M t - n\pi)}{\omega_M t - n\pi}.$$

Mathematically, (7.16) indicates that each sample of our function is multiplied by a "sampling" function

$$Sa\,[\omega_M(t - nT)] = \frac{\sin \omega_M(t - nT)}{\omega_M(t - nT)},$$

and all of the resulting waveforms are added to obtain $f(t)$. This is illustrated in Fig. 7.2(c).

The *sampling theorem in the frequency domain* states that if a function $f(t)$ is zero everywhere except in the interval $-T < t < T$, then its Fourier transform

$F(\omega)$ can be uniquely determined from its values $F(n\pi/T)$ at a series of equidistant points spaced π/T apart. In fact, $F(\omega)$ is given by

$$F(\omega) = \sum_{n=-\infty}^{\infty} F\left(\frac{n\pi}{T}\right) \frac{\sin(\omega T - n\pi)}{\omega T - n\pi}. \tag{7.22}$$

PROBLEM 7.3   Verify (7.22).

Solution: Suppose that

$$f(t) = 0 \quad \text{for } |t| > T. \tag{7.23}$$

Then, in the interval $-T < t < T$, the function $f(t)$ can be expanded in a Fourier series

$$f(t) = \sum_{n=-\infty}^{\infty} c_n e^{j2\pi nt/2T} = \sum_{n=-\infty}^{\infty} c_n e^{jn\pi t/T}, \tag{7.24}$$

where

$$c_n = \frac{1}{2T} \int_{-T}^{T} f(t) e^{-j2\pi nt/2T} \, dt = \frac{1}{2T} \int_{-T}^{T} f(t) e^{-jn\pi t/T} \, dt. \tag{7.25}$$

Since $f(t) = 0$ for $t > T$ and $t < -T$, (7.25) can be written as

$$c_n = \frac{1}{2T} \int_{-\infty}^{\infty} f(t) e^{-jn\pi t/T} \, dt = \frac{1}{2T} F\left(\frac{n\pi}{T}\right), \tag{7.26}$$

where

$$F(\omega) = \mathcal{F}[f(t)] = \int_{-\infty}^{\infty} f(t) e^{-j\omega t} \, dt$$

and

$$\omega = \frac{n\pi}{T}.$$

Substituting (7.26) into (7.24),

$$f(t) = \sum_{n=-\infty}^{\infty} \frac{1}{2T} F\left(\frac{n\pi}{T}\right) e^{jn\pi t/T}. \tag{7.27}$$

Now,

$$F(\omega) = \int_{-\infty}^{\infty} f(t) e^{-j\omega t} \, dt = \int_{-T}^{T} f(t) e^{-j\omega t} \, dt, \tag{7.28}$$

in view of (7.23).

Substituting (7.27) into (7.28) and interchanging the order of summation and integration,

$$F(\omega) = \int_{-T}^{T} \left[\sum_{n=-\infty}^{\infty} \frac{1}{2T} F\left(\frac{n\pi}{T}\right) e^{jn\pi t/T} \right] e^{-j\omega t} \, dt$$

$$= \sum_{n=-\infty}^{\infty} \left[F\left(\frac{n\pi}{T}\right) \frac{1}{2T} \int_{-T}^{T} e^{-j(\omega - n\pi/T)t} \, dt \right]$$

$$= \sum_{n=-\infty}^{\infty} F\left(\frac{n\pi}{T}\right) \frac{\sin(\omega T - n\pi)}{\omega T - n\pi}.$$

Hence we complete the proof of the frequency sampling theorem.

7.2 Amplitude Modulation

The method of processing a signal for more efficient transmission is called *modulation*. One commonly used type of modulation is based on the following *frequency translation theorem* (sometimes called the *modulation theorem*) of the Fourier transform. The theorem states that the multiplication of a signal $f(t)$ by a sinusoidal signal of the frequency ω_c translates its spectrum by $\pm\omega_c$.

PROBLEM 7.4 Verify the frequency translation theorem.

Solution: Let $\mathcal{F}[f(t)] = F(\omega)$. From (5.22) and (5.23),

$$\mathcal{F}[\cos \omega_c t] = \pi \delta(\omega - \omega_c) + \pi \delta(\omega + \omega_c),$$

$$\mathcal{F}[\sin \omega_c t] = -j\pi \delta(\omega - \omega_c) + j\pi \delta(\omega + \omega_c).$$

Therefore, according to the frequency convolution theorem (4.125),

$$\mathcal{F}[f(t) \cos \omega_c t] = \frac{1}{2\pi} F(\omega) * [\pi \delta(\omega - \omega_c) + \pi \delta(\omega + \omega_c)]$$

$$= \frac{1}{2} F(\omega) * \delta(\omega - \omega_c) + \frac{1}{2} F(\omega) * \delta(\omega + \omega_c)$$

$$= \frac{1}{2} F(\omega - \omega_c) + \frac{1}{2} F(\omega + \omega_c) \tag{7.29}$$

with the use of (4.120). Similarly,

$$\mathcal{F}[f(t) \sin \omega_c t] = \frac{1}{2\pi} F(\omega) * [-j\pi \delta(\omega - \omega_c) + j\pi \delta(\omega + \omega_c)]$$

$$= -\frac{1}{2} j F(\omega) * \delta(\omega - \omega_c) + \frac{1}{2} j F(\omega) * \delta(\omega + \omega_c)$$

$$= -\frac{1}{2} j F(\omega - \omega_c) + \frac{1}{2} j F(\omega + \omega_c). \tag{7.30}$$

Equations (7.29) and (7.30) indicate that the multiplication of a signal $f(t)$ by a sinusoidal signal of the frequency ω_c translates its spectrum by $\pm\omega_c$. This is illustrated in Fig. 7.3.

PROBLEM 7.5 Show that if $f(t)$ is a band-limited signal with no spectral components above the frequency ω_M, then the spectrum of the signal $f(t) \cos \omega_c t$ is also band-limited.

Solution: Since the signal $f(t)$ is a band-limited signal,

$$\mathcal{F}[f(t)] = F(\omega) = 0 \quad \text{for } |\omega| > \omega_M.$$

From the results (7.29) of Prob. 7.4 and Fig. 7.3, it follows, therefore, that the signal $f(t) \cos \omega_c t$ is also band-limited, and its spectrum is zero outside the band $(\omega_c - \omega_M)$ to $(\omega_c + \omega_M)$ for $\omega > 0$. It must be noted that this result is based on the assumption $\omega_c > \omega_M$.

An ordinary amplitude modulated (AM) signal is usually written in the form

$$f(t) = K[1 + m(t)] \cos \omega_c t, \tag{7.31}$$

where $m(t)$ is a band-limited signal, such that

$$\mathcal{F}[m(t)] = M(\omega) = 0 \quad \text{for } |\omega| > \omega_M \quad \text{and} \quad |m(t)| < 1 \quad \text{for } \omega_c > \omega_M. \tag{7.32}$$

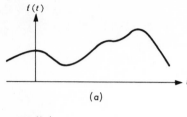

(a)

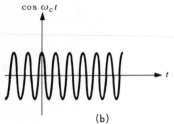

(b)

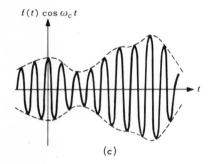

(c)

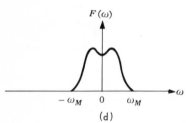

(d)

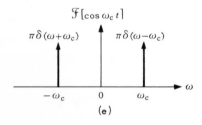

(e)

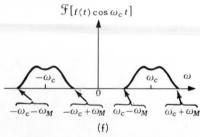

(f)

Fig. 7.3 (a) The band-limited signal $f(t)$ of Prob. 7.5. (b) The function $\cos \omega_c t$. (c) The function $f(t) \cos \omega_c t$. (d) The spectrum of $f(t)$. (e) The spectrum of $\cos \omega_c t$. (f) The spectrum of $f(t) \cos \omega_c t$.

In (7.31), the sinusoid $\cos \omega_c t$ is called the *carrier*, and the frequency $f_c = \omega_c / 2\pi$ is called the *carrier frequency*. In Fig. 7.4, an example of the waveform of an ordinary AM signal is shown. Since $|m(t)| < 1$, it is noted that $K[1 + m(t)] > 0$ for $K > 0$.

PROBLEM 7.6   Find the frequency spectrum of an ordinary AM signal (7.31).

Solution: Using the superposition property and frequency translation theorem (7.29), the Fourier transform of $f(t)$ is given by

$$
\begin{aligned}
F(\omega) &= \mathcal{F}[f(t)] \\
&= \mathcal{F}\{K[1 + m(t)]\cos \omega_c t\} \\
&= \mathcal{F}[K \cos \omega_c t] + \mathcal{F}[K \, m(t)\cos \omega_c t] \\
&= K \, \pi \delta(\omega - \omega_c) + K \, \pi \delta(\omega + \omega_c) \\
&\quad + \frac{1}{2} K \, M(\omega - \omega_c) + \frac{1}{2} K \, M(\omega + \omega_c),
\end{aligned}
\tag{7.33}
$$

where $\mathcal{F}[m(t)] = M(\omega)$.

In Fig. 7.5, the spectrum consists of impulses at the carrier frequency ω_c and the frequency-translated spectrum of $m(t)$. The portion of the spectrum above ω_c is called the *upper side band* of the spectrum, and the symmetrical portion below ω_c is called the *lower side band*. Note that the sidebands are the information-bearing components of the modulated signal.

PROBLEM 7.7   Assume that the message signal $m(t)$ in the ordinary AM signal (7.31) is a sinusoidal signal

$$
m(t) = m_0 \cos \omega_m t, \quad \omega_m < \omega_c, \quad 0 < m_0 < 1.
$$

Find the spectrum of the AM signal for this case.

Solution: The AM signal for this case is given by

$$
f(t) = K(1 + m_0 \cos \omega_m t) \cos \omega_c t.
\tag{7.34}
$$

Using trigonometric identities, we can rewrite (7.34) as

$$
f(t) = K \cos \omega_c t + \frac{1}{2} K \, m_0 \cos (\omega_m - \omega_c)t + \frac{1}{2} K \, m_0 \cos (\omega_m + \omega_c)t.
\tag{7.35}
$$

Hence, using (5.22),

$$
\begin{aligned}
F(\omega) = \mathcal{F}[f(t)] &= K \, \pi [\delta(\omega - \omega_c) + \delta(\omega + \omega_c)] \\
&\quad + \frac{1}{2} K \, m_0 \, \pi [\delta(\omega - \omega_m + \omega_c) + \delta(\omega + \omega_m - \omega_c) \\
&\quad + \delta(\omega - \omega_m - \omega_c) + \delta(\omega + \omega_m + \omega_c)].
\end{aligned}
\tag{7.36}
$$

The spectrum for this example is shown in Fig. 7.6. In this case, the side bands consist of the impulses at $\omega = \omega_c \pm \omega_m$.

PROBLEM 7.8   For the AM signal of Prob. 7.7, find the relative contents of power in the carrier and in the side bands which carry the information.

Solution: The AM signal of Prob. 7.7 is given by

$$
f(t) = K[1 + m_0 \cos \omega_m t] \cos \omega_c t
$$

$$
= \underbrace{K \cos \omega_c t}_{\text{carrier}} + \underbrace{\frac{1}{2} K \, m_0 \cos (\omega_m - \omega_c)t + \frac{1}{2} K \, m_0 \cos (\omega_m + \omega_c)t.}_{\text{side bands}}
$$

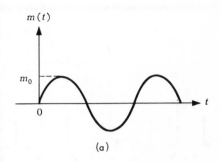

(a)

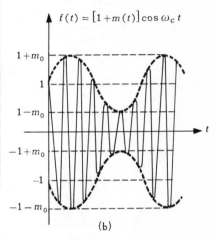

(b)

Fig. 7.4 (a) The band-limited message signal $m(t)$. (b) The waveform of an ordinary AM signal.

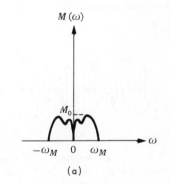

(a)

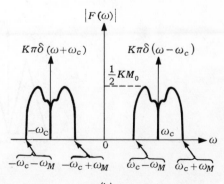

(b)

Fig. 7.5 (a) The spectrum of $m(t)$. (b) The spectrum of an ordinary AM signal.

The carrier and side band terms are shown in the above. It is obvious that the average total power P_t delivered by $f(t)$ (referred to a 1-Ω resistor) is given by

$$P_t = \frac{1}{2} K^2 + \frac{1}{8} K^2 m_0^2 + \frac{1}{8} K^2 m_0^2 = \frac{1}{2} K^2 \left(1 + \frac{1}{2} m_0^2\right). \qquad (7.37)$$

Thus the power in the carrier P_c and the power carried by the side bands P_s are given by

$$P_c = \frac{1}{2} K^2, \qquad P_s = \frac{1}{4} K^2 m_0^2.$$

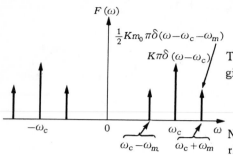

$\frac{1}{2} K m_0 \pi \delta (\omega - \omega_c - \omega_m)$

$K \pi \delta (\omega - \omega_c)$

Fig. 7.6 The spectrum of the AM signal of Prob. 7.7.

Note that $P_s = K^2 m_0^2/8$ in each of the side bands. The percentage of power carried by the side bands is

$$\frac{P_s}{P_t} \times 100 = \frac{m_0^2}{2 + m_0^2} \times 100\%. \qquad (7.38)$$

For example, if $m_0 = 1/2$, then

$$\frac{P_s}{P_t} = \frac{\dfrac{1}{4}}{2 + \dfrac{1}{4}} = \frac{1}{9}, \qquad \text{or about } 11\%,$$

when $m_0 = 1$, $[P_s/P_t]_{\max} = 1/3$, or about 33%.

We now recall that the information-bearing signal $m(t)$ gives rise to the side bands, and only a fraction of the power of $f(t)$ given by (7.38) is in the side bands. The power carried by the carrier represents waste.

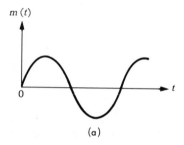

(a)

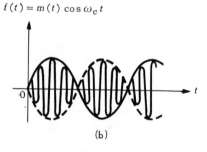

(b)

Fig. 7.7 (a) The sinusoidal band-limited signal $m(t)$. (b) The function $f(t) = m(t) \cos \omega_c t$.

A *double-side-band-suppressed carrier* (DSBSC) AM signal is given by

$$f(t) = m(t) \cos \omega_c t, \qquad (7.39)$$

where $m(t)$ is a band-limited signal as before. Figure 7.7 shows $f(t)$ for a sinusoidal $m(t)$.

PROBLEM 7.9 Find the spectrum of a DSBSC AM signal (7.39).

Solution: If $\mathcal{F}[m(t)] = M(\omega)$, then

$$F(\omega) = \mathcal{F}[f(t)] = \mathcal{F}[m(t) \cos \omega_c t] = \frac{1}{2} [M(\omega - \omega_c) + M(\omega + \omega_c)], \qquad (7.40)$$

in view of the frequency translation theorem (7.29). The spectrum of a DSBSC signal is shown in Fig. 7.8.

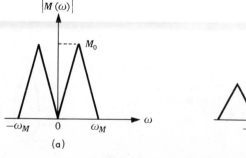

(a)

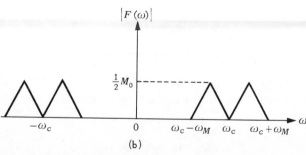

(b)

Fig. 7.8 (a) The spectrum of $m(t)$. (b) The spectrum of the DSBSC signal.

The process of separating a modulating signal from a modulated signal is called *demodulation* or *detection*.

PROBLEM 7.10 Show that the spectrum of the modulated signal can be conveniently retranslated to the original position by multiplying the modulated signal by $\cos \omega_c t$ at the receiving end.

Solution: Let the modulated signal be expressed as

$$f(t) = m(t) \cos \omega_c t. \tag{7.41}$$

Then as shown in Fig. 7.9(a), at the receiver we multiply the received signal $f(t)$ with $\cos \omega_c t$ to obtain, by the use of a trigonometric identity,

$$f(t) \cos \omega_c t = m(t) \cos^2 \omega_c t$$

$$= m(t) \frac{1}{2} (1 + \cos 2\omega_c t)$$

$$= \frac{1}{2} m(t) + \frac{1}{2} m(t) \cos 2\omega_c t. \tag{7.42}$$

Now if $\mathcal{F}[m(t)] = M(\omega)$ and $M(\omega) = 0$ for $|\omega| > \omega_M$, then

$$\mathcal{F}[f(t) \cos \omega_c t] = \mathcal{F}[m(t) \cos^2 \omega_c t]$$

$$= \mathcal{F}\left[\frac{1}{2} m(t)\right] + \mathcal{F}\left[\frac{1}{2} m(t) \cos 2\omega_c t\right]$$

$$= \frac{1}{2} M(\omega) + \frac{1}{4} M(\omega - 2\omega_c) + \frac{1}{4} M(\omega + 2\omega_c). \tag{7.43}$$

The spectrum of $f(t) \cos \omega_c t = m(t) \cos^2 \omega_c t$ is shown in Fig. 7.9(c). From the spectrum in Fig. 7.9(b), we conclude that the original signal $m(t)$ can be recovered by using a low-pass filter which passes the spectrum up to ω_M. The demodulation process is shown in block diagram form in Fig. 7.9(a).

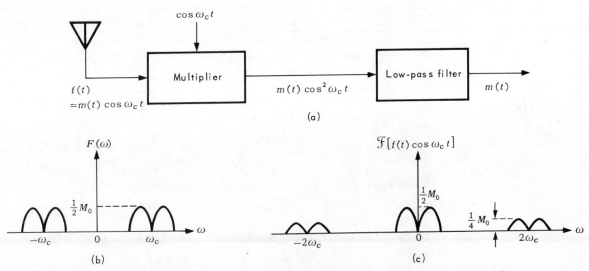

Fig. 7.9 (a) Demodulation system. (b) The spectrum of the modulated signal $f(t)$.
(c) The spectrum of the signal $f(t) \cos \omega_c t$.

PROBLEM 7.11 Show that demodulation may also be accomplished by multiplying the modulated signal $f(t) = m(t) \cos \omega_c t$ by any periodic signal of frequency ω_c.

Solution: If $p(t)$ is a periodic signal of frequency ω_c and of the form

$$p(t) = \sum_{n=-\infty}^{\infty} c_n e^{jn\omega_c t}, \tag{7.44}$$

then from (5.57), its Fourier transform can be written as

$$\mathcal{F}[p(t)] = 2\pi \sum_{n=-\infty}^{\infty} c_n \, \delta(\omega - n\omega_c). \tag{7.45}$$

Now from (7.40),

$$\mathcal{F}[f(t)] = \frac{1}{2} M(\omega - \omega_c) + \frac{1}{2} M(\omega + \omega_c).$$

Hence according to (4.125), the Fourier transform of $f(t)\,p(t)$ is given by

$$\mathcal{F}[f(t)p(t)] = \pi[M(\omega - \omega_c) + M(\omega + \omega_c)] * \sum_{n=-\infty}^{\infty} c_n \, \delta(\omega - n\omega_c)$$

$$= \pi \sum_{n=-\infty}^{\infty} c_n \, [M(\omega - \omega_c) + M(\omega + \omega_c)] * \delta(\omega - n\omega_c)$$

$$= \pi \sum_{n=-\infty}^{\infty} c_n \, \{M[\omega - (n+1)\,\omega_c] + M[\omega - (n-1)\,\omega_c]\} \tag{7.46}$$

with the use of (4.121).

It is obvious that this spectrum contains a term $M(\omega)$, the spectrum of $m(t)$. This can be recovered by using a low-pass filter that passes only up to $\omega = \omega_M$.

7.3 Angle Modulation

In amplitude modulation, the amplitude of the carrier is modulated by the information-bearing signal $m(t)$, and hence the information content is carried by the amplitude variation of the carrier. Amplitude modulation, however, is not the only means of modulating a sinusoidal carrier. We can also modulate either the frequency or the phase of the carrier in accordance with the information-bearing signal.

The signal

$$f(t) = A \cos [\omega_c t + \phi(t)] \tag{7.47}$$

is said to be an *angle-modulated signal*.

If

$$\phi(t) = k_p \, m(t),$$

where k_p is a constant, then the angle-modulated signal

$$f_{PM}(t) = A \cos [\omega_c t + k_p \, m(t)] \tag{7.48}$$

is said to be *phase-modulated* (PM) with the modulating signal $m(t)$, and

$$\phi_m = \left| k_p \, m(t) \right|_{\max} \text{ radians} \tag{7.49}$$

is called the *modulation index* of the PM signal.

If

$$\phi(t) = k_f \int_{-\infty}^{t} m(\tau)\, d\tau,$$

where k_f is a constant, then

$$f_{FM}(t) = A \cos \left[\omega_c t + k_f \int_{-\infty}^{t} m(\tau)\, d\tau \right] \tag{7.50}$$

is said to be *frequency-modulated* (FM), and

$$\phi_m = \left| k_f \int_{-\infty}^{t} m(\tau)\, d\tau \right|_{max} \tag{7.51}$$

is called the *modulation index* of the FM signal.

Let

$$\theta(t) = \omega_c t + \phi(t); \tag{7.52}$$

then the angle-modulated signal (7.47) can be rewritten as

$$f(t) = A \cos \theta(t). \tag{7.53}$$

We now define the *instantaneous radian frequency* ω_i of the angle-modulated signal (7.53) as

$$\omega_i(t) = \frac{d}{dt}\,\theta(t). \tag{7.54}$$

PROBLEM 7.12　Show that ω_i for PM and FM signals are given by

$$\omega_{iPM}(t) = \omega_c + k_p \frac{d}{dt}\,m(t), \tag{7.55}$$

$$\omega_{iFM}(t) = \omega_c + k_f\, m(t), \tag{7.56}$$

respectively.

Solution:　In the case of the PM signal,

$$\omega_i(t) = \frac{d}{dt}\,\theta(t) = \frac{d}{dt}\,[\omega_c t + k_p\, m(t)] = \omega_c + k_p\, m'(t).$$

In the case of the FM signal,

$$\omega_i(t) = \frac{d}{dt}\,\theta(t) = \frac{d}{dt}\left[\omega_c t + k_f \int_{-\infty}^{t} m(\tau)\, d\tau\right] = \omega_c + k_f\, m(t).$$

Equations (7.55) and (7.56) indicate that in phase modulation, the instantaneous frequency varies *linearly with the derivative* of the modulating signal, while in frequency modulation, the instantaneous frequency varies *directly* with the modulating signal.

PROBLEM 7.13　If the modulating signal $m(t)$ is sinusoidal, i.e.,

$$m(t) = m_0 \cos \omega_m t, \quad \omega_m < \omega_c, \tag{7.57}$$

show that the PM and FM signals will have the form

$$f_{PM}(t) = A \cos (\omega_c t + \phi_m \cos \omega_m t), \tag{7.58}$$

$$f_{FM}(t) = A \cos (\omega_c t + \phi_m \sin \omega_m t), \tag{7.59}$$

respectively, where ϕ_m is the modulation index of the PM (or FM) signal.

Solution:　If $m(t) = m_0 \cos \omega_m t$, then from (7.48),

$$f_{PM}(t) = A \cos (\omega_c t + k_p m_0 \cos \omega_m t).$$

From (7.49), $\phi_m = k_p m_0$ because the maximum magnitude of $m(t)$ is m_0; thus,

$$f_{PM}(t) = A \cos (\omega_c t + \phi_m \cos \omega_m t), \quad \phi_m = k_p m_0.$$

Since for the FM signal $\phi(t) = k_f \int m(t)\, dt = \dfrac{k_f m_0}{\omega_m}\sin \omega_m t$,

$$f_{FM}(t) = A \cos\left(\omega_c t + \frac{k_f m_0}{\omega_m}\sin \omega_m t\right)$$

$$= A \cos(\omega_c t + \phi_m \sin \omega_m t), \quad \phi_m = \frac{k_f m_0}{\omega_m}.$$

PROBLEM 7.14 Show that in a sinusoidal modulating FM signal, the modulation index ϕ_m can be defined as

$$\phi_m = \frac{\Delta f}{f_m}, \tag{7.60}$$

where f_m is the modulating signal frequency, and Δf is the frequency deviation defined as

$$\Delta f = \left[\frac{1}{2\pi}(\omega_i - \omega_c)\right]_{\max}.$$

Solution: For the FM signal, from (7.56),

$$\omega_i = \omega_c + k_f\, m(t) = \omega_c + k_f m_0 \cos \omega_m t.$$

Hence,

$$\omega_i - \omega_c = k_f m_0 \cos \omega_m t. \tag{7.61}$$

It is seen from (7.61) that

$$(\omega_i - \omega_c)_{\max} = k_f m_0 = 2\pi\, \Delta f,$$

i.e., the maximum difference between ω_i and ω_c is called *the radian frequency deviation* of the FM signal. Therefore,

$$\phi_m = \frac{k_f m_0}{\omega_m} = \frac{2\pi\, \Delta f}{2\pi\, f_m} = \frac{\Delta f}{f_m}.$$

There is no simple, general theorem which relates the spectrum of $\cos[\omega_c t + \phi(t)]$ to the spectrum of $\phi(t)$, and the spectral analysis of a general angle-modulated signal is thus quite involved. In the following, therefore, we shall consider only the special case of a sinusoidal modulation signal.

PROBLEM 7.15 Find the spectrum of the sinusoidal modulated FM signal.

Solution: From (7.59),

$$f(t) = A \cos(\omega_c t + \phi_m \sin \omega_m t)$$

$$= A \cos \omega_c t \cos(\phi_m \sin \omega_m t) - A \sin \omega_c t \sin(\phi_m \sin \omega_m t). \tag{7.62}$$

In (7.62), the terms

$$\cos(\phi_m \sin \omega_m t) \qquad \text{and} \qquad \sin(\phi_m \sin \omega_m t)$$

are periodic functions with period $T = 2\pi/\omega_m$. Hence they can be expanded by the Fourier series. Note that

$$e^{j\phi_m \sin \omega_m t} = \cos(\phi_m \sin \omega_m t) + j \sin(\phi_m \sin \omega_m t). \tag{7.63}$$

Hence let us consider the Fourier series expansion of (7.63), i.e.,

$$e^{j\phi_m \sin \omega_m t} = \sum_{n=-\infty}^{\infty} c_n\, e^{jn\omega_m t}, \tag{7.64}$$

where

$$c_n = \frac{1}{T} \int_{-T/2}^{T/2} e^{(j\phi_m \sin \omega_m t)} e^{(-jn\omega_m t)} \, dt \qquad (7.65)$$

and $T = 2\pi/\omega_m$. Thus,

$$c_n = \frac{\omega_m}{2\pi} \int_{-T/2}^{T/2} e^{j(\phi_m \sin \omega_m t - n\omega_m t)} \, dt. \qquad (7.66)$$

Letting $\omega_m t = x$,

$$c_n = \frac{1}{2\pi} \int_{-\pi}^{\pi} e^{j(\phi_m \sin x - nx)} \, dx. \qquad (7.67)$$

The Fourier coefficients (7.67) turn out to be Bessel functions of the first kind. From the generating function for the Bessel functions,

$$e^{z(x^2-1)/2x} = \sum_{n=-\infty}^{\infty} J_n(z) \, x^n, \qquad (7.68)$$

where $J_n(z)$ is the Bessel function of the first kind, order n, argument z.

Letting $x = e^{j\omega t}$ in (7.68),

$$\frac{z(x^2-1)}{2x} = z\,\frac{1}{2}\left(x - \frac{1}{x}\right) = jz\,\frac{1}{2j}\,(e^{j\omega t} - e^{-j\omega t}) = jz \sin \omega t. \qquad (7.69)$$

Hence,

$$e^{jz \sin \omega t} = \sum_{n=-\infty}^{\infty} J_n(z) \, e^{jn\omega t}. \qquad (7.70)$$

Comparing (7.70) with (7.64),

$$e^{j\phi_m \sin \omega_m t} = \sum_{n=-\infty}^{\infty} c_n \, e^{jn\omega_m t} = \sum_{n=-\infty}^{\infty} J_n(\phi_m) \, e^{jn\omega_m t}. \qquad (7.71)$$

Thus, from (7.67),

$$c_n = J_n(\phi_m) = \frac{1}{2\pi} \int_{-\pi}^{\pi} e^{j(\phi_m \sin x - nx)} \, dx. \qquad (7.72)$$

The properties of Bessel functions and curves illustrating their behavior may be found in many places. From (7.72),

$$J_{-n}(\phi_m) = (-1)^n \, J_n(\phi_m). \qquad (7.73)$$

Now from (7.71),

$$e^{j\phi_m \sin \omega_m t} = \sum_{n=-\infty}^{\infty} J_n(\phi_m) \, e^{jn\omega_m t}$$

$$= J_0(\phi_m) + J_1(\phi_m) \, (\cos \omega_m t + j \sin \omega_m t)$$

$$+ J_{-1}(\phi_m) \, (\cos \omega_m t - j \sin \omega_m t)$$

$$+ J_2(\phi_m) \, (\cos 2\omega_m t + j \sin 2\omega_m t)$$

$$+ J_{-2}(\phi_m) \, (\cos 2\omega_m t - j \sin 2\omega_m t)$$

$$+ \cdots. \qquad (7.74)$$

Equating real and imaginary parts and using (7.73),

$$\cos(\phi_m \sin \omega_m t) = J_0(\phi_m) + 2J_2(\phi_m) \cos 2\omega_m t + 2J_4(\phi_m) \cos 4\omega_m t + \cdots$$

$$= J_0(\phi_m) + 2 \sum_{n=1}^{\infty} J_{2n}(\phi_m) \cos 2n\,\omega_m t, \qquad (7.75)$$

$$\sin(\phi_m \sin \omega_m t) = 2J_1(\phi_m) \sin \omega_m t + 2J_3(\phi_m) \sin 3\omega_m t + \cdots$$

$$= 2\sum_{n=0}^{\infty} J_{2n+1}(\phi_m) \sin(2n+1)\omega_m t. \qquad (7.76)$$

Equations (7.75) and (7.76) are the desired Fourier series expansions for the terms $\cos(\phi_m \sin \omega_m t)$ and $\sin(\phi_m \sin \omega_m t)$.

The spectral distribution of the FM signal can now be obtained by substituting (7.75) and (7.76) into (7.62); thus,

$$f(t) = A \cos(\omega_c t + \phi_m \sin \omega_m t)$$

$$= A \cos \omega_c t \{J_0(\phi_m) + 2[J_2(\phi_m)\cos 2\omega_m t + J_4(\phi_m)\cos 4\omega_m t + \cdots]\}$$

$$-2A \sin \omega_c t \,[J_1(\phi_m)\sin \omega_m t + J_3(\phi_m)\sin 3\omega_m t + \cdots]. \qquad (7.77)$$

Utilizing the trigonometric sum and difference formulas

$$\cos A \cos B = \frac{1}{2}[\cos(A-B) + \cos(A+B)],$$

$$\sin A \sin B = \frac{1}{2}[\cos(A-B) - \cos(A+B)],$$

we obtain

$$f(t) = A\{J_0(\phi_m)\cos \omega_c t - J_1(\phi_m)\,[\cos(\omega_c - \omega_m)t - \cos(\omega_c + \omega_m)t]$$

$$+ J_2(\phi_m)\,[\cos(\omega_c - 2\omega_m)t + \cos(\omega_c + 2\omega_m)t]$$

$$- J_3(\phi_m)\,[\cos(\omega_c - 3\omega_m)t - \cos(\omega_c + 3\omega_m)t]$$

$$+ \cdots \}. \qquad (7.78)$$

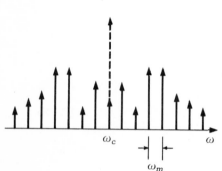

Fig. 7.10 The spectrum of the FM signal of (7.78).

Equation (7.78) shows that the FM signal $f(t)$ consists of a carrier and an infinite number of side bands, spaced at frequencies $(\omega_c \pm \omega_m)$, $(\omega_c \pm 2\omega_m)$, $(\omega_c \pm 3\omega_m)$, etc., as shown in Fig. 7.10. The amplitudes of the carrier and side band terms depend on ϕ_m, the modulation index, this dependence being expressed by the appropriate Bessel functions.

7.4 Pulse Modulation

In a pulse modulation system, a periodic sequence of pulses constitutes the carrier. Either pulse amplitude, pulse duration, or pulse position can be modulated in accordance with the input signal. The theoretical basis for pulse modulation technique is the sampling theory of Sec. 7.1. In a pulse system, we start with an unmodulated pulse train consisting of identical, equally spaced pulses that occur at a sampling rate appropriate for the modulating signal (i.e., at a rate greater than twice the highest frequency component of the modulating signal).

In this section, we shall consider only the case of *pulse amplitude modulation* (PAM). A PAM signal is defined as follows:

Let $m(t)$ be a band-limited signal with $M(\omega) = \mathcal{F}[m(t)] = 0$ for $|\omega| > \omega_M(= 2\pi f_M)$, and let $g(t)$ be a periodic pulse train with period T. Then the product

$$f(t) = m(t)\,g(t) \qquad (7.79)$$

is a PAM signal provided that $T \leq 1/(2f_M)$.

PROBLEM 7.16 Find the spectrum of the PAM signal (7.79) if $g(t)$ is a train of periodic rectangular pulses of width d seconds and repeating every $T = 1/(2f_M)$ seconds.

Solution: Let

$$\mathcal{F}[m(t)] = M(\omega), \tag{7.80}$$

$$M(\omega) = 0 \quad \text{for} \quad |\omega| > \omega_M.$$

According to the frequency convolution theorem (4.125), the Fourier transform of $f(t) = m(t)\,g(t)$ is therefore

$$F(\omega) = \mathcal{F}[f(t)] = \mathcal{F}[m(t)\,g(t)]$$

$$= \frac{1}{2\pi}\,M(\omega) * G(\omega), \tag{7.81}$$

where $G(\omega) = \mathcal{F}[g(t)]$.

From (5.77), $G(\omega)$ can be obtained by setting

$$T = \frac{1}{(2f_M)} = \frac{\pi}{\omega_M} \quad \text{and} \quad \omega_0 = \frac{2\pi}{T} = 2\omega_M.$$

Then,

$$G(\omega) = 2\omega_M d \sum_{n=-\infty}^{\infty} Sa(n\omega_M d)\,\delta(\omega - 2n\,\omega_M). \tag{7.82}$$

Substituting (7.82) into (7.81),

$$F(\omega) = 2\omega_M d\,M(\omega) * \sum_{n=-\infty}^{\infty} Sa(n\omega_M d)\,\delta(\omega - 2n\,\omega_M)$$

$$= 2\omega_M d \sum_{n=-\infty}^{\infty} Sa(n\omega_M d)\,M(\omega) * \delta(\omega - 2n\,\omega_M)$$

$$= 2\omega_M d \sum_{n=-\infty}^{\infty} Sa(n\,\omega_M d)\,M(\omega - 2n\,\omega_M), \tag{7.83}$$

with the use of (4.120).

If $m(t)$ is band-limited as shown in Fig. 7.11(a), the amplitude spectrum of the PAM signal is as illustrated in Fig. 7.11(f).

In Prob. 7.16, a rectangular pulse train is used for $g(t)$. The spectral analysis of the following example shows that the pulse waveform is not relevant.

PROBLEM 7.17   Find the spectrum of a PAM signal (7.79) if $g(t)$ is a train of periodic pulses of arbitrary waveform and repeating every $T < 1/(2f_M)$ seconds.

Solution: Since $g(t)$ is a periodic function, it can be expanded into a Fourier series; thus,

$$g(t) = \sum_{n=-\infty}^{\infty} c_n\,e^{jn\omega_0 t}, \quad \omega_0 = \frac{2\pi}{T}.$$

Then from (7.79), the PAM signal $f(t) = m(t)\,g(t)$ can be written as

$$f(t) = m(t)\left(\sum_{n=-\infty}^{\infty} c_n\,e^{jn\omega_0 t}\right)$$

$$= \sum_{n=-\infty}^{\infty} c_n\,m(t)\,e^{jn\omega_0 t}. \tag{7.84}$$

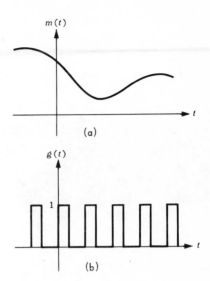

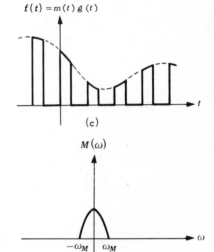

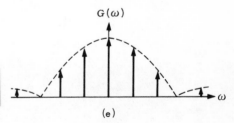

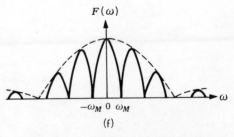

Fig. 7.11 (a) The band-limited signal $m(t)$ of Prob. 7.16. (b) A train of periodic rectangular pulses $g(t)$. (c) The PAM signal $f(t) = m(t)\,g(t)$. (d) $M(\omega)$; the spectrum of $m(t)$. (e) $G(\omega)$; the spectrum of $g(t)$. (f) $F(\omega)$; the spectrum of the PAM signal $f(t)$.

Thus,

$$F(\omega) = \mathcal{F}[f(t)] = \mathcal{F}\left[\sum_{n=-\infty}^{\infty} c_n \, m(t) \, e^{jn\omega_0 t}\right]$$

$$= \sum_{n=-\infty}^{\infty} c_n \, \mathcal{F}[m(t) \, e^{jn\omega_0 t}]. \qquad (7.85)$$

Now according to the frequency-shifting property of the Fourier transform (4.74), if $\mathcal{F}[m(t)] = M(\omega)$, then

$$\mathcal{F}[m(t) \, e^{jn\omega_0 t}] = M(\omega - n\,\omega_0).$$

Hence,

$$F(\omega) = \sum_{n=-\infty}^{\infty} c_n \, M(\omega - n\,\omega_0). \qquad (7.86)$$

Figure 7.12(b) illustrates the amplitude spectrum of the PAM signal which consists of periodically spaced pulses with amplitude modified by the Fourier coefficients of $g(t)$. In Fig. 7.12, ω_0 is selected such that $T < 1/(2f_M)$.

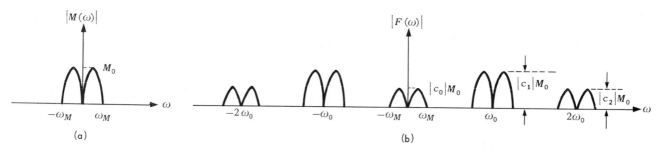

(a)   (b)

Fig. 7.12 (a) The spectrum of the band-limited signal $m(t)$ of Prob. 7.17. (b) The spectrum of the PAM signal of Prob. 7.17.

7.5 Average Correlation Functions

The concept of correlation functions was introduced in Sec. 4.9. For periodic or random noise signals which exist over the entire time interval $(-\infty, \infty)$, the energy content will be infinite, i.e.,

$$\int_{-\infty}^{\infty} [f(t)]^2 \, dt = \infty.$$

Thus it is obvious that the correlation functions as defined in Sec. 4.9 do not exist. In such cases, we consider the following average correlation functions.

The *average autocorrelation* function of $f_1(t)$, denoted by $\overline{R}_{11}(\tau)$, is defined as the limit

$$\overline{R}_{11}(\tau) = \lim_{T \to \infty} \frac{1}{T} \int_{-T/2}^{T/2} f_1(t) f_1(t - \tau) \, dt. \qquad (7.87)$$

Similarly, the *average cross-correlation* function of $f_1(t)$ and $f_2(t)$, denoted by $\overline{R}_{12}(\tau)$, is defined as the limit

$$\overline{R}_{12}(\tau) = \lim_{T \to \infty} \frac{1}{T} \int_{-T/2}^{T/2} f_1(t) f_2(t - \tau) \, dt. \qquad (7.88)$$

PROBLEM 7.18   For periodic functions (with period T_1), show that

$$\overline{R}_{11}(\tau) = \frac{1}{T_1} \int_{-T_1/2}^{T_1/2} f_1(t) f_1(t - \tau)\, dt, \qquad (7.89)$$

$$\overline{R}_{12}(\tau) = \frac{1}{T_1} \int_{-T_1/2}^{T_1/2} f_1(t) f_2(t - \tau)\, dt. \qquad (7.90)$$

Solution: Let $f_1(t)$ and $f_2(t)$ both be periodic functions of period T_1.   Then,

$$f_1(t) = f_1(t + T_1), \qquad (7.91)$$

$$f_1(t - \tau) = f_1(t - \tau + T_1), \qquad (7.92)$$

$$f_2(t - \tau) = f_2(t - \tau + T_1). \qquad (7.93)$$

Hence the integrands in (7.87) and (7.88) are periodic functions in variable t with period T_1. The integral of such a function over each period is the same, therefore it is immaterial whether the correlation functions are averaged over a very large interval, $T \longrightarrow \infty$, or over one period T_1.

Thus for periodic functions,

$$\overline{R}_{11}(\tau) = \lim_{T \to \infty} \frac{1}{T} \int_{-T/2}^{T/2} f_1(t) f_1(t - \tau)\, dt = \frac{1}{T_1} \int_{-T_1/2}^{T_1/2} f_1(t) f_1(t - \tau)\, dt,$$

$$\overline{R}_{12}(\tau) = \lim_{T \to \infty} \frac{1}{T} \int_{-T/2}^{T/2} f_1(t) f_2(t - \tau)\, dt = \frac{1}{T_1} \int_{-T_1/2}^{T_1/2} f_1(t) f_2(t - \tau)\, dt.$$

PROBLEM 7.19   Show that the average autocorrelation and cross-correlation functions of periodic signals of period T_1 are also periodic with the same period.

Solution: From (7.89),

$$\overline{R}_{11}(\tau - T_1) = \frac{1}{T_1} \int_{-T_1/2}^{T_1/2} f_1(t) f_1[t - (\tau - T_1)]\, dt$$

$$= \frac{1}{T_1} \int_{-T_1/2}^{T_1/2} f_1(t) f_1(t - \tau + T_1)\, dt.$$

But from (7.93),

$$\overline{R}_{11}(\tau - T_1) = \frac{1}{T_1} \int_{-T_1/2}^{T_1/2} f_1(t) f_1(t - \tau)\, dt = \overline{R}_{11}(\tau). \qquad (7.94)$$

Similarly, from (7.90) and (7.93),

$$\overline{R}_{12}(\tau - T_1) = \frac{1}{T_1} \int_{-T_1/2}^{T_1/2} f_1(t) f_2[t - (\tau - T_1)]\, dt$$

$$= \frac{1}{T_1} \int_{-T_1/2}^{T_1/2} f_1(t) f_2(t - \tau + T_1)\, dt$$

$$= \frac{1}{T_1} \int_{-T_1/2}^{T_1/2} f_1(t) f_2(t - \tau)\, dt = \overline{R}_{12}(\tau).$$

$$= \overline{R}_{12}(\tau). \qquad (7.95)$$

Equations (7.94) and (7.95) show that $\overline{R}_{11}(\tau)$ and $\overline{R}_{12}(\tau)$ are periodic with the period T_1.

PROBLEM 7.20   Find the average autocorrelation function of the sine wave given by

$$f(t) = A \sin (\omega_1 t + \phi), \qquad \omega_1 = \frac{2\pi}{T_1}.$$

Solution: Since $f(t)$ is periodic, from (7.89),

$$\overline{R}_{ff}(\tau) = \lim_{T \to \infty} \frac{1}{T} \int_{-T/2}^{T/2} f(t) f(t - \tau)\, dt$$

$$= \frac{1}{T_1} \int_{-T_1/2}^{T_1/2} f(t) f(t - \tau)\, dt$$

$$= \frac{A^2}{T_1} \int_{-T_1/2}^{T_1/2} \sin (\omega_1 t + \phi) \sin [\omega_1(t - \tau) + \phi]\, dt$$

$$= \frac{A^2}{T_1} \int_{-T_1/2}^{T_1/2} \sin (\omega_1 t + \phi) \sin (\omega_1 t + \phi - \omega_1 \tau)\, dt. \qquad (7.96)$$

Using the trigonometric identity $\sin A \sin B = \dfrac{1}{2} [\cos (A - B) - \cos (A + B)]$,

$$\overline{R}_{ff}(\tau) = \frac{A^2}{2T_1} \int_{-T_1/2}^{T_1/2} [\cos \omega_1 \tau - \cos (2\omega_1 t + 2\phi - \omega_1 \tau)]\, dt$$

$$= \frac{A^2}{2T_1} \cos \omega_1 \tau \int_{-T_1/2}^{T_1/2} dt$$

$$= \frac{A^2}{2} \cos (\omega_1 \tau). \qquad (7.97)$$

Equation (7.97) shows that $\overline{R}_{ff}(\tau)$ is independent of the phase ϕ of $f(t)$.

PROBLEM 7.21   Show that if $f_1(t)$ and $f_2(t)$ are real periodic functions having the same period T_1, then

$$\overline{R}_{12}(\tau) = \sum_{n=-\infty}^{\infty} [c_{1n}^* \, c_{2n}] \, e^{-jn\omega_1 \tau}, \qquad (7.98)$$

where $\omega_1 = 2\pi/T_1$ and c_{1n}, c_{2n} are the complex Fourier coefficients of $f_1(t)$ and $f_2(t)$, respectively, and c_{1n}^* denotes complex conjugate of c_{1n}.

Solution: In the case of periodic functions, from (7.90),

$$\overline{R}_{12}(\tau) = \frac{1}{T_1} \int_{-T_1/2}^{T_1/2} f_1(t) f_2(t - \tau)\, dt.$$

Let the complex Fourier series expansions for $f_1(t)$ and $f_2(t)$ be

$$f_1(t) = \sum_{n=-\infty}^{\infty} c_{1n} \, e^{jn\omega_1 t}, \qquad (7.99)$$

$$f_2(t) = \sum_{n=-\infty}^{\infty} c_{2n} \, e^{jn\omega_1 t}, \qquad (7.100)$$

where

$$c_{1n} = \frac{1}{T_1} \int_{-T_1/2}^{T_1/2} f_1(t) \, e^{-jn\omega_1 t}\, dt, \qquad (7.101)$$

$$c_{2n} = \frac{1}{T_1} \int_{-T_1/2}^{T_1/2} f_2(t) \, e^{-jn\omega_1 t} \, dt. \tag{7.102}$$

By writing $f_2(t - \tau)$ of (7.90) in the form (7.100),

$$\overline{R}_{12}(\tau) = \frac{1}{T_1} \int_{-T_1/2}^{T_1/2} f_1(t) \, f_2(t - \tau) \, dt$$

$$= \frac{1}{T_1} \int_{-T_1/2}^{T_1/2} f_1(t) \left[\sum_{n=-\infty}^{\infty} c_{2n} \, e^{jn\omega_1(t-\tau)} \right] dt. \tag{7.103}$$

Interchanging the order of summation and integration,

$$\overline{R}_{12}(\tau) = \sum_{n=-\infty}^{\infty} c_{2n} \, e^{-jn\omega_1 \tau} \left[\frac{1}{T_1} \int_{-T_1/2}^{T_1/2} f_1(t) \, e^{jn\omega_1 t} \, dt \right]. \tag{7.104}$$

The integral in the bracket is recognized, by comparison with (7.101), as the complex conjugate of c_{1n}. Hence,

$$\overline{R}_{12}(\tau) = \sum_{n=-\infty}^{\infty} [c_{1n}^* \, c_{2n}] \, e^{-jn\omega_1 \tau}.$$

Note that $\overline{R}_{12}(\tau)$ is also a periodic function of τ with period T_1.

PROBLEM 7.22 Show that if $f(t)$ is a real periodic function having the period T, then

$$\overline{R}_{ff}(\tau) = \sum_{n=-\infty}^{\infty} |c_n|^2 \, e^{jn\omega_0 \tau}, \tag{7.105}$$

where $\omega_0 = 2\pi/T$ and c_n are the complex Fourier coefficients of $f(t)$.

Solution: In Prob. 7.21, if we let $f_1(t) = f_2(t) = f(t)$ and $T_1 = T$, then from (7.98),

$$\overline{R}_{ff}(\tau) = \sum_{n=-\infty}^{\infty} c_n^* \, c_n \, e^{-jn\omega_0 \tau} = \sum_{n=-\infty}^{\infty} |c_n|^2 \, e^{-jn\omega_0 \tau} = \sum_{n=-\infty}^{\infty} |c_n|^2 \, e^{jn\omega_0 \tau}$$

since $|c_{-n}|^2 = |c_n|^2$.

Note that (7.105) is exactly a complex Fourier series expansion form of $\overline{R}_{ff}(\tau)$, and hence $\overline{R}_{ff}(\tau)$ is a periodic function of τ with the same period as that of $f(t)$. Equation (7.105) also shows that the Fourier coefficients of $\overline{R}_{ff}(\tau)$ only contain absolute values of the Fourier coefficients of $f(t)$. It therefore follows that all periodic time functions which have the same Fourier coefficient magnitudes and periodicities also have the same autocorrelation even though their Fourier coefficient phases may be different.

7.6 Signal Identification Using Correlation

We now turn to the case of signals that are contaminated with noise. By noise we normally mean any spurious or undesired disturbances that tend to obscure or mask the signal transmitted. The noise signal encountered in practice is a signal with random amplitude variation. In the following, the noise signal $n(t)$ is assumed to have a zero average value, i.e.,

$$\lim_{T \to \infty} \frac{1}{T} \int_{-T/2}^{T/2} n(t) \, dt = 0. \tag{7.106}$$

In general, two signals $f_1(t)$ and $f_2(t)$ are said to be *uncorrelated* if

$$\overline{R}_{12}(\tau) = \lim_{T \to \infty} \frac{1}{T} \int_{-T/2}^{T/2} f_1(t) f_2(t - \tau) \, dt$$

$$= \left[\lim_{T \to \infty} \frac{1}{T} \int_{-T/2}^{T/2} f_1(t) \, dt \right] \left[\lim_{T \to \infty} \frac{1}{T} \int_{-T/2}^{T/2} f_2(t) \, dt \right]. \tag{7.107}$$

PROBLEM 7.23 Let $s(t)$ be a useful signal and $n(t)$ be a noise signal. Show that if $s(t)$ and $n(t)$ are uncorrelated, then

$$\lim_{T \to \infty} \frac{1}{T} \int_{-T/2}^{T/2} s(t) n(t - \tau) \, dt = 0 \quad \text{for all } \tau. \tag{7.108}$$

Solution: If $s(t)$ and $n(t)$ are uncorrelated, then according to (7.107),

$$\lim_{T \to \infty} \frac{1}{T} \int_{-T/2}^{T/2} s(t) n(t - \tau) \, dt = \left[\lim_{T \to \infty} \frac{1}{T} \int_{-T/2}^{T/2} s(t) \, dt \right] \left[\lim_{T \to \infty} \frac{1}{T} \int_{-T/2}^{T/2} n(t) \, dt \right] = 0$$

in view of (7.106).

If we denote $\overline{R}_{sn}(\tau)$ as the average cross-correlation function of $s(t)$ and $n(t)$, then (7.108) can be expressed as

$$\overline{R}_{sn}(\tau) = 0 \quad \text{for all } \tau. \tag{7.109}$$

For random noise signals, with zero average value,

$$\lim_{\tau \to \infty} \overline{R}_{nn}(\tau) = 0. \tag{7.110}$$

PROBLEM 7.24 Show that the average autocorrelation function of the sum of signal and noise is the sum of the individual autocorrelation functions of signal and noise, respectively.

Solution: Let $f(t) = s(t) + n(t)$. Then,

$$\overline{R}_{ff}(\tau) = \lim_{T \to \infty} \frac{1}{T} \int_{-T/2}^{T/2} f(t) f(t - \tau) \, dt$$

$$= \lim_{T \to \infty} \frac{1}{T} \int_{-T/2}^{T/2} [s(t) + n(t)] [s(t - \tau) + n(t - \tau)] \, dt$$

$$= \overline{R}_{ss}(\tau) + \overline{R}_{nn}(\tau) + \overline{R}_{sn}(\tau) + \overline{R}_{ns}(\tau). \tag{7.111}$$

Since the signal $s(t)$ and the noise signal $n(t)$ are uncorrelated,

$$\overline{R}_{sn}(\tau) = \overline{R}_{ns}(\tau) = 0.$$

Thus,

$$\overline{R}_{ff}(\tau) = \overline{R}_{ss}(\tau) + \overline{R}_{nn}(\tau). \tag{7.112}$$

PROBLEM 7.25 Show that from the result (7.112) of Prob. 7.24, autocorrelation can be used for signal detection.

Solution: Let $f(t)$ be the received signal which is the sum of the useful signal $s(t)$ and the noise $n(t)$. Now, if we know the nature of the noise such as the power spectrum which will be discussed in the following section, then the average autocorrelation function of the noise $\overline{R}_{nn}(\tau)$ can be computed. If $\overline{R}_{nn}(\tau)$ differs from $\overline{R}_{ff}(\tau)$, then we can conclude that a useful signal $s(t)$ exists in the received signal $f(t)$, since $\overline{R}_{ss}(\tau)$ is not zero.

Equation (7.112) also offers a means of detecting a periodic signal masked by random noise. Since in this case $s(t)$ is a periodic signal and $n(t)$ is a non-periodic signal, from the result of Prob. 7.19 and (7.110), it follows that $\overline{R}_{ss}(\tau)$ is periodic, whereas $\overline{R}_{nn}(\tau)$ becomes very small for large values of τ. Therefore, for sufficiently large values of τ, $\overline{R}_{ff}(\tau)$ will be almost equal to $\overline{R}_{ss}(\tau)$, and $\overline{R}_{ff}(\tau)$ will exhibit a periodic nature at sufficiently large values of τ.

PROBLEM 7.26   Show that the cross-correlation function between transmitted and received signals is the same as that between transmitted and useful received signals.

Solution: Let $g(t)$ and $f(t)$ be the transmitted signal and the received signal, respectively. Then,

$$f(t) = s(t) + n(t),$$

where $s(t)$ is the useful received signal and $n(t)$ is the noise. Now if we cross-correlate the received signal $f(t)$ with the transmitted signal,

$$\overline{R}_{fg}(\tau) = \lim_{T \to \infty} \frac{1}{T} \int_{-T/2}^{T/2} [s(t) + n(t)] g(t - \tau)\, dt = \overline{R}_{sg}(\tau) + \overline{R}_{ng}(\tau). \quad (7.113)$$

Since $n(t)$ and $g(t)$ are not correlated, i.e., $\overline{R}_{ng}(\tau) = 0$,

$$\overline{R}_{fg}(\tau) = \overline{R}_{sg}(\tau). \qquad (7.114)$$

PROBLEM 7.27   From the result (7.114) of Prob. 7.25, show that average cross-correlation can be used for signal detection.

Solution: If the received signal $f(t)$ is only noise, i.e., if $s(t) = 0$, then the average cross-correlation function $\overline{R}_{sg}(\tau) = 0$, and hence $\overline{R}_{fg} = 0$. Therefore, we conclude that if the average cross-correlation between transmitted and received signal is not identically zero, then a useful signal exists in the received signal. Equation (7.114) also can be used in the detection of a periodic signal contaminated by noise. Since the useful signal $s(t)$ and the transmitted signal $g(t)$ are signals of the same frequency, it follows from the result of Prob. 7.19 that $\overline{R}_{sg}(\tau)$ is also a periodic function of the same period. Hence from (7.114), we conclude that if the average cross-correlation of the received signal $f(t)$ and the transmitted signal $g(t)$ is periodic, then $f(t)$ must contain a periodic signal.

It should be noted that in the cross-correlation method, $\overline{R}_{fg}(\tau) = \overline{R}_{sg}(\tau)$, without any additional noise term such as $\overline{R}_{nn}(\tau)$ encountered in the autocorrelation technique of detection; hence, it is possible to detect a periodic signal in the received signal $f(t)$ at any value of τ.

7.7 Average Power Spectra: Random Signal

In Sec. 4.8 we introduced the idea of the energy spectrum or energy-density function of $f(t)$. There we assumed that the energy content of $f(t)$ is finite; i.e.,

$$\int_{-\infty}^{\infty} [f(t)]^2\, dt = \text{finite}. \qquad (7.115)$$

For such functions, the average power over the interval T approaches zero as T approaches infinity; thus,

$$\lim_{T \to \infty} \frac{1}{T} \int_{-T/2}^{T/2} [f(t)]^2 \, dt = 0. \tag{7.116}$$

In connection with noise calculations, we have to consider signals which do not have finite energy content. Then in this case, the average power of $f(t)$ is the quantity

$$\lim_{T \to \infty} \frac{1}{T} \int_{-T/2}^{T/2} [f(t)]^2 \, dt. \tag{7.117}$$

When this limit exists, the quantity

$$P(\omega) = \lim_{T \to \infty} \frac{1}{T} \left| \int_{-T/2}^{T/2} f(t) \, e^{-j\omega t} \, dt \right|^2 \tag{7.118}$$

is called the *power spectrum* or the *power spectral density* of the function $f(t)$.

If only the power spectral density of a function $f(t)$ is specified, we do not know the waveform, because only a time-average spectrum is known. Signals specified in this fashion may be called *random signals*. Random signals are usually described in terms of their statistical properties; however, we shall not discuss these properties here.

Although the quantity (7.118) is referred to as the power spectral density of the function $f(t)$, the power spectral density (or simply spectral density) of the function $f(t)$ is usually defined as the Fourier transform of the average autocorrelation function of $f(t)$. Thus, we define

$$P(\omega) = \mathcal{F}[\overline{R}_{ff}(\tau)] = \int_{-\infty}^{\infty} \overline{R}_{ff}(\tau) \, e^{-j\omega\tau} d\tau, \tag{7.119}$$

$$\overline{R}_{ff}(\tau) = \mathcal{F}^{-1}[P(\omega)] = \frac{1}{2\pi} \int_{-\infty}^{\infty} P(\omega) \, e^{j\omega\tau} d\omega. \tag{7.120}$$

PROBLEM 7.28 Show that the total average power (or the mean-square value) of a function $f(t)$ is given by

$$\lim_{T \to \infty} \frac{1}{T} \int_{-T/2}^{T/2} [f(t)]^2 \, dt = \frac{1}{2\pi} \int_{-\infty}^{\infty} P(\omega) \, d\omega = \int_{-\infty}^{\infty} P(2\pi\nu) \, d\nu, \tag{7.121}$$

where $\omega = 2\pi\nu$.

Solution: It follows from (7.120) that

$$\overline{R}_{ff}(0) = \frac{1}{2\pi} \int_{-\infty}^{\infty} P(\omega) \, d\omega = \int_{-\infty}^{\infty} P(2\pi\nu) \, d\nu. \tag{7.122}$$

Now from (7.87),

$$\overline{R}_{ff}(\tau) = \lim_{T \to \infty} \frac{1}{T} \int_{-T/2}^{T/2} f(t) \, f(t - \tau) \, dt. \tag{7.87}$$

Hence,

$$\overline{R}_{ff}(0) = \lim_{T \to \infty} \frac{1}{T} \int_{-T/2}^{T/2} [f(t)]^2 \, dt. \tag{7.123}$$

Comparing (7.123) and (7.122),

$$\lim_{T \to \infty} \frac{1}{T} \int_{-T/2}^{T/2} [f(t)]^2 \, dt = \frac{1}{2\pi} \int_{-\infty}^{\infty} P(\omega) \, d\omega = \int_{-\infty}^{\infty} P(2\pi\nu) \, d\nu.$$

Equation (7.121) states that the total average power (or the mean-square value) of a function $f(t)$ is given by the integration of $P(\omega)$ over the entire frequency range. For this reason the quantity $P(\omega)$ is called the *power spectrum* or *power spectral density* of $f(t)$.

PROBLEM 7.29 Find the power spectral density of a periodic function $f(t)$ with period T.

Solution: Let the Fourier series of a periodic function $f(t)$ be given by

$$f(t) = \sum_{n=-\infty}^{\infty} c_n\, e^{jn\omega_0 t}, \quad \omega_0 = \frac{2\pi}{T}. \tag{7.124}$$

It was shown in Prob. 7.22 that the average autocorrelation function for $f(t)$ is

$$\overline{R}_{ff}(\tau) = \sum_{n=-\infty}^{\infty} |c_n|^2\, e^{jn\omega_0 \tau}. \tag{7.105}$$

If we take the Fourier transform of $\overline{R}_{ff}(\tau)$,

$$P(\omega) = \mathcal{F}[\overline{R}_{ff}(\tau)] = \sum_{n=-\infty}^{\infty} |c_n|^2\, \mathcal{F}[e^{jn\omega_0 \tau}]$$

$$= \sum_{n=-\infty}^{\infty} 2\pi\, |c_n|^2\, \delta(\omega - n\omega_0) \tag{7.125}$$

with the use of (5.21).

Hence $P(\omega)$ consists of a series of impulses at the harmonic frequencies of $f(t)$. Each impulse has a strength equal to the power contained in that component frequency, and is clearly a measure of the distribution of the power in $f(t)$.

PROBLEM 7.30 Show that the average power per period in a periodic function $f(t)$ is given by

$$\frac{1}{T_1} \int_{-T_1/2}^{T_1/2} [f(t)]^2\, dt = \sum_{n=-\infty}^{\infty} |c_n|^2. \tag{7.126}$$

Solution: Since $f(t)$ is periodic, from (7.89),

$$\lim_{T \to \infty} \frac{1}{T} \int_{-T/2}^{T/2} [f(t)]^2\, dt = \frac{1}{T_1} \int_{-T_1/2}^{T_1/2} [f(t)]^2\, dt, \tag{7.127}$$

where T_1 is the period of $f(t)$.

Substituting (7.125) into (7.121) and using the relation (7.127),

$$\frac{1}{T_1} \int_{-T_1/2}^{T_1/2} [f(t)]^2\, dt = \frac{1}{2\pi} \int_{-\infty}^{\infty} P(\omega)\, d\omega = \int_{-\infty}^{\infty} \left[\sum_{n=-\infty}^{\infty} |c_n|^2\, \delta(\omega - n\omega_0) \right] d\omega.$$

Interchanging the order of summation and integration and using a property of the δ-function,

$$\frac{1}{T_1} \int_{-T_1/2}^{T_1/2} [f(t)]^2\, dt = \sum_{n=-\infty}^{\infty} |c_n|^2 \int_{-\infty}^{\infty} \delta(\omega - n\omega_0)\, d\omega = \sum_{n=-\infty}^{\infty} |c_n|^2.$$

Equation (7.126) is exactly Parseval's theorem for a periodic function (3.85).

White noise is defined as any random signal whose power spectral density is a constant (independent of frequency).

PROBLEM 7.31 Find the average autocorrelation function of white noise.

Solution: From the definition of white noise,

$$P(\omega) = K. \tag{7.128}$$

It follows from (7.120) that

$$\overline{R}(\tau) = \mathcal{F}^{-1}[P(\omega)] = \frac{1}{2\pi}\int_{-\infty}^{\infty} P(\omega) e^{j\omega\tau}d\omega = K\frac{1}{2\pi}\int_{-\infty}^{\infty} e^{j\omega\tau}d\omega.$$

From the identity (5.4) of the δ-function, i.e.,

$$\frac{1}{2\pi}\int_{-\infty}^{\infty} e^{j\omega\tau}d\omega = \delta(\tau),$$

we have

$$\overline{R}(\tau) = K\,\delta(\tau). \tag{7.129}$$

Hence, the average autocorrelation function for white noise is found to be an impulse.

PROBLEM 7.32 The average autocorrelation function of the thermal-noise current $i_n(t)$ is given by

$$\overline{R}_{ii}(\tau) = kTG\alpha\, e^{-\alpha|\tau|}, \tag{7.130}$$

where

k = Boltzmann constant, $k = 1.38 \times 10^{-23}$ joule/$^{\circ}$K,
T = ambient temperature in degrees Kelvin,
G = conductance of the resistor in mhos,
α = average number of collisions per second of an electron.

Find the average power spectral density of the thermal-noise current.

Solution: Taking the Fourier transform of (7.130),

$$P(\omega) = \mathcal{F}[\overline{R}_{ii}(\tau)]$$

$$= kTG\alpha\int_{-\infty}^{\infty} e^{-\alpha|\tau|}\, e^{-j\omega\tau}\,d\tau$$

$$= kTG\alpha\int_{-\infty}^{0} e^{\alpha\tau} e^{-j\omega\tau}\,d\tau + \int_{0}^{\infty} e^{-\alpha\tau} e^{-j\omega\tau}\,d\tau$$

$$= \frac{2kTG\alpha^2}{\alpha^2 + \omega^2} = \frac{2kTG}{1 + \dfrac{\omega^2}{\alpha^2}}. \tag{7.131}$$

Since α, the number of collisions per second, is of the order of 10^{12}, the factor $1 + \omega^2/\alpha^2$ is close to unity for frequencies below about 10^{10} cps. Therefore, for frequencies below about 10^{10} cps, the average power spectral density of the thermal-noise current may be approximated by

$$P(\omega) = 2kTG. \tag{7.132}$$

7.8 Input-Output Relations: Noise Calculation

The input-output relations discussed in Chap. 6 determine the output of a constant-parameter linear system when the input is a known function of time. Since random signals such as noise can not be expressed as deterministic functions of time, the techniques developed in Chap. 6 are not directly applicable when the input is a random signal.

In this section, we shall study the application of correlation functions and power spectral densities to system analysis problems involving random signals.

PROBLEM 7.33 Let $x(t)$ and $y(t)$ be the random input and output signals, respectively, for a constant-parameter stable linear system characterized by the system function $H(\omega)$. Show that the average autocorrelations of the input and the output are related by

$$\overline{R}_{yy}(\tau) = \int_{-\infty}^{\infty} h(\lambda) \int_{-\infty}^{\infty} h(\sigma) \overline{R}_{xx}(\tau + \sigma - \lambda) \, d\sigma \, d\lambda, \qquad (7.133)$$

where $h(t) = \mathcal{F}^{-1}[H(\omega)]$ = unit impulse response of the system.

Solution: It was shown in (6.87) that the output $y(t)$ is related to the input $x(t)$ by the convolution integral; i.e.,

$$y(t) = \int_{-\infty}^{\infty} h(\tau) x(t - \tau) \, d\tau. \qquad (7.134)$$

Now from (7.87),

$$\overline{R}_{yy}(\tau) = \lim_{T \to \infty} \frac{1}{T} \int_{-T/2}^{T/2} y(t) y(t - \tau) \, dt. \qquad (7.135)$$

From (7.134), we may write $y(t)$ and $y(t - \tau)$ as

$$y(t) = \int_{-\infty}^{\infty} h(\lambda) x(t - \lambda) \, d\lambda, \qquad (7.136)$$

$$y(t - \tau) = \int_{-\infty}^{\infty} h(\sigma) x(t - \tau - \sigma) \, d\sigma. \qquad (7.137)$$

Substituting (7.136) and (7.137) into (7.135),

$$\overline{R}_{yy}(\tau) = \lim_{T \to \infty} \frac{1}{T} \int_{-T/2}^{T/2} \left[\int_{-\infty}^{\infty} h(\lambda) x(t - \lambda) d\lambda \int_{-\infty}^{\infty} h(\sigma) x(t - \tau - \sigma) d\sigma \right] dt. \qquad (7.138)$$

By interchanging the order of integration, we can write (7.138) as

$$\overline{R}_{yy}(\tau) = \int_{-\infty}^{\infty} h(\lambda) \int_{-\infty}^{\infty} h(\sigma) \left[\lim_{T \to \infty} \frac{1}{T} \int_{-T/2}^{T/2} x(t - \lambda) x(t - \tau - \sigma) dt \right] d\sigma \, d\lambda. \qquad (7.139)$$

Since

$$\overline{R}_{xx}(\tau + \sigma - \lambda) = \lim_{T \to \infty} \frac{1}{T} \int_{-T/2}^{T/2} x(t - \lambda) x(t - \tau - \sigma) \, dt, \qquad (7.140)$$

(7.139) becomes

$$\bar{R}_{yy}(\tau) = \int_{-\infty}^{\infty} h(\lambda) \int_{-\infty}^{\infty} h(\sigma) \bar{R}_{xx}(\tau + \sigma - \lambda) d\sigma d\lambda.$$

PROBLEM 7.34   Show that the output power spectral density $P_0(\omega)$ and the input power spectral density $P_i(\omega)$ of a linear system are related by

$$P_0(\omega) = |H(\omega)|^2 P_i(\omega), \tag{7.141}$$

where $H(\omega)$ is the system function of the system.

Solution: From (7.119), $P_0(\omega)$ is given by

$$P_0(\omega) = \mathcal{F}[\bar{R}_{yy}(\tau)] = \int_{-\infty}^{\infty} \bar{R}_{yy}(\tau) e^{-j\omega\tau} d\tau. \tag{7.142}$$

Substituting (7.133) into (7.142),

$$P_0(\omega) = \int_{-\infty}^{\infty} \left[\int_{-\infty}^{\infty} h(\lambda) \int_{-\infty}^{\infty} h(\sigma) \bar{R}_{xx}(\tau + \sigma - \lambda) d\sigma d\lambda \right] e^{-j\omega\tau} d\tau. \tag{7.143}$$

With the change of variable $\mu = \tau + \sigma - \lambda$, followed by a separation of variables,

$$P_0(\omega) = \int_{-\infty}^{\infty} h(\lambda) d\lambda \int_{-\infty}^{\infty} h(\sigma) d\sigma \int_{-\infty}^{\infty} \bar{R}_{xx}(\mu) e^{-j\omega(\mu - \sigma + \lambda)} d\mu$$

$$= \int_{-\infty}^{\infty} h(\lambda) e^{-j\omega\lambda} d\lambda \int_{-\infty}^{\infty} h(\sigma) e^{j\omega\sigma} d\sigma \int_{-\infty}^{\infty} \bar{R}_{xx}(\mu) e^{-j\omega\mu} d\mu. \tag{7.144}$$

Since

$$P_i(\omega) = \int_{-\infty}^{\infty} R_{xx}(\tau) e^{-j\omega\tau} d\tau,$$

$$H(\omega) = \int_{-\infty}^{\infty} h(\tau) e^{-j\omega\tau} d\tau,$$

and $h(t)$ is always real,

$$H^*(\omega) = \int_{-\infty}^{\infty} h(\tau) e^{j\omega\tau} d\tau.$$

Then (7.144) can be written as

$$P_0(\omega) = H(\omega) H^*(\omega) P_i(\omega). \tag{7.145}$$

Since $H(\omega) H^*(\omega) = |H(\omega)|^2$,

$$P_0(\omega) = |H(\omega)|^2 P_i(\omega).$$

For random signals, we neither have nor can we get an explicit expression for an input noise source or for the response of a system to such a source. Consequently, a relationship such as (6.92) is not available for random signals. However, by means of power spectral densities, we are able to establish and to utilize the relationship (7.141) for problems involving random signals applied to a linear system.

PROBLEM 7.35 Find the average autocorrelation function of the output of a low-pass *RC* network shown in Fig. 7.13 when the input is a white noise. Also find the mean-square noise voltage at the output.

Solution: From the result (6.100) of Prob. 6.19, the impulse response $h(t)$ of the network is given by

$$h(t) = \frac{1}{RC} \, e^{-t/RC} \, u(t),$$

while from (7.129), the average input (white noise) autocorrelation function is given by

$$\overline{R}_{xx}(\tau) = K\delta(\tau).$$

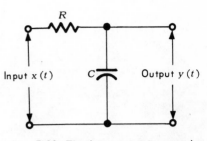

Fig. 7.13 The low-pass *RC* network of Prob. 7.35.

Then by use of (7.133),

$$\overline{R}_{yy}(\tau) = \int_{-\infty}^{\infty} \frac{1}{RC} e^{-\lambda/RC} u(\lambda) \int_{-\infty}^{\infty} \frac{K}{RC} e^{-\sigma/RC} u(\sigma) \delta(\tau + \sigma - \lambda) d\sigma \, d\lambda$$

$$= \frac{K}{(RC)^2} \int_{-\infty}^{\infty} e^{-\sigma/RC} u(\sigma) \int_{-\infty}^{\infty} \delta(\tau + \sigma - \lambda) e^{-\lambda/RC} u(\lambda) d\lambda \, d\sigma. \qquad (7.146)$$

Recalling a property (2.68) of the δ-function,

$$\overline{R}_{yy}(\tau) = \frac{K}{(RC)^2} \int_{-\infty}^{\infty} e^{-\sigma/RC} u(\sigma) e^{-(\tau+\sigma)/RC} \, d\sigma$$

$$= \frac{K}{(RC)^2} \int_{0}^{\infty} e^{-\tau/RC} e^{-2\sigma/RC} \, d\sigma$$

since $u(\sigma) = 0$ for $\sigma < 0$ and $u(\sigma) = 1$ for $\sigma > 0$.

Hence,

$$\overline{R}_{yy}(\tau) = \frac{K}{(RC)^2} e^{-\tau/RC} \int_{0}^{\infty} e^{-2\sigma/RC} \, d\sigma = \frac{K}{2RC} e^{-\tau/RC}. \qquad (7.147)$$

Equation (7.147) is only valid for τ positive; however, since the autocorrelation function is an even function of τ [see (4.148)],

$$\overline{R}_{yy}(\tau) = \frac{K}{2RC} e^{-|\tau|/RC}, \quad -\infty < \tau < \infty. \qquad (7.148)$$

The mean-square noise voltage at the output is given by

$$\lim_{T \to \infty} \frac{1}{T} \int_{-T/2}^{T/2} [y(t)]^2 \, dt = \overline{R}_{yy}(0) = \frac{K}{2RC}. \qquad (7.149)$$

PROBLEM 7.36 Find the power spectral density of the output of the *RC* network of Fig. 7.13 when the input is the same white noise. Also check the mean-square noise voltage at the output by (7.121).

Solution: From (6.99), the system function $H(\omega)$ of the *RC* network is given by

$$H(\omega) = \frac{\dfrac{1}{RC}}{j\omega + \dfrac{1}{RC}}. \qquad [6.99]$$

The power spectral density of the input white noise is given by

$$P_i(\omega) = K. \qquad [7.128]$$

Thus, from (7.141), the output power spectral density is given by

$$P_0(\omega) = |H(\omega)|^2 P_i(\omega) = \frac{\left(\dfrac{1}{RC}\right)^2}{\omega^2 + \left(\dfrac{1}{RC}\right)^2} K. \qquad (7.150)$$

From (7.121), the mean-square output voltage may be evaluated from $P_0(\omega)$; thus,

$$\lim_{T \to \infty} \frac{1}{T} \int_{-T/2}^{T/2} [y(t)]^2 \, dt = \frac{1}{2\pi} \int_{-\infty}^{\infty} P_0(\omega) \, d\omega$$

$$= \frac{K}{2\pi \, (RC)^2} \int_{-\infty}^{\infty} \frac{d\omega}{\omega^2 + \left(\dfrac{1}{RC}\right)^2}$$

$$= \frac{K}{2 RC} \qquad (7.151)$$

which agrees with (7.149).

7.9 Supplementary Problems

PROBLEM 7.37 Show that a band-limited periodic function, with no harmonics of order higher than N, is uniquely specified by its value at $2N + 1$ instants in one period.

[Hint: With $2N + 1$ unknowns, a band-limited periodic function has the form

$$f(t) = C_0 + \sum_{n=1}^{N} C_n \cos (\omega_0 t + \phi_n), \qquad \omega_0 = \frac{2\pi}{T} .]$$

PROBLEM 7.38 Consider the sampling functions

$$\phi_n(t) = \frac{\sin \omega_M (t - nT)}{\omega_M (t - nT)}, \qquad n = 0, \pm 1, \pm 2, \cdots,$$

where $\omega_M = 2\pi f_M$ and $T = 1/(2 f_M)$. Show that (a) $\phi_n(t)$ are orthogonal over the interval $-\infty < t < \infty$, and (b)

$$\int_{-\infty}^{\infty} \phi_n(t) \, \phi_m(t) \, dt = T \delta_{nm},$$

where δ_{nm} is the Kronecker's delta.

[Hint: Use the result of Prob. 4.23 and Parseval's theorem.]

PROBLEM 7.39 If $f(t)$ is band-limited, that is, $F(\omega) = \mathcal{F}[f(t)] = 0$ for $|\omega| > \omega_c$, show that

$$\int_{-\infty}^{\infty} f(t) \phi_n(t) \, dt = T f(nT),$$

where $\phi_n(t)$ is the sampling function of Prob. 7.38, for every $\phi_n(t)$ of Prob. 7.38 with $\omega_M > \omega_c$.

[Hint: Multiply (7.16) by $\phi_n(t)$ and integrate over $[-\infty, \infty]$, and use the result of Prob. 7.38.]

PROBLEM 7.40 Using the time convolution theorem (4.122), verify the result of Prob. 7.39.

[Hint: See Prob. 4.59.]

PROBLEM 7.41 Let $f(t)$ be a band-limited signal whose spectrum is zero outside the range from $-f_M$ to f_M Hertz. If $f(t)$ is sampled at a rate of $2f_M$ samples per second, prove that

$$\frac{1}{2f_M} \sum_{n=-\infty}^{\infty} \left[f\left(\frac{n}{2f_M}\right) \right]^2 = \int_{-\infty}^{\infty} f^2(t)\, dt.$$

PROBLEM 7.42 Show that the product of an ordinary AM signal, with a periodic waveform whose fundamental frequency is the carrier frequency of the ordinary AM signal, includes a term proportional to the signal $m(t)$.

PROBLEM 7.43 Show that the DSBSC signal can be demodulated by multiplying the signal by any periodic signal whose fundamental frequency is the carrier frequency of the DSBSC signal.

PROBLEM 7.44 Elimination of one side band in a DSBSC signal results in a *single-side band* (SSB) AM signal. Figure 7.14 shows a block diagram of a phase-shift method for producing an SSB signal. Form the (a) DSBSC signal $f_1(t)$ by multiplying a given message signal $m(t)$ by a carrier $\cos \omega_c t$, and (b) DSBSC signal $f_2(t)$ by multiplying the $-\frac{1}{2}\pi$-phase shifted carrier by the $-\frac{1}{2}\pi$-phase shifted message signal. Show that $f_1(t) - f_2(t)$ results in a SSB signal.

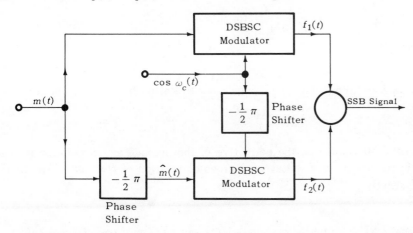

Fig. 7.14 Block diagram of a phase-shift method of producing SSB signal.

PROBLEM 7.45 (a) Show that the signal $f(t) = m(t) \cos \omega_c t$, where $m(t)$ is a periodic square wave, can be written as the phase-modulated signal $\cos[\omega_c t + \phi(t)]$. (b) Find $\phi(t)$.

Answer: If

$$m(t) = \begin{cases} 1 & \text{for } 0 < t < T/2 \\ -1 & \text{for } T/2 < t < T \end{cases} \quad \text{and} \quad m(t + T) = m(t),$$

then $\phi(t)$ is also a periodic square wave; i.e.,

$$\phi(t) = \begin{cases} 0 & \text{for } 0 < t < T/2 \\ \pi & \text{for } T/2 < t < T \end{cases} \quad \text{and} \quad \phi(t + T) = \phi(t).$$

PROBLEM 7.46 The FM signals with $\phi(t) = k_f \displaystyle\int_{-\infty}^{t} m(\tau)\, d\tau \ll \frac{1}{2}\pi$ for all values of t are called *narrowband* FM signals. Find the equation and the frequency spectrum of a narrowband FM signal.

Answer: $A \cos \omega_c t - A \phi(t) \sin \omega_c t$,

$$\frac{A}{2}\left[\delta(\omega - \omega_c) + \delta(\omega + \omega_c)\right] - \frac{Ak_f}{2\omega}\left[M(\omega - \omega_c) - M(\omega + \omega_c)\right],$$

where $M(\omega) = \mathcal{F}[m(t)]$.

PROBLEM 7.47 Compare and contrast the narrowband FM signal with an ordinary AM signal. (Cf., Prob. 7.46.)

PROBLEM 7.48 Find the spectrum of the PAM signal (7.79) if $g(t)$ is the periodic symmetrical rectangular pulse shown in Fig. 7.15. This special PAM signal is also called a *chopped* signal.

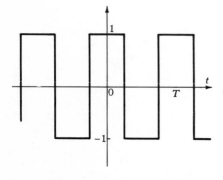

Fig. 7.15 The periodic symmetrical rectangular pulse of Prob. 7.48.

Answer: $\displaystyle\sum_{n=1}^{\infty} \frac{1}{2}\, a_{2n-1} \left[M\{\omega - (2n-1)\omega_0\} + M\{\omega + (2n-1)\omega_0\}\right]$, with

$$a_{2n-1} = \begin{cases} \dfrac{4}{(2n-1)\pi} & \text{for } (2n-1) = 1, 5, \cdots \\ \dfrac{-4}{(2n-1)\pi} & \text{for } (2n-1) = 3, 7, \cdots \end{cases}$$

(Cf., Prob. 2.13.)

PROBLEM 7.49 Show that the average autocorrelation function $\overline{R}_{11}(\tau)$ is an even function of τ.

PROBLEM 7.50 Show that the derivative of the average autocorrelation function of $f(t)$ is the negative of the average cross-correlation of $f(t)$ and df/dt; that is, $d\overline{R}_{ff}/d\tau = -\overline{R}_{f\,df/dt}$.

PROBLEM 7.51 Two periodic signals $f_1(t)$ and $f_2(t)$ with period T are said to be *uncorrelated* or *noncoherent* if for all τ,

$$\overline{R}_{12}(\tau) = \frac{1}{T}\int_{-T/2}^{T/2} f_1(t)\, f_2(t - \tau)\, dt = \frac{1}{T}\int_{-T/2}^{T/2} f_1(t)\, dt \times \frac{1}{T}\int_{-T/2}^{T/2} f_2(t)\, dt;$$

i.e., the average cross-correlation function of $f_1(t)$ and $f_2(t)$ is equal to the product of the average of $f_1(t)$ and $f_2(t)$ over one period.

Show that the mean-squared value of the sum of two periodic noncoherent signals is the sum of the mean-squared values of the two signals when the average value of each signal is zero.

PROBLEM 7.52 Show that the power density spectrum of a sinusoidal waveform $A \sin \omega_1 t$ (or $A \cos \omega_1 t$) is $P(\omega) = \frac{1}{4} A^2 [\delta(\omega - \omega_1) + \delta(\omega + \omega_1)]$.
[Hint: Use the result of Prob. 7.20.]

PROBLEM 7.53 Two signals $f_a(t)$ and $f_b(t)$ are applied to two systems, as shown in Fig. 7.16. The resultant outputs are $f_1(t)$ and $f_2(t)$. Express the average cross-correlation function $\overline{R}_{12}$ of $f_1(t)$ and $f_2(t)$ in terms of $\overline{R}_{ab}$, $h_1(t)$, and $h_2(t)$, where $h_1(t)$ and $h_2(t)$ are the respective unit impulse responses of the two systems.

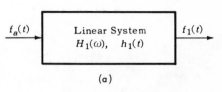
(a)

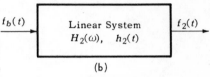
(b)

Fig. 7.16 The two systems of Prob. 7.53.

Answer: $\overline{R}_{12}(\tau) = \int_{-\infty}^{\infty} h_1(\lambda) \int_{-\infty}^{\infty} \overline{R}_{ab}(\tau + \sigma - \lambda) h_2(\sigma) \, d\sigma \, d\lambda$.

PROBLEM 7.54 If the *cross spectral density* $S_{12}(\omega)$ of two functions $f_1(t)$ and $f_2(t)$ is defined by $S_{12}(\omega) = \mathcal{F}[\overline{R}_{12}(\tau)]$, show that for the two systems of Prob. 7.53,

$$S_{12}(\omega) = H_1(\omega) H_2^*(\omega) S_{ab}(\omega),$$

where $S_{ab}(\omega)$ is the cross spectral density of $f_a(t)$ and $f_b(t)$, and $H_1(\omega)$ and $H_2(\omega)$ are the respective system functions of the two systems.

PROBLEM 7.55 Find the average autocorrelation function of the output of the low-pass network shown in Fig. 7.13 when the input has an average autocorrelation function of the form $\overline{R}_{xx}(\tau) = \frac{1}{2} \alpha K e^{-\alpha |\tau|}$.

Answer: $\overline{R}_{yy}(\tau) = \dfrac{b^2 \alpha K}{2(b^2 - \alpha^2)} \left[e^{-\alpha |\tau|} - \dfrac{\alpha}{b} e^{-b|\tau|} \right]$, where $b = \dfrac{1}{RC}$.

PROBLEM 7.56 The coefficient $\frac{1}{2} \alpha K$ of $\overline{R}_{xx}(\tau)$ of Prob. 7.55 has been chosen so that the input has a spectral density K at $\omega = 0$. Thus, at low frequencies the spectral density is the same as the white-noise spectrum. Show that when $\alpha \gg 1/RC = b$, the result of Prob. 7.55 approaches the white-noise result of (7.148).
[Hint: Rewrite $\overline{R}_{yy}(\tau)$ as

$$\overline{R}_{yy}(\tau) = \frac{bK}{2} e^{-b|\tau|} \left[\frac{1}{(1 - b^2/\alpha^2)} \left(1 - \frac{b}{\alpha} e^{-(\alpha - b)|\tau|} \right) \right].]$$

PROBLEM 7.57 Let $F(\omega) = R(\omega) + jX(\omega)$ be the Fourier transform of a real function $f(t)$, and let $\hat{F}(\omega)$ be the Fourier transform of $\hat{f}(t)$, where $\hat{f}(t)$ is defined by

$$\hat{f}(t) = \frac{1}{\pi} \int_0^{\infty} [X(\omega) \cos \omega t + R(\omega) \sin \omega t] \, d\omega.$$

Show that (a) the relationship between $\hat{f}(t)$ and $f(t)$ is

$$\hat{f}(t) = \frac{1}{\pi} \int_0^{\infty} \int_{-\infty}^{\infty} f(x) \sin \omega(t - x) \, dx \, d\omega;$$

(b) the relationship between $\hat{F}(\omega)$ and $F(\omega)$ is

$$\hat{F}(\omega) = -j \operatorname{sgn} \omega F(\omega).$$

[Hint: (a) Use (4.19-20); (b) substitute

$$R(\omega) = \frac{1}{2}[F(\omega) + F(-\omega)] \quad \text{and} \quad X(\omega) = \frac{1}{2j}[F(\omega) - F(-\omega)]$$

into the definition of $\hat{f}(t)$, and note that $\hat{f}(t) = \dfrac{1}{2\pi}\displaystyle\int_{-\infty}^{\infty} \hat{F}(\omega)\, e^{j\omega t}\, d\omega$. See Probs. 6.50 and 9.55.]

PROBLEM 7.58 The *analytic signal* $f_+(t)$ associated with the real signal $f(t)$ is defined by

$$f_+(t) = f(t) + j\hat{f}(t),$$

where $\hat{f}(t)$ is the signal defined in Prob. 7.57. Show that if $\mathcal{F}[f_+(t)] = F_+(\omega)$, then

$$F_+(\omega) = 2F(\omega)\,u(\omega) = \begin{cases} 2F(\omega), & \omega > 0 \\ \\ 0, & \omega < 0, \end{cases}$$

where $u(\omega)$ is the unit step function.

PROBLEM 7.59 Find the analytic signal associated with the signal $f(t) = \cos \omega t$.
[Hint: See Prob. 6.51.]

Answer: $f_+(t) = \cos \omega t + j \sin \omega t = e^{j\omega t}$.

PROBLEM 7.60 It is often convenient to represent an arbitrary real signal $f(t)$ as an amplitude- and angle-modulated sinusoid of the form $f(t) = A(t)\cos\theta(t)$, where $A(t)$ is called the *envelope function*, $\theta(t)$ the *phase function*, and $\omega_i = d\theta(t)/dt$ the *instantaneous frequency* of the signal $f(t)$. Let $\hat{f}(t)$ be the signal defined in Prob. 7.57. Then the envelope function $A(t)$ can be defined by

$$A(t) = \frac{f(t)}{\cos\{\tan^{-1}[\hat{f}(t)/f(t)]\}},$$

and the phase function $\theta(t)$ can be defined by

$$\theta(t) = \tan^{-1}[\hat{f}(t)/f(t)].$$

(a) Using the above definitions, express $f(t) = A \sin \omega t$, where A and ω are constant, in the form of an amplitude- and angle-modulated sinusoid.

Answer: $f(t) = A \cos\left(\omega t - \dfrac{\pi}{2}\right)$.

PROBLEM 7.61 Find the instantaneous frequency of the signal $f(t) = 1/(1 + t^2)$.
[Hint: See Prob. 6.51(b).]

Answer: $\omega_i = 1/(1 + t^2)$.

APPLICATIONS TO BOUNDARY - VALUE PROBLEMS

8 CHAPTER

8.1 Separation of Variables and Fourier Series

Many boundary-value problems in engineering mathematics can be solved conveniently by a method referred to as "separation of variables." We shall illustrate the essence of the method by means of particular examples.

PROBLEM 8.1 Consider the following equation governing small transverse vibrations of an elastic string which is stretched to length l and then fixed at the end points:

$$\frac{\partial^2 u(x,t)}{\partial x^2} - \frac{1}{c^2}\frac{\partial^2 u(x,t)}{\partial t^2} = 0, \tag{8.1}$$

where $u(x,t)$ is the deflection of the string, and $c^2 = T/\rho$, where ρ is the mass of the string per unit length, and T is the tension of the string. Equation (8.1) is known as the *one-dimensional wave equation*. The boundary conditions are

$$u(0,t) = 0 \quad \text{and} \quad u(l,t) = 0 \quad \text{for all } t. \tag{8.2}$$

The initial conditions are

$$u(x,0) = f(x), \quad \text{and} \quad \frac{\partial u(x,t)}{\partial t}\bigg|_{t=0} = \acute{g}(x). \tag{8.3}$$

Find the solution $u(x,t)$ of (8.1) satisfying the conditions (8.2) and (8.3).

Solution: First, assume that the solution $u(x,t)$ of (8.1) will be of the form

$$u(x,t) = X(x)\,T(t), \tag{8.4}$$

which is a product of two functions, each depending on only one of the variables x and t. By differentiating (8.4),

$$\frac{\partial^2 u(x,t)}{\partial x^2} = X''(x)\,T(t) \quad \text{and} \quad \frac{\partial^2 u(x,t)}{\partial t^2} = X(x)\,T''(t), \tag{8.5}$$

where primes denote differentiation with respect to the appropriate argument variable of each factor. By substituting (8.5) into (8.1),

$$X''(x)\,T(t) = \frac{1}{c^2}\,X(x)\,T''(t). \tag{8.6}$$

Dividing by $X(x)\,T(t)$, thus separating the variables one to each side of the equation,

$$\frac{X''(x)}{X(x)} = \frac{T''(t)}{c^2 T(t)}.$$

(8.7)

Now, the left side of (8.7) is independent of t, and so therefore is the right side. The right side is independent of x, and thus the left side must be also. Hence, the expressions on the left and right side of (8.7) must be equal to a constant, independent of both x and t. Thus,

$$\frac{X''(x)}{X(x)} = \frac{T''(t)}{c^2 T(t)} = -k^2.$$

(8.8)

The constant, which is denoted by $-k^2$, is called the *separation constant*. Equation (8.8) yields the two ordinary linear differential equations

$$X''(x) + k^2 X(x) = 0,$$

(8.9)

$$T''(t) + c^2 k^2 T(t) = 0.$$

(8.10)

We next determine solutions $X(x)$ and $T(t)$ of (8.9) and (8.10) so that $u(x, t) = X(x) T(t)$ satisfies the conditions (8.2) and (8.3). The general solutions of (8.9) and (8.10) are

$$X(x) = A \cos kx + B \sin kx,$$

(8.11)

$$T(t) = C \cos kct + D \sin kct.$$

(8.12)

From the boundary conditions (8.2),

$$u(0, t) = X(0) T(t) = 0.$$

Here we have a product of two terms which equals zero. Since $T(t)$ is not identically zero, $X(0)$ must be equal to zero. Similarly the second condition

$$u(l, t) = X(l) T(t) = 0$$

implies that $X(l) = 0$.

From $X(0) = 0$, we conclude that

$$X(0) = A \cos 0 + B \sin 0 = A = 0;$$

(8.13)

hence,

$$X(x) = B \sin kx.$$

From the second condition,

$$X(l) = B \sin kl = 0.$$

But if $B = 0$, $X(x) = 0$ and hence $u(x, t) = 0$. This contradicts the initial conditions (8.3) that $u(x, 0) = f(x) \neq 0$. We therefore conclude that

$$\sin kl = 0,$$

from which

$$kl = n\pi \quad \text{or} \quad k = \frac{n\pi}{l}, \quad n = 1, 2, \cdots.$$

(8.14)

Thus we obtain an infinite set of solutions $X(x) = X_n(x)$, where

$$X_n(x) = B_n \sin \frac{n\pi x}{l}, \quad n = 1, 2, \cdots.$$

(8.15)

The solution (8.12) now becomes

$$T_n(t) = C_n \cos \frac{cn\pi}{l} t + D_n \sin \frac{cn\pi}{l} t.$$

(8.16)

Hence the functions

$$u_n(x, t) = X_n(x)\, T_n(t) = \sin \frac{n\pi x}{l} \left(E_n \cos \frac{cn\pi}{l} t + F_n \sin \frac{cn\pi}{l} t \right) \qquad (8.17)$$

are the solutions of (8.1), satisfying the boundary conditions (8.2). In (8.17) the coefficients E_n and F_n are as yet undetermined. Note that $B_n C_n = E_n$ and $B_n D_n = F_n$.

Clearly, a single solution $u_n(x, t)$ of (8.17) in general will not satisfy the initial conditions (8.3). As (8.1) is linear, we consider the infinite series

$$u(x, t) = \sum_{n=1}^{\infty} u_n(x, t) = \sum_{n=1}^{\infty} \sin \frac{n\pi x}{l} \left(E_n \cos \frac{cn\pi}{l} t + F_n \sin \frac{cn\pi}{l} t \right). \qquad (8.18)$$

Now let us require that (8.18) satisfy the initial conditions (8.3). Hence we find that the coefficients E_n and F_n must satisfy the equations

$$u(x, 0) = \sum_{n=1}^{\infty} E_n \sin \frac{n\pi x}{l} = f(x), \qquad (8.19)$$

$$\left. \frac{\partial u(x, t)}{\partial t} \right|_{t=0} = \sum_{n=1}^{\infty} F_n \frac{cn\pi}{l} \sin \frac{n\pi x}{l} = g(x). \qquad (8.20)$$

Equation (8.19) shows that the coefficients E_n must be chosen such that $u(x, 0)$ becomes the Fourier sine series of $f(x)$ (see Sec. 2.3); i.e.,

$$E_n = \frac{2}{l} \int_0^l f(x) \sin \frac{n\pi x}{l}\, dx, \quad n = 1, 2, \cdots . \qquad (8.21)$$

Similarly (8.20) indicates that the coefficients F_n must be chosen such that $\partial u(x, t)/\partial t \big|_{t=0}$ becomes the Fourier sine series of $g(x)$; i.e.,

$$F_n \frac{cn\pi}{l} = \frac{2}{l} \int_0^l g(x) \sin \frac{n\pi x}{l}\, dx \qquad (8.22)$$

or

$$F_n = \frac{2}{cn\pi} \int_0^l g(x) \sin \frac{n\pi x}{l}\, dx, \quad n = 1, 2, \cdots . \qquad (8.23)$$

Hence with the coefficients E_n and F_n given by (8.21) and (8.23), (8.18) is the desired solution.

PROBLEM 8.2 Find the solution of (8.1) with the same boundary conditions as (8.2) but with the triangular initial deflection (Fig. 8.1) and zero initial velocity; i.e.,

$$u(x, 0) = f(x) = \begin{cases} \dfrac{2k}{l}\, x & \text{for } 0 < x < \dfrac{1}{2}\, l \\[2mm] \dfrac{2k}{l}\, (l - x) & \text{for } \dfrac{1}{2}\, l < x < l, \end{cases} \qquad (8.24)$$

$$\left. \frac{\partial u(x, t)}{\partial t} \right|_{t=0} = g(x) = 0. \qquad (8.25)$$

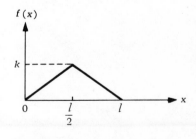

Fig. 8.1 Triangular initial deflection.

Solution: Since $g(x) = 0$, from (8.23), $F_n = 0$. From the result of Prob. 2.19, we see that the coefficients E_n of (8.21) are given by (2.63); i.e.,

$$E_n = \frac{8k}{n^2 \pi^2} \sin \frac{n\pi}{2} .$$

Hence the Fourier sine series of $f(x)$ is given by (2.64); i.e.,

$$u(x, 0) = \frac{8k}{\pi^2} \left(\sin \frac{\pi x}{l} - \frac{1}{3^2} \sin \frac{3 \pi x}{l} + \frac{1}{5^2} \sin \frac{5 \pi x}{l} - \cdots \right).$$

Thus, from (8.18),

$$u(x, t) = \frac{8k}{\pi^2} \left(\sin \frac{\pi x}{l} \cos \frac{c \pi t}{l} - \frac{1}{3^2} \sin \frac{3 \pi x}{l} \cos \frac{3c \pi t}{l} + \cdots \right). \tag{8.26}$$

PROBLEM 8.3 In Prob. 8.1, if $u(x, 0) = f(x)$ but $\partial u(x, t)/\partial t \big|_{t=0} = g(x) = 0$, show that the solution of (8.1) can be expressed as

$$u(x, t) = \frac{1}{2} f_1(x - ct) + \frac{1}{2} f_1(x + ct), \tag{8.27}$$

where $f_1(x)$ is the odd periodic extension of $f(x)$ with the period $2l$. Also give the physical interpretation of (8.27).

Solution: The general solution of (8.1) is given by (8.18); i.e.,

$$u(x, t) = \sum_{n=1}^{\infty} \sin \frac{n \pi x}{l} \left(E_n \cos \frac{cn \pi t}{l} + F_n \sin \frac{cn \pi t}{l} \right). \tag{8.18}$$

Since the initial velocity $g(x)$ is identically zero, from (8.22) the coefficients F_n are zero, and (8.18) reduces to

$$u(x, t) = \sum_{n=1}^{\infty} E_n \sin \frac{n \pi x}{l} \cos \frac{cn \pi t}{l}. \tag{8.28}$$

Using the trigonometric identity

$$\sin A \cos B = \frac{1}{2} \left[\sin (A - B) + \sin (A + B) \right],$$

it follows that

$$\sin \frac{n \pi x}{l} \cos \frac{cn \pi t}{l} = \frac{1}{2} \left[\sin \frac{n \pi}{l} (x - ct) + \sin \frac{n \pi}{l} (x + ct) \right].$$

Hence, we can rewrite (8.28) in the form

$$u(x, t) = \frac{1}{2} \sum_{n=1}^{\infty} E_n \sin \frac{n \pi}{l} (x - ct) + \frac{1}{2} \sum_{n=1}^{\infty} E_n \sin \frac{n \pi}{l} (x + ct). \tag{8.29}$$

Comparing with (8.19), we conclude that the above two series are those obtained by substituting $(x - ct)$ and $(x + ct)$, respectively, for the variable x in the Fourier sine series (8.19) for $f(x)$. Therefore,

$$u(x, t) = \frac{1}{2} f_1(x - ct) + \frac{1}{2} f_1(x + ct),$$

where $f_1(x)$ is the odd periodic extension of $f(x)$ with the period $2l$ shown in Fig. 8.2.

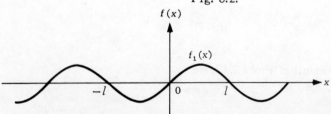

Fig. 8.2 Periodic extension of $f(x)$ of Prob. 8.3.

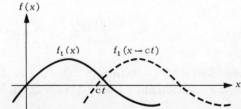

Fig. 8.3 Graph of $f_1(x)$ and $f_1(x - ct)$ of Prob. 8.3.

Now, the graph of $f_1(x - ct)$ is obtained from the graph of $f_1(x)$ by shifting ct units to the right (Fig. 8.3). Also we recognize that we may stay on a particular reference value of the function by keeping the argument, $x - ct$, a constant, i.e., by moving in the positive x direction with velocity c as time increases. This means that $f_1(x - ct)$, $(c > 0)$, represents a wave which is travelling to the right as t increases. Similarly, $f_1(x + ct)$ represents a wave which is travelling to the left with velocity c. Hence the solution $u(x, t)$ is the superposition of these two waves.

PROBLEM 8.4 In stationary heat flow or electrostatic potential problems in a plane, taken as the xy-plane, the temperature distribution function or the electrostatic potential function $u(x, y)$ in a source free region, satisfies the following equation in two-dimensional space:

$$\frac{\partial^2 u(x, y)}{\partial x^2} + \frac{\partial^2 u(x, y)}{\partial y^2} = 0. \tag{8.30}$$

This is known as *Laplace's equation*.

Find the solution of (8.30) with the following boundary conditions:

$$u(x, y) = 0 \quad \text{at} \quad x = 0, \ y = 0, \ \text{and} \ y = b; \tag{8.31}$$

$$u(x, y) = U_o \quad \text{at} \quad x = d, \ \text{and} \ 0 < y < b. \tag{8.32}$$

Solution: Assume that the solution of (8.30) is of the form

$$u(x, y) = X(x) Y(y), \tag{8.33}$$

where $X(x)$ is a function of x only, and $Y(y)$ a function of y only. By substituting (8.33) into (8.30),

$$X''(x) Y(y) + X(x) Y''(y) = 0. \tag{8.34}$$

Dividing by $X(x) Y(y)$, thus separating the variables,

$$\frac{X''(x)}{X(x)} + \frac{Y''(y)}{Y(y)} = 0 \tag{8.35}$$

or

$$\frac{X''(x)}{X(x)} = -\frac{Y''(y)}{Y(y)}. \tag{8.36}$$

Now, the left side of (8.36) is independent of y, and therefore, so is the right side. The right side is independent of x and thus the left side must be also. This means that the expressions on the left and right sides of (8.36) must be independent of both x and y and equal to a constant. Let this separation constant be denoted by k^2; then,

$$\frac{X''(x)}{X(x)} = -\frac{Y''(y)}{Y(y)} = k^2. \tag{8.37}$$

The sign of the separation constant was chosen in such a way that the boundary conditions could be satisfied. Equation (8.37) yields the two ordinary linear differential equations

$$X''(x) - k^2 X(x) = 0, \tag{8.38}$$

$$Y''(y) + k^2 Y(y) = 0. \tag{8.39}$$

The general solutions of (8.38) and (8.39) are

$$X(x) = A \, e^{kx} + B \, e^{-kx}, \tag{8.40}$$

$$Y(y) = C \cos ky + D \sin ky. \tag{8.41}$$

From the boundary conditions (8.31),

$$X(0) = A + B = 0,$$

$$Y(0) = C = 0, \qquad Y(b) = D \sin kb = 0.$$

Hence,

$$A = -B, \tag{8.42}$$

$$\sin kb = 0,$$

from which

$$kb = n\pi \qquad \text{or} \qquad k = \frac{n\pi}{b}, \quad n = 1, 2, \cdots . \tag{8.43}$$

Thus we obtain an infinite set of solutions $Y(y) = Y_n(y)$, where

$$Y_n(y) = D_n \sin \frac{n\pi y}{b}, \quad n = 1, 2, \cdots . \tag{8.44}$$

The corresponding general solutions (8.40) now become

$$X_n(x) = A_n(e^{kx} - e^{-kx}) = 2A_n \sinh kx$$

$$= 2A_n \sinh \frac{n\pi x}{b}, \quad n = 1, 2, \cdots . \tag{8.45}$$

Hence the functions

$$u_n(x, y) = X_n(x)Y_n(y) = E_n \sinh \frac{n\pi x}{b} \sin \frac{n\pi y}{b}, \quad n = 1, 2, \cdots , \tag{8.46}$$

are the solutions of (8.30) satisfying the boundary conditions (8.31).   Note that $2A_n D_n$ was replaced by the new arbitrary constant E_n.

Clearly, a single solution $u_n(x, y)$ of (8.46) will not satisfy the other boundary condition of (8.32). Since (8.30) is linear, we consider the infinite series

$$u(x, y) = \sum_{n=1}^{\infty} u_n(x, y) = \sum_{n=1}^{\infty} E_n \sinh \frac{n\pi x}{b} \sin \frac{n\pi y}{b}. \tag{8.47}$$

Applying the boundary condition of (8.32),

$$u(d, y) = U_o = \sum_{n=1}^{\infty} E_n \sinh \frac{n\pi d}{b} \sin \frac{n\pi y}{b}$$

$$= \sum_{n=1}^{\infty} c_n \sin \frac{n\pi y}{b}, \quad 0 < y < b, \tag{8.48}$$

where

$$c_n = E_n \sinh \frac{n\pi d}{b}.$$

Equation (8.48) is a Fourier sine series and the coefficients c_n may be determined as [see (2.51)]

$$c_n = \frac{2}{b} \int_0^b U_o \sin \frac{n\pi y}{b} \, dy = \frac{2U_o}{n\pi} (1 - \cos n\pi) = \begin{cases} \dfrac{4U_o}{n\pi}, & n = 1, 3, \cdots \\ 0, & n = 2, 4, \cdots . \end{cases}$$

However,

$$c_n = E_n \sinh \frac{n\pi d}{b},$$

and therefore,

$$E_n = \frac{4U_o}{n\pi \sinh\left(\dfrac{n\pi d}{b}\right)}, \qquad n = 1, 3, 5, \cdots, \tag{8.49}$$

which may be substituted into (8.47) to give the desired solution:

$$u(x,y) = \frac{4U_o}{\pi} \sum_{n=\text{odd}}^{\infty} \frac{1}{n} \frac{\sinh\left(\dfrac{n\pi x}{b}\right)}{\sinh\left(\dfrac{n\pi d}{b}\right)} \sin \frac{n\pi y}{b}. \tag{8.50}$$

In this section we have obtained formal solutions of certain linear second-order partial differential equations that satisfy given boundary and initial conditions, but we have not shown that any of the solutions are unique. Since the proof of uniqueness is quite involved and unfortunately no general uniqueness theorem exists, we shall not prove the uniqueness of the solutions obtained in either this section or in those to follow.

8.2 Vibration

The vibration of a string and its governing equation, the one-dimensional wave equation, have been discussed in Prob. 8.1. In the following, we shall apply the Fourier analysis technique to the various problems of vibration.

PROBLEM 8.5 The governing equation for the small transversal vibration of a membrane is given by

$$\left(\frac{\partial^2 u}{\partial x^2} + \frac{\partial^2 u}{\partial y^2}\right) - \frac{1}{c^2} \frac{\partial^2 u}{\partial t^2} = 0, \tag{8.51}$$

where $u(x,y,t)$ is the deflection of the membrane, and $c^2 = T/\rho$, where ρ is the mass of the membrane per unit area, and T is the tension of the membrane. Equation (8.51) is called the *two-dimensional wave equation*. Consider the rectangular membrane of Fig. 8.4 and find the solution of (8.51) that satisfies the following boundary condition:

$$u(x,y,t) = 0 \quad \text{on the boundary of the membrane for all } t;$$

that is

$$u(x,y,t) = 0 \quad \text{for } x = 0, \quad x = a, \quad y = 0, \quad \text{and} \quad y = b. \tag{8.52}$$

The initial conditions are

$$u(x,y,0) = f(x,y), \tag{8.53}$$

$$\left.\frac{\partial u(x,y,t)}{\partial t}\right|_{t=0} = g(x,y), \tag{8.54}$$

where $f(x,y)$ and $g(x,y)$ are the given initial displacement and initial velocity of the membrane, respectively.

Solution: Assume that the solution of (8.51) is of the form

$$u(x,y,t) = X(x)Y(y)T(t). \tag{8.55}$$

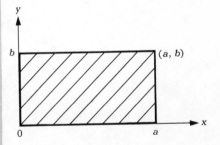

Fig. 8.4 A rectangular membrane.

By substituting (8.55) into (8.51),

$$X''(x)\,Y(y)\,T(t) + X(x)\,Y''(y)\,T(t) - \frac{1}{c^2}\,X(x)\,Y(y)\,T''(t) = 0, \qquad (8.56)$$

where primes denote differentiation with respect to the arguments of each function. Dividing through by $X(x)\,Y(y)\,T(t)$ and separating the variables,

$$\frac{X''(x)}{X(x)} + \frac{Y''(y)}{Y(y)} = \frac{1}{c^2}\,\frac{T''(t)}{T(t)}. \qquad (8.57)$$

Since the right side of (8.57) depends only on t while the left side does not depend on t, the expressions on both sides must be equal to a constant. Denoting this constant by $-k^2$,

$$\frac{X''(x)}{X(x)} + \frac{Y''(y)}{Y(y)} = \frac{1}{c^2}\,\frac{T''(t)}{T(t)} = -k^2.$$

This yields the two differential equations

$$T''(t) + c^2 k^2 T(t) = 0, \qquad (8.58)$$

$$\frac{X''(x)}{X(x)} + \frac{Y''(y)}{Y(y)} = -k^2,$$

or

$$\frac{X''(x)}{X(x)} = -k^2 - \frac{Y''(y)}{Y(y)}. \qquad (8.59)$$

Again, since the left side of (8.59) depends only on x while the right side depends only on y, the expressions on both sides must be equal to a constant. This constant must be negative (otherwise the boundary conditions could not be satisfied), say $-k_x^2$. Then,

$$\frac{X''(x)}{X(x)} = -k^2 - \frac{Y''(y)}{Y(y)} = -k_x^2.$$

This yields the following differential equations:

$$X''(x) + k_x^2 X(x) = 0, \qquad (8.60)$$

$$Y''(y) + k_y^2 Y(y) = 0, \qquad (8.61)$$

where

$$k_y^2 = k^2 - k_x^2 \quad \text{or} \quad k_x^2 + k_y^2 = k^2. \qquad (8.62)$$

The general solutions of (8.58), (8.60), and (8.61) have the forms

$$X(x) = A \cos k_x x + B \sin k_x x, \qquad (8.63)$$

$$Y(y) = C \cos k_y y + D \sin k_y y, \qquad (8.64)$$

$$T(t) = E \cos kct + F \sin kct. \qquad (8.65)$$

From the boundary condition (8.52),

$$X(0) = 0, \qquad X(a) = 0, \qquad Y(0) = 0, \qquad Y(b) = 0.$$

Therefore,

$$X(0) = A = 0, \qquad X(a) = B \sin k_x a = 0,$$

from which

$$k_x a = m\pi \quad \text{or} \quad k_x = \frac{m\pi}{a} \quad (m = 1, 2, \cdots). \qquad (8.66)$$

Similarly, $Y(0) = C = 0$ and $Y(b) = D \sin k_y b = 0$; hence,

$$k_y b = n\pi \qquad \text{or} \qquad k_y = \frac{n\pi}{b}, \qquad n = 1, 2, \cdots . \qquad (8.67)$$

In this way we obtain the solutions

$$X_m(x) = B_m \sin \frac{m\pi x}{a}, \qquad m = 1, 2, \cdots ,$$

$$Y_n(y) = D_n \sin \frac{n\pi y}{b}, \qquad n = 1, 2, \cdots .$$

Since $k^2 = k_x^2 + k_y^2$,

$$k^2 = k_{mn}^2 = \frac{m^2 \pi^2}{a^2} + \frac{n^2 \pi^2}{b^2} \qquad (8.68)$$

and the corresponding general solution of (8.58) is

$$T_{mn}(t) = E_{mn} \cos k_{mn} ct + F_{mn} \sin k_{mn} ct.$$

It follows that the functions

$$u_{mn}(x, y, t) = X_m(x) Y_n(y) T_{mn}(t)$$

$$= (G_{mn} \cos k_{mn} ct + H_{mn} \sin k_{mn} ct) \sin \frac{m\pi x}{a} \sin \frac{n\pi y}{b}, \quad (8.69)$$

where $m = 1, 2, \cdots$, $n = 1, 2, \cdots$, and with k_{mn} given by (8.68), are solutions of the wave equation (8.51). These are zero on the boundary of the rectangular membrane in Fig. 8.4. We must now evaluate the arbitrary constants G_{mn} and H_{mn}.

To obtain the solution which also satisfies the initial conditions (8.53) and (8.54), we proceed in a manner similar to that used in Prob. 8.1.

Consider the following double series

$$u(x, y, t) = \sum_{m=1}^{\infty} \sum_{n=1}^{\infty} u_{mn}(x, y, t)$$

$$= \sum_{m=1}^{\infty} \sum_{n=1}^{\infty} (G_{mn} \cos k_{mn} ct + H_{mn} \sin k_{mn} ct) \sin \frac{m\pi x}{a} \sin \frac{n\pi y}{b}. \quad (8.70)$$

From (8.70) and (8.53),

$$u(x, y, 0) = f(x, y) = \sum_{m=1}^{\infty} \sum_{n=1}^{\infty} G_{mn} \sin \frac{m\pi x}{a} \sin \frac{n\pi y}{b}. \qquad (8.71)$$

The series (8.71) is called the *double Fourier series* representing $f(x, y)$ in the region $0 < x < a$ and $0 < y < b$. The Fourier coefficients G_{mn} of $f(x, y)$ in (8.71) can be determined as follows:

Setting

$$J_m(y) = \sum_{n=1}^{\infty} G_{mn} \sin \frac{n\pi y}{b}, \qquad (8.72)$$

we may write (8.71) in the form

$$f(x, y) = \sum_{m=1}^{\infty} J_m(y) \sin \frac{m\pi x}{a}. \qquad (8.73)$$

For fixed y, (8.73) is the Fourier sine series of $f(x, y)$, and is considered as a function of x. It follows from (2.52) that the coefficients of this expansion are given by

$$J_m(y) = \frac{2}{a} \int_0^a f(x, y) \sin \frac{m \pi x}{a} \, dx. \tag{8.74}$$

Now, (8.72) is the Fourier sine series of $J_m(y)$ and hence the coefficients G_{mn} are given by

$$G_{mn} = \frac{2}{b} \int_0^b J_m(y) \sin \frac{n \pi y}{b} \, dy. \tag{8.75}$$

Substituting (8.74) into (8.75),

$$G_{mn} = \frac{4}{ab} \int_0^b \int_0^a f(x, y) \sin \frac{m \pi x}{a} \sin \frac{n \pi y}{b} \, dx \, dy, \tag{8.76}$$

where $m = 1, 2, \cdots, \ n = 1, 2, \cdots$.

To determine the H_{mn} of (8.70), we differentiate (8.70) term-by-term with respect to t, and using (8.54),

$$\frac{\partial u}{\partial t} \bigg|_{t=0} = g(x, y)$$

$$= \sum_{m=1}^{\infty} \sum_{n=1}^{\infty} H_{mn} \, ck_{mn} \sin \frac{m \pi x}{a} \sin \frac{n \pi y}{b}. \tag{8.77}$$

Proceeding as before,

$$H_{mn} = \frac{4}{ab \, ck_{mn}} \int_0^b \int_0^a g(x, y) \sin \frac{m \pi x}{a} \sin \frac{n \pi y}{b} \, dx \, dy, \tag{8.78}$$

where $m = 1, 2, \cdots, \ n = 1, 2, \cdots$.

Hence (8.70) with the coefficients given by (8.76) and (8.78) is the desired solution.

PROBLEM 8.6 Find the solution of (8.51) with the following boundary and initial conditions:

$$u(x, y, t) = 0 \text{ for } x = 0, \quad x = a, \quad y = 0, \text{ and } y = b,$$

$$u(x, y, 0) = xy(x - a)(y - b),$$

$$\frac{\partial u}{\partial t} \bigg|_{t=0} = 0.$$

Solution: From (8.70),

$$u(x, y, t) = \sum_{m=1}^{\infty} \sum_{n=1}^{\infty} (G_{mn} \cos k_{mn} ct + H_{mn} \sin k_{mn} ct) \sin \frac{m \pi x}{a} \sin \frac{n \pi y}{b}.$$

Letting $t = 0$,

$$u(x, y, 0) = \sum_{m=1}^{\infty} \sum_{n=1}^{\infty} G_{mn} \sin \frac{m \pi x}{a} \sin \frac{n \pi y}{b}.$$

According to (8.76),

$$G_{mn} = \frac{4}{ab} \int_0^b \int_0^a u(x,y,0) \sin \frac{m\pi x}{a} \sin \frac{n\pi y}{b} \, dx \, dy$$

$$= \frac{4}{ab} \int_0^a x(x-a) \sin \frac{m\pi x}{a} \, dx \int_0^b y(y-b) \sin \frac{n\pi y}{b} \, dy$$

$$= \frac{4}{ab} \frac{2a^3}{m^3 \pi^3} [(-1)^m - 1] \frac{2b^3}{n^3 \pi^3} [(-1)^n - 1]$$

$$= \begin{cases} \dfrac{64 a^2 b^2}{\pi^6 m^3 n^3} & \text{if } n \text{ and } m \text{ are odd} \\ 0 & \text{otherwise.} \end{cases}$$

Since $\partial u/\partial t\big|_{t=0} = 0$ and according to (8.78), $H_{mn} = 0$, the final solution is

$$u(x,y,t) = \frac{64 a^2 b^2}{\pi^6} \sum_{m=\text{odd}}^{\infty} \sum_{n=\text{odd}}^{\infty} \frac{1}{m^3 n^3} \cos k_{mn} ct \sin \frac{m\pi x}{a} \sin \frac{n\pi y}{b}, \quad (8.79)$$

where $k_{mn}^2 = (m\pi/a)^2 + (n\pi/b)^2$.

PROBLEM 8.7 The small free transverse vibrations of a uniform cantilever beam lying along the x-axis are governed by the fourth-order equation

$$\frac{\partial^4 u(x,t)}{\partial x^4} + \frac{1}{c^2} \frac{\partial^2 u(x,t)}{\partial t^2} = 0, \quad (8.80)$$

where $c^2 = EI/(\rho A)$, E = Young's modulus of elasticity, I = moment of inertia of the cross-section, ρ = density, A = cross-sectional area. Find the solution of (8.80) that satisfies the following conditions:

$$u(0,t) = 0, \quad u(l,t) = 0, \quad (8.81)$$

$$\frac{\partial^2 u}{\partial x^2}\bigg|_{x=0} = \frac{\partial^2 u}{\partial x^2}\bigg|_{x=l} = 0, \quad (8.82)$$

$$u(x,0) = x(l-x), \quad (8.83)$$

$$\frac{\partial u}{\partial t}\bigg|_{t=0} = 0. \quad (8.84)$$

Solution: Assume that the solution of (8.80) will be of the form

$$u(x,t) = X(x)T(t). \quad (8.85)$$

Substituting (8.85) into (8.80),

$$X^{(4)}(x) T(t) + \frac{1}{c^2} X(x) T''(t) = 0.$$

Dividing by $X(x)T(t)$ and separating the variables,

$$\frac{X^{(4)}(x)}{X(x)} = -\frac{1}{c^2} \frac{T''(t)}{T(t)}. \quad (8.86)$$

Since the left side of (8.86) depends on only x and the right side depends on only t, the expressions on both sides must be equal to a constant. The constant, say k^4, must be positive from physical considerations; namely, to make $T(t)$ oscillatory. Thus we obtain the two ordinary differential equations

$$X^{(4)}(x) - k^4 X(x) = 0, \tag{8.87}$$

$$T''(t) + c^2 k^4 T(t) = 0. \tag{8.88}$$

The general solutions of (8.87) and (8.88) are

$$X(x) = A \cos kx + B \sin kx + C \cosh kx + D \sinh kx, \tag{8.89}$$

$$T(t) = E \cos k^2 ct + F \sin k^2 ct. \tag{8.90}$$

Now, from the boundary conditions (8.81),

$$X(0) = A + C = 0, \tag{8.91}$$

$$X(l) = A \cos kl + B \sin kl + C \cosh kl + D \sinh kl = 0. \tag{8.92}$$

Since

$$X''(x) = -k^2 (A \cos kx + B \sin kx - C \cosh kx - D \sinh kx),$$

using the boundary conditions (8.82),

$$X''(0) = -k^2 (A - C) = 0, \tag{8.93}$$

$$X''(l) = -k^2 (A \cos kl + B \sin kl - C \cosh kl - D \sinh kl) = 0. \tag{8.94}$$

From (8.91) and (8.93), $A + C = 0$, $A - C = 0$ and hence $A = C = 0$. Then from (8.92) and (8.94),

$$B \sin kl + D \sinh kl = 0,$$

$$B \sin kl - D \sinh kl = 0,$$

and hence,

$$B \sin kl = 0, \qquad D \sinh kl = 0.$$

The second condition gives $D = 0$ since if $\sinh kl = 0$, then $k = 0$ and hence $X(x) = 0$, which would give a trivial solution. Then from the first condition,

$$\sin kl = 0,$$

that is,

$$kl = n\pi \qquad \text{or} \qquad k = \frac{n\pi}{l}, \quad n = 1, 2, \cdots. \tag{8.95}$$

Thus we obtain the infinite set of solutions $X(x) = X_n(x)$; i.e.,

$$X_n(x) = B_n \sin \frac{n\pi x}{l}, \quad n = 1, 2, \cdots. \tag{8.96}$$

Next, since

$$T'(t) = k^2 c (-E \sin k^2 ct + F \cos k^2 ct),$$

from the initial condition (8.84),

$$T'(0) = k^2 c \, F = 0.$$

Hence $F = 0$, and the corresponding solutions $T_n(t)$ become

$$T_n(t) = E_n \cos \frac{n^2 \pi^2 ct}{l^2}. \tag{8.97}$$

Therefore the functions

$$u_n(x, t) = X_n(x) T_n(t) = b_n \sin \frac{n\pi x}{l} \cos \frac{n^2 \pi^2 ct}{l^2}, \tag{8.98}$$

where $b_n = B_n E_n$, are the solutions of (8.80), satisfying the boundary conditions (8.81), (8.82) and the zero initial velocity condition (8.84).

In order to satisfy the initial condition (8.83), we consider

$$u(x, t) = \sum_{n=1}^{\infty} u_n(x, t)$$

$$= \sum_{n=1}^{\infty} b_n \sin \frac{n \pi x}{l} \cos \frac{n^2 \pi^2 ct}{l^2}. \tag{8.99}$$

Hence from (8.83),

$$u(x, 0) = x(l - x) = \sum_{n=1}^{\infty} b_n \sin \frac{n \pi x}{l}. \tag{8.100}$$

Thus the b_n are the sine Fourier coefficients of $x(l - x)$ and are given as

$$b_n = \frac{2}{l} \int_0^l x(l - x) \sin \frac{n \pi x}{l} \, dx$$

$$= \begin{cases} \dfrac{8\,l^2}{n^3 \pi^3} & \text{for } n \text{ odd} \\[2ex] 0 & \text{for } n \text{ even.} \end{cases} \tag{8.101}$$

The final solution is therefore,

$$u(x, t) = \frac{8\,l^2}{\pi^3} \sum_{n=\text{odd}}^{\infty} \frac{1}{n^3} \sin \frac{n \pi x}{l} \cos \frac{n^2 \pi^2 ct}{l^2}. \tag{8.102}$$

In the following example, we shall consider the vibration of an infinite string. In this case we do not have boundary conditions but only the initial conditions.

PROBLEM 8.8 Determine the displacement $u(x, t)$ of an infinite string with zero initial velocity. The initial displacement is given by $f(x)$ for $-\infty < x < \infty$.

Solution: The function $u(x, t)$ satisfies the one-dimensional wave equation

$$\frac{\partial^2 u(x, t)}{\partial x^2} - \frac{1}{c^2} \frac{\partial^2 u(x, t)}{\partial t^2} = 0, \tag{8.1}$$

and the initial conditions

$$u(x, 0) = f(x), \quad -\infty < x < \infty, \tag{8.103}$$

$$\left. \frac{\partial u(x, t)}{\partial t} \right|_{t=0} = 0. \tag{8.104}$$

Proceeding as in Prob. 8.1, we substitute

$$u(x, t) = X(x)\,T(t)$$

into (8.1). This yields two ordinary differential equations

$$X''(x) + k^2 X(x) = 0, \tag{8.105}$$

$$T''(t) + c^2 k^2 T(t) = 0. \tag{8.106}$$

The functions

$$X(x) = A \cos kx + B \sin kx,$$

$$T(t) = C \cos kct + D \sin kct$$

are solutions of (8.105) and (8.106), respectively.

By using the initial condition (8.104),

$$T'(0) = kc\,D = 0.$$

Hence $D = 0$, and

$$u(x, t; k) = (F\cos kx + G\sin kx)\cos kct \qquad (8.107)$$

is a solution of (8.1) satisfying (8.104).

Any series of functions (8.107), found in the usual manner by taking k as multiples of a fixed number, would lead to a function which is periodic in x when $t = 0$. However, since $f(x)$ in (8.103) is not assumed periodic, it is natural to use the Fourier integral in the present case instead of Fourier series.

Since F and G in (8.107) are arbitrary, we may consider them as functions of k and write $F = F(k)$ and $G = G(k)$. Since the wave equation (8.1) is linear and homogeneous, the function

$$u(x, t) = \int_0^\infty u(x, t; k)\, dk = \int_0^\infty [F(k)\cos kx + G(k)\sin kx]\cos kct\, dk \qquad (8.108)$$

is also a solution of (8.1).

From (8.103),

$$u(x, 0) = f(x) = \int_0^\infty [F(k)\cos kx + G(k)\sin kx]\, dk. \qquad (8.109)$$

Now, from the Fourier's integral theorem

$$f(t) = \frac{1}{\pi}\int_0^\infty \left[\int_{-\infty}^\infty f(x)\cos \omega(t-x)\, dx\right] d\omega, \qquad [4.12]$$

we may write

$$f(x) = \frac{1}{\pi}\int_0^\infty \left[\int_{-\infty}^\infty f(y)\cos k(x-y)\, dy\right] dk \qquad (8.110)$$

$$= \frac{1}{\pi}\int_0^\infty \left[\int_{-\infty}^\infty f(y)(\cos kx\cos ky + \sin kx\sin ky)\, dy\right] dk$$

$$= \frac{1}{\pi}\int_0^\infty \left[\cos kx\int_{-\infty}^\infty f(y)\cos ky\, dy + \sin kx\int_{-\infty}^\infty f(y)\sin ky\, dy\right] dk. \qquad (8.111)$$

If we set

$$F(k) = \frac{1}{\pi}\int_{-\infty}^\infty f(y)\cos ky\, dy, \qquad G(k) = \frac{1}{\pi}\int_{-\infty}^\infty f(y)\sin ky\, dy,$$

then (8.111) can be written in the form

$$f(x) = \int_0^\infty [F(k)\cos kx + G(k)\sin kx]\, dk. \qquad (8.112)$$

Comparing (8.112) and (8.109), we may write (8.109) as

$$u(x, 0) = f(x) = \frac{1}{\pi}\int_0^\infty \left[\int_{-\infty}^\infty f(y)\cos k(x-y)\, dy\right] dk. \qquad (8.113)$$

Then from (8.108),

$$u(x, t) = \frac{1}{\pi}\int_0^\infty \left[\int_{-\infty}^\infty f(y)\cos k(x-y)\cos kct\, dy\right] dk. \qquad (8.114)$$

By use of the trigonometric identity

$$\cos k(x-y)\cos kct = \frac{1}{2}[\cos k(x+ct-y)+\cos k(x-ct-y)],$$

(8.114) becomes

$$u(x,t) = \frac{1}{2}\frac{1}{\pi}\int_0^\infty\left[\int_{-\infty}^\infty f(y)\cos k(x+ct-y)\,dy\right]dk$$

$$+\frac{1}{2}\frac{1}{\pi}\int_0^\infty\left[\int_{-\infty}^\infty f(y)\cos k(x-ct-y)\,dy\right]dk. \qquad (8.115)$$

If we replace x by $x \pm ct$ in (8.110),

$$f(x\pm ct) = \frac{1}{\pi}\int_0^\infty\left[\int_{-\infty}^\infty f(y)\cos k(x\pm ct-y)\,dy\right]dk,$$

and comparing this with (8.115),

$$u(x,t) = \frac{1}{2}f(x+ct)+\frac{1}{2}f(x-ct) \qquad (8.116)$$

which is the familiar equation for the traveling waves (see Prob. 8.3).

In the previous chapters, we have been dealing with the Fourier transform pair $f(t)$ and $F(\omega)$, wherein the first term denotes a function of time and the second, a function of frequency. The use of the Fourier transform is by no means restricted to time-frequency domains. If the function $f(x)$ and $F(s)$ form a Fourier transform pair, then

$$F(s) = \mathcal{F}[f(x)] = \int_{-\infty}^\infty f(x)\,e^{-jsx}\,dx, \qquad (8.117)$$

$$f(x) = \mathcal{F}^{-1}[F(s)] = \frac{1}{2\pi}\int_{-\infty}^\infty F(s)\,e^{jsx}\,ds. \qquad (8.118)$$

In the next example, we shall apply the Fourier transform technique to solve the initial-value problem.

PROBLEM 8.9   Using the Fourier transform technique, rework Prob. 8.8.

Solution: Let the Fourier transform of the solution $u(x,t)$ with respect to x be

$$U(s,t) = \mathcal{F}[u(x,t)] = \int_{-\infty}^\infty u(x,t)\,e^{-jsx}\,dx; \qquad (8.119)$$

then,

$$u(x,t) = \mathcal{F}^{-1}[U(s,t)] = \frac{1}{2\pi}\int_{-\infty}^\infty U(s,t)\,e^{jsx}\,ds. \qquad (8.120)$$

We shall assume that the solution $u(x,t)$ and $\partial u(x,t)/\partial x$ are small for large $|x|$ and approach zero as $x \longrightarrow \pm\infty$.

Let

$$u_{xx}(x,t) = \frac{\partial^2 u(x,t)}{\partial x^2}, \qquad u_x(x,t) = \frac{\partial u(x,t)}{\partial x},$$

$$u_{tt}(x,t) = \frac{\partial^2 u(x,t)}{\partial t^2}, \qquad u_t(x,t) = \frac{\partial u(x,t)}{\partial t}.$$

By applying successive partial integration, the Fourier transform of $u_{xx}(x, t)$ is

$$\mathcal{F}[u_{xx}(x, t)] = \int_{-\infty}^{\infty} u_{xx}(x, t)\, e^{-jsx}\, dx$$

$$= \int_{(x=-\infty)}^{(x=\infty)} e^{-jsx}\, du_x(x, t)$$

$$= e^{-jsx}\, u_x(x, t)\Big|_{-\infty}^{\infty} + js \int_{-\infty}^{\infty} u_x(x, t)\, e^{-jsx}\, dx$$

$$= js \int_{(x=-\infty)}^{(x=\infty)} e^{-jsx}\, du(x, t)$$

$$= js\, e^{-jsx}\, u(x, t)\Big|_{-\infty}^{\infty} - js(-js) \int_{-\infty}^{\infty} u(x, t)\, e^{-jsx}\, dx$$

$$= -s^2\, U(s, t) \tag{8.121}$$

since $u_x(\pm\infty, t) = u(\pm\infty, t) = 0$.

The Fourier transform of $u_{tt}(x, t)$ is (since we are taking the transform with respect to x)

$$\mathcal{F}[u_{tt}(x, t)] = \int_{-\infty}^{\infty} u_{tt}(x, t)\, e^{-jsx}\, dx$$

$$= \frac{\partial^2}{\partial t^2} \int_{-\infty}^{\infty} u(x, t)\, e^{-jsx}\, dx$$

$$= U_{tt}(s, t). \tag{8.122}$$

Now applying the Fourier transform to the wave equation (8.1) and from (8.121) and (8.122),

$$-s^2\, U(s, t) - \frac{1}{c^2}\, U_{tt}(s, t) = 0,$$

or

$$\frac{\partial^2 U(s, t)}{\partial t^2} + s^2 c^2\, U(s, t) = 0 \tag{8.123}$$

which is the equation for the transform $U(s, t)$.

The general solution of (8.123) is

$$U(s, t) = A(s)\, e^{jsct} + B(s)\, e^{-jsct}, \tag{8.124}$$

where $A(s)$ and $B(s)$ are constants with respect to t. Applying the Fourier transform to the initial conditions (8.103) and (8.104),

$$U(s, 0) = \mathcal{F}[u(x, 0)] = \int_{-\infty}^{\infty} u(x, 0)\, e^{-jsx}\, dx$$

$$= \int_{-\infty}^{\infty} f(x)\, e^{-jsx}\, dx$$

$$= F(s), \tag{8.125}$$

$$U_t(s, 0) = \mathcal{F}[u_t(x, t)|_{t=0}] = 0. \tag{8.126}$$

From (8.125) and (8.126), $A(s)$ and $B(s)$ of (8.124) can now be evaluated; thus,

$$F(s) = U(s, 0) = A(s) + B(s), \qquad 0 = U_t(s, 0) = jsc\,[A(s) - B(s)].$$

Solving $A(s)$ and $B(s)$ from these two algebraic equations,

$$A(s) = B(s) = \frac{1}{2} F(s).$$

Hence, from (8.124),

$$U(s,t) = \frac{1}{2} F(s) e^{jsct} + \frac{1}{2} F(s) e^{-jsct}. \tag{8.127}$$

The desired solution $u(x,t)$ is the inverse Fourier transform of $U(s,t)$, namely,

$$u(x,t) = \mathcal{F}^{-1}[U(s,t)] = \frac{1}{2} \mathcal{F}^{-1}[F(s) e^{jsct}] + \frac{1}{2} \mathcal{F}^{-1}[F(s) e^{-jsct}]. \tag{8.128}$$

By means of the time-shifting property (4.73),

$$\mathcal{F}^{-1}[F(s) e^{jsct}] = f(x + ct), \tag{8.129}$$

$$\mathcal{F}^{-1}[F(s) e^{-jsct}] = f(x - ct). \tag{8.130}$$

Thus,

$$u(x,t) = \frac{1}{2} f(x + ct) + \frac{1}{2} f(x - ct)$$

which is exactly the result obtained in (8.116).

8.3 Heat Conduction

The heat flow in a body of homogeneous material is governed by the heat equation

$$\nabla^2 u(x,y,z,t) - \frac{1}{c^2} \frac{\partial u(x,y,z,t)}{\partial t} = 0, \tag{8.131}$$

where $u(x,y,z,t)$ is the temperature in the body, and $c^2 = K/(\rho\sigma)$, where K is the thermal conductivity, σ is the specific heat, and ρ is the density of material of the body. The *Laplacian* of u is $\nabla^2 u$, and in rectangular coordinates, it can be expressed as

$$\nabla^2 u = \frac{\partial^2 u}{\partial x^2} + \frac{\partial^2 u}{\partial y^2} + \frac{\partial^2 u}{\partial z^2}. \tag{8.132}$$

PROBLEM 8.10 Consider the temperature in a uniform bar of length l which is oriented along the x-axis. Both ends of the bar are held at zero temperature. If the initial temperature in the bar is

$$f(x) = \begin{cases} x & \text{for} \quad 0 < x < \frac{1}{2} l \\ \\ l - x & \text{for} \quad \frac{1}{2} l < x < l, \end{cases}$$

where x is the distance measured from one end, find the temperature distribution after time t.

Solution: Since the temperature $u(x, t)$ depends only on x and t, the heat equation (8.131) becomes the so-called one-dimensional heat equation

$$\frac{\partial^2 u(x,t)}{\partial x^2} - \frac{1}{c^2} \frac{\partial u(x,t)}{\partial t} = 0. \tag{8.133}$$

The boundary conditions are

$$u(0, t) = 0, \quad u(l, t) = 0, \tag{8.134}$$

and the initial condition is

$$u(x, 0) = f(x) = \begin{cases} x & \text{for} \quad 0 < x < \dfrac{1}{2} l \\[2ex] l - x & \text{for} \quad \dfrac{1}{2} l < x < l. \end{cases} \tag{8.135}$$

Once again, assume the solution to be in the form of the product

$$u(x, t) = X(x) T(t) \tag{8.136}$$

and substitute into (8.133). Hence,

$$X''(x) T(t) - \frac{1}{c^2} X(x) T'(t) = 0. \tag{8.137}$$

Dividing by $X(x) T(t)$ and separating variables,

$$\frac{X''(x)}{X(x)} = \frac{1}{c^2} \frac{T'(t)}{T(t)}. \tag{8.138}$$

The expression on the left depends only on x, while the right side depends only on t; therefore we conclude that both expressions must be equal to a constant. This constant, say K, must be negative since if $K > 0$, the only solution $u(x, t) = X(x) T(t)$ that satisfies (8.134) is $u(x, t) = 0$. This is shown as follows: If

$$\frac{X''(x)}{X(x)} = K = k^2,$$

then

$$X''(x) - k^2 X(x) = 0,$$

and the general solution will be

$$X(x) = A e^{kx} + B e^{-kx}.$$

Applying the boundary condition (8.134),

$$A + B = 0 \quad \text{and} \quad Ae^{kl} + Be^{-kl} = 0.$$

Solving for A and B, we have $A = -B = 0$. Thus $X(x) = 0$ and consequently $u(x, t) = 0$. This gives only a trivial solution. Hence, letting $K = -k^2$,

$$\frac{X''(x)}{X(x)} = \frac{1}{c^2} \frac{T'(t)}{T(t)} = -k^2, \tag{8.139}$$

and from this we get the two ordinary differential equations

$$X''(x) + k^2 X(x) = 0, \tag{8.140}$$

$$T'(t) + c^2 k^2 T(t) = 0. \tag{8.141}$$

The general solutions of (8.140) and (8.141) are

$$X(x) = A \cos kx + B \sin kx, \tag{8.142}$$

$$T(t) = C e^{-c^2 k^2 t}. \tag{8.143}$$

From the boundary condition (8.134),

$$X(0) = A = 0,$$

$$X(l) = B \sin kl = 0.$$

Thus,

$$kl = n\pi \quad \text{or} \quad k = \frac{n\pi}{l}, \quad n = 1, 2, \cdots. \tag{8.144}$$

We thus obtain the solutions of (8.140) which satisfy (8.134) as

$$X_n(x) = B_n \sin \frac{n\pi x}{l}, \quad n = 1, 2, \cdots. \tag{8.145}$$

The corresponding solutions of (8.141) are

$$T_n(t) = C_n e^{-c^2 k^2 t} = C_n e^{-c^2 n^2 \pi^2 t / l^2} = C_n e^{-\lambda_n^2 t}, \quad n = 1, 2, \cdots, \tag{8.146}$$

where

$$\lambda_n = \frac{cn\pi}{l}.$$

Hence the functions

$$u_n(x, t) = X_n(t) T_n(t) = b_n e^{-\lambda_n^2 t} \sin \frac{n\pi x}{l}, \quad n = 1, 2, \cdots, \tag{8.147}$$

where $b_n = B_n C_n$, are the solutions of the heat equation (8.133), satisfying (8.134).

To find a solution also satisfying the initial condition (8.135), we consider the series

$$u(x, t) = \sum_{n=1}^{\infty} u_n(x, t)$$

$$= \sum_{n=1}^{\infty} b_n e^{-\lambda_n^2 t} \sin \frac{n\pi x}{l}. \tag{8.148}$$

From (8.135) and (8.148),

$$u(x, 0) = f(x) = \sum_{n=1}^{\infty} b_n \sin \frac{n\pi x}{l}. \tag{8.149}$$

Hence for (8.148) to satisfy (8.135), the coefficients b_n must be chosen such that (8.149) becomes the Fourier sine series of $f(x)$; i.e.,

$$b_n = \frac{2}{l} \int_0^l f(x) \sin \frac{n\pi x}{l} \, dx$$

$$= \frac{2}{l} \left[\int_0^{l/2} x \sin \frac{n\pi x}{l} \, dx + \int_{l/2}^l (l - x) \sin \frac{n\pi x}{l} \, dx \right]$$

$$= \begin{cases} 0 & \text{for} \quad n \text{ even} \\ \dfrac{4l}{n^2 \pi^2} & \text{for} \quad n = 1, 5, 9, \cdots \\ -\dfrac{4l}{n^2 \pi^2} & \text{for} \quad n = 3, 7, 11, \cdots. \end{cases} \tag{8.150}$$

Hence the solution is

$$u(x, t) = \frac{4l}{\pi^2} \left[\sin \frac{\pi x}{l} e^{-(c\pi/l)^2 t} - \frac{1}{9} \sin \frac{3\pi x}{l} e^{-(3c\pi/l)^2 t} + \cdots \right]. \tag{8.151}$$

It is noted that the solution $u(x, t)$ of (8.151) becomes small after a long period of time, i.e., it tends to zero as $t \longrightarrow \infty$.

In the next example, we shall consider solutions of the one-dimensional heat equation (8.133) in the case of a bar which extends to infinity on both sides. In this case, similar to the case of the vibration of an infinite string (Prob. 8.8), we do not have boundary conditions but only the initial conditions.

PROBLEM 8.11   Find the temperature distribution $u(x, t)$ in the case of an infinite bar. The initial temperature distribution is given by $f(x)$ for $-\infty < x < \infty$.

Solution: The function $u(x, t)$ satisfies

$$\frac{\partial^2 u(x, t)}{\partial x^2} - \frac{1}{c^2} \frac{\partial u(x, t)}{\partial t} = 0 \qquad [8.133]$$

and the initial condition is

$$u(x, 0) = f(x) \quad \text{for} \quad -\infty < x < \infty. \qquad (8.152)$$

Proceeding as in Prob. 8.10, we substitute

$$u(x, t) = X(x) T(t)$$

into (8.133). This yields two ordinary differential equations

$$X''(x) + k^2 X(x) = 0, \qquad (8.153)$$

$$T'(t) + c^2 k^2 T(t) = 0. \qquad (8.154)$$

The general solutions of (8.153) and (8.154) are

$$X(x) = A \cos kx + B \sin kx,$$

$$T(t) = C e^{-c^2 k^2 t}.$$

Hence,

$$u(x, t; k) = X(x) T(t) = (D \cos kx + E \sin kx) e^{-c^2 k^2 t} \qquad (8.155)$$

is a solution of (8.133), where D and E are the arbitrary constants. Since $f(x)$ in (8.138) is in general not periodic, following the similar argument for the case of an infinite string vibration (Prob. 8.8), we may consider D and E as functions of k. Then the function

$$u(x, t) = \int_0^\infty u(x, t; k) \, dk$$

$$= \int_0^\infty [D(k) \cos kx + E(k) \sin kx] e^{-c^2 k^2 t} \, dk \qquad (8.156)$$

is also a solution of (8.133).
From (8.152),

$$u(x, 0) = f(x) = \int_0^\infty [D(k) \cos kx + E(k) \sin kx] \, dk. \qquad (8.157)$$

Now if

$$D(k) = \frac{1}{\pi} \int_{-\infty}^\infty f(y) \cos ky \, dy,$$

$$E(k) = \frac{1}{\pi} \int_{-\infty}^\infty f(y) \sin ky \, dy,$$

then with the Fourier integral theorem (4.12), we may write (8.157) as

$$u(x, 0) = \frac{1}{\pi} \int_0^\infty \left[\int_{-\infty}^\infty f(y) \cos k(x - y) \, dy \right] dk. \qquad (8.158)$$

Thus, from (8.156),

$$u(x, t) = \frac{1}{\pi} \int_0^\infty \left[\int_{-\infty}^\infty f(y) \cos k(x - y) e^{-c^2 k^2 t} \, dy \right] dk. \qquad (8.159)$$

Assuming that we can interchange the order of integration,

$$u(x, t) = \frac{1}{\pi} \int_{-\infty}^\infty f(y) \left[\int_0^\infty e^{-c^2 k^2 t} \cos k(x - y) \, dk \right] dy. \qquad (8.160)$$

In order to evaluate the inner integral we proceed as follows:
    From a table of integral formulas,

$$\int_0^\infty e^{-s^2} \cos 2bs \, ds = \frac{\sqrt{\pi}}{2} e^{-b^2}. \qquad (8.161)$$

Introducing a new variable of integration k by setting $s = ck\sqrt{t}$ and choosing

$$b = \frac{x - y}{2c\sqrt{t}},$$

the formula (8.161) becomes

$$\int_0^\infty e^{-c^2 k^2 t} \cos k(x - y) \, dk = \frac{\sqrt{\pi}}{2c\sqrt{t}} e^{-(x-y)^2/(4c^2 t)}. \qquad (8.162)$$

Substituting (8.162) into (8.160),

$$u(x, t) = \frac{1}{2c\sqrt{\pi t}} \int_{-\infty}^\infty f(y) e^{-(x-y)^2/(4c^2 t)} \, dy. \qquad (8.163)$$

Introducing the new variable of integration, $q = (x - y)/(2c\sqrt{t})$, (8.163) can be written as

$$u(x, t) = \frac{1}{\sqrt{\pi}} \int_{-\infty}^\infty f(x - 2cq\sqrt{t}) e^{-q^2} \, dq. \qquad (8.164)$$

PROBLEM 8.12   Using the Fourier transform technique, rework Prob. 8.11.

Solution: Let the Fourier transform of the solution $u(x, t)$ with respect to x be

$$U(s, t) = \mathscr{F}[u(x, t)] = \int_{-\infty}^\infty u(x, t) e^{-jsx} \, dx; \qquad (8.165)$$

then,

$$u(x, t) = \mathscr{F}^{-1}[U(s, t)] = \frac{1}{2\pi} \int_{-\infty}^\infty U(s, t) e^{jsx} \, ds. \qquad (8.166)$$

We shall assume that the solution $u(x, t)$ and $\partial u(x, t)/\partial x$ are small for large $|x|$ and approach zero as $x \longrightarrow \pm\infty$.
    From (8.121), the Fourier transform of $u_{xx}(x, t)$ is

$$\mathscr{F}[u_{xx}(x, t)] = \int_{-\infty}^\infty u_{xx}(x, t) e^{-jsx} \, dx = -s^2 U(s, t). \qquad (8.167)$$

The Fourier transform of $u_t(x, t)$ is

$$\mathscr{F}[u_t(x, t)] = \int_{-\infty}^\infty u_t(x, t) e^{-jsx} \, dx = \frac{\partial}{\partial t} U(s, t)$$

$$= U_t(s, t). \qquad (8.168)$$

Now applying the Fourier transform to the heat equation (8.133),

$$-s^2\, U(s,t) - \frac{1}{c^2}\, U_t(s,t) = 0$$

or

$$\frac{\partial U(s,t)}{\partial t} + c^2 s^2\, U(s,t) = 0. \tag{8.169}$$

The solution of (8.169) is

$$U(s,t) = U(s,0)\, e^{-c^2 s^2 t}. \tag{8.170}$$

But by applying the Fourier transform to the initial condition (8.152),

$$U(s,0) = \int_{-\infty}^{\infty} u(x,0)\, e^{-jsx}\, dx$$

$$= \int_{-\infty}^{\infty} f(x)\, e^{-jsx}\, dx$$

$$= \int_{-\infty}^{\infty} f(y)\, e^{-jsy}\, dy. \tag{8.171}$$

Substituting (8.171) into (8.170),

$$U(s,t) = e^{-c^2 s^2 t} \int_{-\infty}^{\infty} f(y)\, e^{-jsy}\, dy. \tag{8.172}$$

Now, the solution $u(x,t)$ can be obtained by taking the inverse Fourier transform of (8.172); that is,

$$u(x,t) = \frac{1}{2\pi} \int_{-\infty}^{\infty} U(s,t)\, e^{jsx}\, ds$$

$$= \frac{1}{2\pi} \int_{-\infty}^{\infty} e^{(jsx - c^2 s^2 t)} \left[\int_{-\infty}^{\infty} f(y)\, e^{-jsy}\, dy \right] ds. \tag{8.173}$$

Assuming that we can interchange the order of integration,

$$u(x,t) = \frac{1}{2\pi} \int_{-\infty}^{\infty} f(y) \left\{ \int_{-\infty}^{\infty} e^{\left[js(x-y) - c^2 s^2 t\right]}\, ds \right\} dy. \tag{8.174}$$

In order to evaluate the inner integral, we proceed as follows:
From the integral table,

$$\int_{-\infty}^{\infty} e^{-w^2}\, dw = \sqrt{\pi}. \tag{8.175}$$

Now,

$$\int_{-\infty}^{\infty} e^{\left[js(x-y) - c^2 s^2 t\right]}\, ds = \int_{-\infty}^{\infty} \exp\left[\left(\frac{x-y}{2c\sqrt{t}} + jcs\sqrt{t} \right)^2 - \left(\frac{x-y}{2c\sqrt{t}} \right)^2 \right] ds$$

$$= e^{-(x-y)^2/(4c^2 t)} \int_{-\infty}^{\infty} \exp\left(\frac{x-y}{2c\sqrt{t}} + jcs\sqrt{t} \right)^2 ds.$$

Introducing a new variable of integration w by setting

$$\frac{x-y}{2c\sqrt{t}} + jcs\sqrt{t} = jw,$$

we have

$$\int_{-\infty}^{\infty} e^{\left[js(x-y)-c^2 s^2 t\right]} ds = \frac{1}{c\sqrt{t}} e^{-(x-y)^2/(4c^2 t)} \int_{-\infty}^{\infty} e^{-w^2} dw$$

$$= \frac{1}{c} \sqrt{\frac{\pi}{t}} e^{-(x-y)^2/(4c^2 t)}, \qquad (8.176)$$

in view of (8.175).

Substituting (8.176) into (8.174), we finally obtain

$$u(x,t) = \frac{1}{2c\sqrt{\pi t}} \int_{-\infty}^{\infty} f(y) e^{-(x-y)^2/(4c^2 t)} dy \qquad (8.177)$$

which is exactly (8.163).

Now (8.174) or (8.177) can be expressed as

$$u(x,t) = \int_{-\infty}^{\infty} f(y) G(x-y,t) dy, \qquad (8.178)$$

where

$$G(x-y,t) = \frac{1}{2\pi} \int_{-\infty}^{\infty} e^{\left[js(x-y)-c^2 s^2 t\right]} ds = \frac{1}{2c\sqrt{\pi t}} e^{-(x-y)^2/(4c^2 t)} \qquad (8.179)$$

is called *Green's function* of the heat equation (8.133) for the infinite interval.

PROBLEM 8.13 Assume a bar to be semi-infinite, extending from 0 to ∞. The end at $x = 0$ is held at zero temperature and the initial temperature distribution is $f(x)$ for $0 < x < \infty$. Find the temperature $u(x,t)$ in the bar. It is assumed that the condition at the infinite end is such that $u(x,t) \longrightarrow 0$ as $x \longrightarrow \infty$.

Solution: There are several ways to solve this problem, but we shall use the method of images in this case.

Since the temperature at $x = 0$ is held at 0, we extend the given initial function $f(x)$, $x > 0$, to be an odd function for $-\infty < x < \infty$. Then this becomes an infinite bar problem. (See Prob. 8.11.)

From (8.177),

$$u(x,t) = \frac{1}{2c\sqrt{\pi t}} \int_{-\infty}^{\infty} f(y) e^{-(x-y)^2/(4c^2 t)} dy. \qquad [8.177]$$

Using the fact $f(-y) = -f(y)$,

$$u(x,t) = \frac{1}{2c\sqrt{\pi t}} \int_{0}^{\infty} f(y) e^{-(x-y)^2/(4c^2 t)} dy + \frac{1}{2c\sqrt{\pi t}} \int_{0}^{\infty} f(-y) e^{-(x+y)^2/(4c^2 t)} dy$$

$$= \frac{1}{2c\sqrt{\pi t}} \int_{0}^{\infty} f(y) \left[e^{-(x-y)^2/(4c^2 t)} - e^{-(x+y)^2/(4c^2 t)} \right] dy \qquad (8.180)$$

which is the desired solution.

8.4 Potential Theory

In this section we shall apply Fourier analysis to potential theory. *Potential theory* is the theory of the solution of *Laplace's equation*

$$\nabla^2 u = 0, \qquad (8.181)$$

where $\nabla^2 u$ is the Laplacian of u. Laplace's equation occurs in connection with

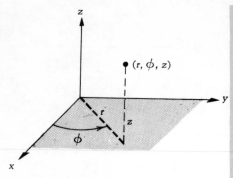

Fig. 8.5 Cylindrical coordinates.

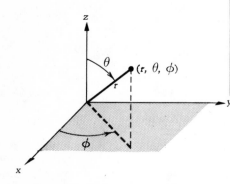

Fig. 8.6 Spherical coordinates.

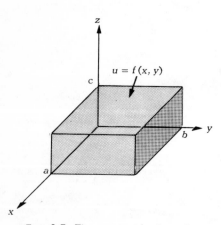

Fig. 8.7 The rectangular box of Prob. 8.14.

gravitational potentials, electrostatic potentials, stationary heat problems, potentials of incompressible inviscid fluid flow, etc.

In rectangular coordinates, the Laplacian of a function u in three-dimensional space is expressed as

$$\nabla^2 u = \frac{\partial^2 u}{\partial x^2} + \frac{\partial^2 u}{\partial y^2} + \frac{\partial^2 u}{\partial z^2}. \tag{8.182}$$

As shown in Fig. 8.5, in cylindrical coordinates (r, ϕ, z),

$$\nabla^2 u = \frac{\partial^2 u}{\partial r^2} + \frac{1}{r}\frac{\partial u}{\partial r} + \frac{1}{r^2}\frac{\partial^2 u}{\partial \phi^2} + \frac{\partial^2 u}{\partial z^2}. \tag{8.183}$$

As shown in Fig. 8.6, in spherical coordinates (r, θ, ϕ),

$$\nabla^2 u = \frac{1}{r^2}\frac{\partial}{\partial r}\left(r^2\frac{\partial u}{\partial r}\right) + \frac{1}{\sin\theta}\frac{\partial}{\partial\theta}\left(\sin\theta\frac{\partial u}{\partial\theta}\right) + \frac{1}{\sin^2\theta}\frac{\partial^2 u}{\partial\phi^2}. \tag{8.184}$$

The separation of variables technique applied to the two-dimensional Laplace's equation $u_{xx} + u_{yy} = 0$ has been discussed in Prob. 8.2. In the following example, we shall consider the three-dimensional case.

PROBLEM 8.14 Consider the rectangular box shown in Fig. 8.7. Find the potential distribution if the potential is zero on all sides and the bottom, and is $f(x, y)$ on the top.

Solution: Let $u(x, y, z)$ be the potential distribution in the rectangular box shown in Fig. 8.7. Then, $u(x, y, z)$ satisfies

$$\nabla^2 u = u_{xx} + u_{yy} + u_{zz} = 0, \tag{8.185}$$

and the boundary conditions

$$u(0, y, z) = u(a, y, z) = u(x, 0, z) = u(x, b, z) = u(x, y, 0) = 0, \tag{8.186}$$

$$u(x, y, c) = f(x, y). \tag{8.187}$$

The method of separation of variables suggests assuming a solution of (8.185) of the form

$$u(x, y, z) = X(x)Y(y)Z(z). \tag{8.188}$$

Substituting this into (8.185) reduces it to

$$X''(x)Y(y)Z(z) + X(x)Y''(y)Z(z) + X(x)Y(y)Z''(z) = 0. \tag{8.189}$$

Dividing by $X(x)Y(y)Z(z)$ and separating the variables,

$$-\frac{X''(x)}{X(x)} = \frac{Y''(y)}{Y(y)} + \frac{Z''(z)}{Z(z)} = k_x^2, \tag{8.190}$$

where k_x^2 is the separation constant. The separation here depends upon the fact that the left side is independent of both y and z and the right side is independent of x.

Hence,

$$X''(x) + k_x^2 X(x) = 0. \tag{8.191}$$

After a second separation,

$$-\frac{Y''(y)}{Y(y)} = \frac{Z''(z)}{Z(z)} - k_x^2 = k_y^2. \tag{8.192}$$

This yields the following equations:

$$Y''(y) + k_y^2 Y(y) = 0, \tag{8.193}$$

$$Z''(z) - k_z^2 \, Z(z) = 0, \tag{8.194}$$

where $k_z^2 = k_x^2 + k_y^2$. The general solutions of (8.191), (8.193), and (8.194) are

$$X(x) = A \cos k_x x + B \sin k_x x, \tag{8.195}$$

$$Y(y) = C \cos k_y y + D \sin k_y y, \tag{8.196}$$

$$Z(z) = E \cosh k_z z + F \sinh k_z z. \tag{8.197}$$

From the boundary conditions (8.186),

$$X(0) = X(a) = 0,$$

$$Y(0) = Y(b) = 0,$$

$$Z(0) = 0.$$

Therefore,

$$X(0) = A = 0,$$

$$X(a) = B \sin k_x a = 0;$$

hence,

$$k_x a = m\pi \quad \text{or} \quad k_x = \frac{m\pi}{a}, \quad m = 1, 2, \cdots. \tag{8.198}$$

Similarly,

$$Y(0) = C = 0,$$

$$Y(b) = D \sin k_y b = 0;$$

hence,

$$k_y b = n\pi \quad \text{or} \quad k_y = \frac{n\pi}{b}, \quad n = 1, 2, \cdots. \tag{8.199}$$

Also

$$Z(0) = E = 0.$$

If we write further

$$k_z^2 = k_x^2 + k_y^2 = \pi^2 \left(\frac{m^2}{a^2} + \frac{n^2}{b^2} \right) = k_{mn}^2$$

or

$$k_z = k_{mn} = \pi \sqrt{\frac{m^2}{a^2} + \frac{n^2}{b^2}}, \tag{8.200}$$

we obtain the solutions

$$X(x) = X_m(x) = B_m \sin \frac{m\pi x}{a}, \quad m = 1, 2, \cdots,$$

$$Y(y) = Y_n(y) = D_n \sin \frac{n\pi y}{b}, \quad n = 1, 2, \cdots,$$

$$Z(z) = Z_{mn}(z) = F_{mn} \sinh k_{mn} z.$$

Thus, writing $b_{mn} = B_m D_n F_{mn}$, it follows that the functions

$$u_{mn}(x, y, z) = X_m(x) Y_n(y) Z_{mn}(z)$$

$$= b_{mn} \sin \frac{m\pi x}{a} \sin \frac{n\pi y}{b} \sinh k_{mn} z, \tag{8.201}$$

where $m = 1, 2, \cdots$, $n = 1, 2, \cdots$, with k_{mn} defined by (8.200), are solutions of (8.185) satisfying the boundary condition (8.186).

In order to satisfy the boundary condition (8.187), we assume the desired solution in the form

$$u(x, y, z) = \sum_{m=1}^{\infty} \sum_{n=1}^{\infty} u_{mn}(x, y, z)$$

$$= \sum_{m=1}^{\infty} \sum_{n=1}^{\infty} b_{mn} \sin \frac{m\pi x}{a} \sin \frac{n\pi y}{b} \sinh k_{mn} z. \qquad (8.202)$$

If we let

$$c_{mn} = b_{mn} \sinh k_{mn} c, \qquad (8.203)$$

the boundary condition (8.187) takes the form

$$f(x, y) = \sum_{m=1}^{\infty} \sum_{n=1}^{\infty} c_{mn} \sin \frac{m\pi x}{a} \sin \frac{n\pi y}{b}, \quad 0 < x < a, \ 0 < y < b. \qquad (8.204)$$

Thus the coefficients c_{mn} are the coefficients of the double Fourier sine series expansion of $f(x, y)$ over the indicated rectangle. From (8.76), these coefficients are readily determined as

$$c_{mn} = \frac{4}{ab} \int_0^b \int_0^a f(x, y) \sin \frac{m\pi x}{a} \sin \frac{n\pi y}{b} \, dx \, dy. \qquad (8.205)$$

With these values of c_{mn}, the solution (8.202) becomes, with the notation of (8.203),

$$u(x, y, z) = \sum_{m=1}^{\infty} \sum_{n=1}^{\infty} c_{mn} \sin \frac{m\pi x}{a} \sin \frac{n\pi y}{b} \frac{\sinh k_{mn} z}{\sinh k_{mn} c}, \qquad (8.206)$$

where k_{mn} is defined by (8.200).

PROBLEM 8.15   Rework Prob. 8.14 when $f(x, y) = U_o$, a constant.

Solution: From (8.205),

$$c_{mn} = \frac{4}{ab} \int_0^b \int_0^a U_o \sin \frac{m\pi x}{a} \sin \frac{n\pi y}{b} \, dx \, dy$$

$$= \frac{4U_o}{ab} \int_0^a \sin \frac{m\pi x}{a} \, dx \int_0^b \sin \frac{n\pi y}{b} \, dy$$

$$= \begin{cases} \dfrac{16U_o}{mn\pi^2} & \text{for} \quad m, n \text{ odd} \\[2mm] 0 & \text{for} \quad m, n \text{ even.} \end{cases}$$

Hence from (8.206),

$$u(x, y, z) = \frac{16U_o}{\pi^2} \sum_{m=\text{odd}}^{\infty} \sum_{n=\text{odd}}^{\infty} \frac{1}{mn} \sin \frac{m\pi x}{a} \sin \frac{n\pi y}{b} \frac{\sinh k_{mn} z}{\sinh k_{mn} c}, \qquad (8.207)$$

where $k_{mn} = \pi [(m^2/a^2) + (n^2/b^2)]^{1/2}$.

In the following example, the solution of Laplace's equation in polar coordinates will be considered.

PROBLEM 8.16   Find the steady-state temperature distribution in a semicircular plate of radius a, insulated on both faces, with its curved boundary kept at a constant temperature U_o, and its bounding diameter kept at zero temperature (Fig. 8.8).

Solution: In Sec. 8.3, the heat flow equation is written as

$$\nabla^2 u - \frac{1}{c^2}\frac{\partial u}{\partial t} = 0. \qquad [8.131]$$

In the steady-state, the temperature u is independent of time, hence $\partial u/\partial t = 0$, and u satisfies Laplace's equation; i.e.,

$$\nabla^2 u = 0.$$

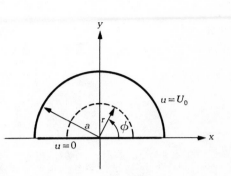

Fig. 8.8 The semicircular plate of Prob. 8.16.

Since in this problem, the space of heat flow is two dimensional and the boundaries are cylindrical, the two-dimensional Laplacian of u in cylindrical coordinates (or polar coordinates) will be used. Hence from (8.183),

$$\nabla^2 u\,(r, \phi) = \frac{\partial^2 u(r, \phi)}{\partial r^2} + \frac{1}{r}\frac{\partial u(r, \phi)}{\partial r} + \frac{1}{r^2}\frac{\partial^2 u(r, \phi)}{\partial \phi^2} = 0. \qquad (8.208)$$

The temperature $u\,(r, \phi)$ considered as a function of r and ϕ satisfies (8.208) and the boundary conditions (Fig. 8.8)

$$u\,(a, \phi) = U_o, \qquad (8.209)$$

$$u\,(r, 0) = 0, \qquad (8.210)$$

$$u\,(r, \pi) = 0. \qquad (8.211)$$

The method of separation of variables suggests assuming a solution of (8.208) of the form

$$u\,(r, \phi) = R\,(r)\,\Phi\,(\phi). \qquad (8.212)$$

Substituting (8.212) into (8.208),

$$R''(r)\,\Phi\,(\phi) + \frac{1}{r}\,R'(r)\,\Phi\,(\phi) + \frac{1}{r^2}\,R\,(r)\,\Phi''(\phi) = 0,$$

or

$$r^2 R''(r)\,\Phi\,(\phi) + r R'(r)\,\Phi\,(\phi) + R\,(r)\,\Phi''(\phi) = 0. \qquad (8.213)$$

Dividing (8.213) by $R\,(r)\,\Phi\,(\phi)$ and separating the variables,

$$r^2\,\frac{R''(r)}{R\,(r)} + r\,\frac{R'(r)}{R\,(r)} = -\frac{\Phi''(\phi)}{\Phi\,(\phi)} = k^2, \qquad (8.214)$$

where k^2 is the separation constant. The separation here results from the fact that the left side is independent of ϕ and the right side is independent of r. The sign of the separation constant was chosen in such a way that sine and cosines rather than exponential functions will be introduced in $\Phi\,(\phi)$. Equation (8.124) then yields the following two equations:

$$r^2 R''(r) + r R'(r) - k^2 R\,(r) = 0, \qquad (8.215)$$

$$\Phi''(\phi) + k^2 \Phi\,(\phi) = 0. \qquad (8.216)$$

The general solution of (8.216) is

$$\Phi\,(\phi) = A\,\cos k\,\phi + B\,\sin k\,\phi. \qquad (8.217)$$

In order to solve (8.215), we make the transformation

$$r = e^s.$$

Then,

$$R'(r) = \frac{dR}{dr} = \frac{dR}{ds}\frac{ds}{dr} = \frac{1}{r}\frac{dR}{ds},$$

$$R''(r) = \frac{1}{r^2}\frac{d^2R}{ds^2} - \frac{1}{r^2}\frac{dR}{ds},$$

and (8.215) reduces to

$$\frac{d^2R}{ds^2} - k^2 R = 0.$$

The general solution of this equation is

$$R = C\,e^{ks} + D\,e^{-ks}.$$

Since $e^s = r$,

$$R(r) = C\,r^k + D\,r^{-k}. \tag{8.218}$$

From the boundary conditions (8.210) and (8.211),

$$\Phi(0) = \Phi(\pi) = 0.$$

Hence,

$$\Phi(0) = A = 0 \quad \text{and} \quad \Phi(\pi) = B \sin k\pi = 0.$$

Since a trivial solution results if $B = 0$, we must have $\sin k\pi = 0$, from which

$$k\pi = n\pi \quad \text{or} \quad k = n, \quad n = 1, 2, \cdots.$$

Hence we find the solutions

$$\Phi(\phi) = \Phi_n(\phi) = B_n \sin n\phi, \quad n = 1, 2, \cdots. \tag{8.219}$$

In (8.218), we see that as $r \longrightarrow 0$, the term $r^{-k} \longrightarrow \infty$ since $k = n > 0$. Since at $r = 0$, $R(0) = 0$, D must be equal to zero. Thus,

$$R(r) = R_n(r) = C_n\,r^n, \quad n = 1, 2, \cdots. \tag{8.220}$$

Then, it follows that the functions

$$u_n(r, \phi) = R_n(r)\Phi_n(\phi) = b_n\,r^n \sin n\phi, \quad n = 1, 2, \cdots, \tag{8.221}$$

where $b_n = B_n C_n$, satisfy (8.208) as well as the boundary conditions (8.210) and (8.211).

In order to satisfy the boundary condition (8.209), we assume the desired solution in the form

$$u(r, \phi) = \sum_{n=1}^{\infty} u_n(r, \phi) = \sum_{n=1}^{\infty} b_n\,r^n \sin n\phi. \tag{8.222}$$

From (8.209),

$$u(a, \phi) = U_o = \sum_{n=1}^{\infty} b_n\,a^n \sin n\phi. \tag{8.223}$$

Thus, the $b_n a^n$ are the sine Fourier coefficients of U_o, and

$$b_n a^n = \frac{2}{\pi} \int_0^\pi U_o \sin n\phi \, d\phi$$

$$= \begin{cases} \dfrac{4U_o}{n\pi} & \text{for } n = 1, 3, \cdots \\[2mm] 0 & \text{for } n = 2, 4, \cdots. \end{cases}$$

Hence,

$$b_n = \frac{4U_o}{\pi n a^n}, \quad n = 1, 3, \cdots .$$

With these values of b_n, the solution (8.222) becomes

$$u(r, \phi) = \frac{4U_o}{\pi} \sum_{n=odd}^{\infty} \frac{1}{r} \left(\frac{r}{a}\right)^n \sin n\phi. \qquad (8.224)$$

In the next example, we shall consider the application of the Fourier transform to the solution of Laplace's equation for the half-plane.

PROBLEM 8.17 Find the solution $u(x, y)$ of the Laplace's equation for the half-plane $y > 0$, when $u(x, 0) = f(x)$ for $-\infty < x < \infty$ (Fig. 8.9).

Solution: To the Laplace's equation

$$u_{xx}(x, y) + u_{yy}(x, y) = 0,$$

we apply the Fourier transform with respect to the variable x, namely,

$$U(s, y) = \mathcal{F}[u(x, y)] = \int_{-\infty}^{\infty} u(x, y) e^{-jsx} dx.$$

Assuming that $u(x, y)$ and $u_x(x, y)$ vanish for $x \longrightarrow \pm\infty$, we obtain the equation for $U(s, y)$ as [see (8.121)]

$$\frac{\partial^2 U(s, y)}{\partial y^2} - s^2 U(s, y) = 0. \qquad (8.225)$$

The general solution of (8.225) is

$$U(s, y) = A(s) e^{sy} + B(s) e^{-sy}. \qquad (8.226)$$

We shall also assume that $u(x, y)$ is bounded as $y \longrightarrow +\infty$. Hence for $s > 0$, we set $A(s) = 0$, and

$$U(s, y) = B(s) e^{-sy} \quad \text{for} \quad s > 0. \qquad (8.227)$$

Since $U(s, 0) = B(s)$, we can rewrite (8.227) as

$$U(s, y) = U(s, 0) e^{-sy} \quad \text{for} \quad s > 0. \qquad (8.228)$$

Similarly, for $s < 0$, we set $B(s) = 0$ in (8.226) and write

$$U(s, y) = A(s) e^{sy} \quad \text{for} \quad s < 0. \qquad (8.229)$$

Again, since $U(s, 0) = A(s)$, we can rewrite (8.229) as

$$U(s, y) = U(s, 0) e^{sy} \quad \text{for} \quad s < 0. \qquad (8.230)$$

The two equations (8.228) and (8.230) can be combined as

$$U(s, y) = U(s, 0) e^{-|s|y}. \qquad (8.231)$$

Since $u(x, 0) = f(x)$,

$$U(s, 0) = \mathcal{F}[u(x, 0)] = \int_{-\infty}^{\infty} f(x') e^{-jsx'} dx'. \qquad (8.232)$$

From (8.231),

$$U(s, y) = \left[\int_{-\infty}^{\infty} f(x') e^{-jsx'} dx'\right] e^{-|s|y}. \qquad (8.233)$$

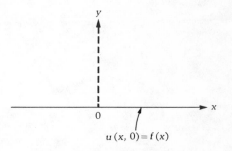

Fig. 8.9 The half-plane of Prob. 8.17.

The desired solution $u(x, y)$ is the inverse Fourier transform of (8.233); i.e.,

$$u(x, y) = \mathcal{F}^{-1}[U(s, y)] = \frac{1}{2\pi} \int_{-\infty}^{\infty} U(s, y) e^{jsx} ds$$

$$= \frac{1}{2\pi} \int_{-\infty}^{\infty} e^{jsx} \left[\int_{-\infty}^{\infty} f(x') e^{-jsx'} dx' \right] e^{-|s|y} ds. \quad (8.234)$$

Interchanging the order of integration,

$$u(x, y) = \frac{1}{2\pi} \int_{-\infty}^{\infty} f(x') \left\{ \int_{-\infty}^{\infty} e^{[js(x-x')-|s|y]} ds \right\} dx'. \quad (8.235)$$

Now,

$$\int_{-\infty}^{\infty} e^{[js(x-x')-|s|y]} ds = \int_{-\infty}^{0} e^{[js(x-x')+sy]} ds + \int_{0}^{\infty} e^{[js(x-x')-sy]} ds$$

$$= \frac{e^{js(x-x')+sy}}{j(x-x')+y} \bigg|_{-\infty}^{0} + \frac{e^{js(x-x')-sy}}{j(x-x')-y} \bigg|_{0}^{\infty}$$

$$= \frac{1}{j(x-x')+y} - \frac{1}{j(x-x')-y}$$

$$= \frac{2y}{(x-x')^2 + y^2}. \quad (8.236)$$

Substituting (8.236) into (8.235), we finally obtain

$$u(x, y) = \frac{y}{\pi} \int_{-\infty}^{\infty} \frac{f(x') dx'}{(x-x')^2 + y^2}, \quad y > 0. \quad (8.237)$$

8.5 Supplementary Problems

PROBLEM 8.18 Solve (8.1) using the boundary conditions of (8.2) and with the initial conditions

$$u(x, 0) = f(x) = \begin{cases} \dfrac{k}{a} x & \text{for } 0 < x < a \\[2ex] \dfrac{k}{l-a} (l-x) & \text{for } a < x < l, \end{cases} \quad \text{and} \quad \frac{\partial u(x, t)}{\partial t} \bigg|_{t=0} = 0.$$

See Fig. 8.10.

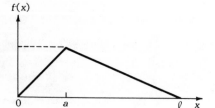

f(x)

0   a   ℓ   x

Fig. 8.10 The elastic string of
Prob. 8.18.

Answer: $u(x, t) = \dfrac{2kl^2}{\pi^2 a(l-a)} \displaystyle\sum_{n=1}^{\infty} \frac{1}{n^2} \sin\left(\frac{n\pi a}{l}\right) \sin\left(\frac{n\pi x}{l}\right) \cos\left(\frac{n\pi ct}{l}\right).$

PROBLEM 8.19 If the instantaneous energy of a vibrating string is

$$W_{KE} = \frac{1}{2} \rho \int_{0}^{l} \left[\frac{\partial u(x, t)}{\partial t} \right]^2 dx,$$

find the kinetic energy of the vibrating string of Prob. 8.18.

Answer: $\dfrac{1}{2} \rho \displaystyle\sum_{n=1}^{\infty} \frac{n^2 \pi^2 c^2}{2l} A_n^2 \sin^2\left(\frac{n\pi ct}{l}\right),$ where $A_n = \dfrac{2kl^2}{\pi^2 a(l-a)} \dfrac{1}{n^2} \sin\left(\frac{n\pi a}{l}\right).$

PROBLEM 8.20 Prove that the function

$$u(x, t) = f(x - ct) + g(x + ct)$$

is a solution of the one-dimensional wave equation (8.1) whenever f and g are twice differentiable functions of a single variable.

PROBLEM 8.21 The temperature in a uniformly insulated bar of length l satisfies the endpoint conditions $u(0, t) = 0$, $u(l, t) = 1$, and the initial condition $u(x, 0) = \sin(\pi x/l)$. Find (a) the temperature distribution after time t and (b) the steady-state temperature, i.e., the temperature as $t \to \infty$, in the bar.

Answer: (a) $u(x, t) = \dfrac{x}{l} + \dfrac{2}{\pi} \displaystyle\sum_{n=1}^{\infty} \dfrac{(-1)^n}{n} e^{-\lambda_n^2 t} \sin\left(\dfrac{n \pi x}{l}\right)$, $\lambda_n = \dfrac{cn\pi}{l}$,

(b) $u(x, t)\Big|_{t=\infty} = \dfrac{x}{l}$.

PROBLEM 8.22 Solve

$$\frac{\partial^2 u}{\partial x^2} - \frac{1}{c^2}\frac{\partial u}{\partial t} = 0 \quad \text{for } 0 < x < \pi, \quad t > 0,$$

with $\dfrac{\partial u}{\partial x}(0, t) = 0$, $\dfrac{\partial u}{\partial x}(\pi, t) = 0$, and $u(x, 0) = \sin x$.

Answer: $u(x, t) = \dfrac{2}{\pi} - \dfrac{4}{\pi} \displaystyle\sum_{n=1}^{\infty} \dfrac{1}{(4n^2 - 1)} e^{-4n^2 c^2 t} \cos 2nx$.

PROBLEM 8.23 Solve

$$\frac{\partial^2 u}{\partial x^2} + \frac{\partial^2 u}{\partial y^2} = 0 \quad \text{for } 0 < x < a, \quad 0 < y < b,$$

with the boundary and initial conditions $u(0, y) = u(a, y) = u(x, b) = 0$, and $u(x, 0) = f(x)$.

Answer: $u(x, y) = \displaystyle\sum_{n=1}^{\infty} b_n \dfrac{\sinh[n\pi(b - y)/a]}{\sinh(n\pi b/a)} \sin\left(\dfrac{n\pi x}{a}\right)$, where

$$b_n = \frac{2}{a} \int_0^a f(x) \sin\left(\frac{n\pi x}{a}\right) dx .$$

PROBLEM 8.24 Solve

$$\frac{\partial^2 u}{\partial x^2} + \frac{\partial^2 u}{\partial y^2} = 0 \quad \text{for } 0 < x < a, \quad 0 < y < \infty,$$

with $u(x, y) \to 0$ when $y \to \infty$, $u(0, y) = 0$, $u(a, y) = 0$, and $u(x, 0) = x(a - x)$.

Answer: $u(x, y) = \dfrac{4a^2}{\pi^3} \displaystyle\sum_{n=1}^{\infty} \dfrac{(1 - \cos n\pi)}{n^3} e^{-n\pi y/a} \sin\left(\dfrac{n\pi x}{a}\right)$.

PROBLEM 8.25 Solve

$$\frac{\partial^2 u}{\partial r^2} + \frac{1}{r}\frac{\partial u}{\partial r} + \frac{1}{r^2}\frac{\partial^2 u}{\partial \phi^2} = 0 \quad \text{for } r < 1, \quad 0 < \phi < \pi,$$

with $u(r, 0) = u(r, \pi) = 0$ and $u(1, \phi) = \phi(\pi - \phi)$.

Answer: $u(r, \phi) = \dfrac{8}{\pi} \displaystyle\sum_{n=1}^{\infty} \dfrac{1}{(2n-1)^3} r^{2n-1} \sin(2n-1)\phi$.

PROBLEM 8.26 Solve

$$\frac{\partial^2 u}{\partial r^2} + \frac{1}{r} \frac{\partial u}{\partial r} + \frac{1}{r^2} \frac{\partial^2 u}{\partial \phi^2} = 0 \quad \text{for } r < 1, \quad 0 < \phi < \frac{\pi}{2},$$

with $u(r, 0) = 0$, $\dfrac{\partial u}{\partial \phi}\left(r, \dfrac{1}{2}\pi\right) = 0$, and $u(1, \phi) = \phi$.

Answer: $u(r, \phi) = \dfrac{4}{\pi} \displaystyle\sum_{n=1}^{\infty} (-1)^{n-1} \dfrac{1}{(2n-1)^2} r^{2n-1} \sin(2n-1)\phi$.

PROBLEM 8.27 Find the temperature distribution $u(x, t)$ for an infinite bar. The initial temperature distribution is

$$f(x) = \begin{cases} 0 & \text{for } x < 0 \\ T & \text{for } x > 0, \end{cases}$$

where T is a constant. (Cf., Prob. 8.11.)

Answer: $u(x, t) = \dfrac{T}{2}\left[1 + \operatorname{erf}\left(\dfrac{x}{2c\sqrt{t}}\right)\right]$, where $\operatorname{erf} y = \dfrac{2}{\sqrt{\pi}} \displaystyle\int_0^y e^{-\xi^2} d\xi$.

PROBLEM 8.28 Using the Fourier transform, solve

$$\frac{\partial^2 u}{\partial x^2} - \frac{\partial u}{\partial t} = f(x, t) \quad \text{for} \quad -\infty < x < \infty, \quad t > 0,$$

with the initial condition $u(x, 0) = 0$ for $t > 0$.

Answer: $u(x, t) = \dfrac{1}{2\sqrt{\pi}} \displaystyle\int_{-\infty}^{\infty} \int_{-\infty}^{\infty} \dfrac{e^{-(x-\xi)^2/4(t-\tau)}}{\sqrt{t-\tau}} H(t-\tau) f(\xi, \tau) d\xi d\tau$, where

$$H(\lambda) = \begin{cases} 1 & \text{for } \lambda > 0 \\ 0 & \text{for } \lambda < 0. \end{cases}$$

PROBLEM 8.29 Using the Fourier sine transform, solve

$$\frac{\partial^2 u}{\partial x^2} - \frac{\partial u}{\partial t} = 0, \quad \text{for } x > 0, \quad t > 0,$$

with $u(x, 0) = 0$ for $x > 0$, and $u(0, t) = g(t)$ for $t > 0$.

Answer: $u(x, t) = \dfrac{x}{2\sqrt{\pi}} \displaystyle\int_0^t \dfrac{g(\tau)}{(t-\tau)^{3/2}} e^{-x^2/[4(t-\tau)]} d\tau$.

MISCELLANEOUS APPLICATIONS OF THE FOURIER TRANSFORM*

9 CHAPTER

9.1 The Fourier Transform in Diffraction and Image Formation

The application of the Fourier transform to optics makes it possible to establish general relations which clarify and simplify the calculation of image formation by an optical system. In this section, we shall consider diffraction and image formation. It is assumed that the reader is familiar with the physics of these phenomena.

In this section, we shall assume that $f(x)$ is a real function; i.e., no phase change is introduced by the screen.

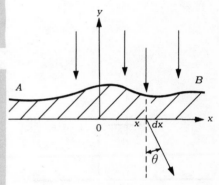

Fig. 9.1 The absorbing screen of Prob. 9.1.

PROBLEM 9.1 In the Fraunhofer diffraction phenomena, derive the relationship between the diffraction pattern and the transmission characteristic of the absorbing screen.

Solution: Consider an absorbing screen AB as shown in Fig. 9.1 whose transmission coefficient at the point x is given by $f(x)$. Assume that the screen is illuminated by a monochromatic plane wave of wavelength λ. Let us examine the complex amplitude of the resulting wave in the direction θ. The contribution of the element dx at the point x has an amplitude proportional to $f(x)$ and a phase given by $[2\pi \sin (\theta/\lambda)]x$. If the incident wave is represented by the complex quantity

$$U_o \, e^{j\omega t},$$

then the contribution due to dx at the point x is given by

$$U_o \, f(x) \, e^{j(\omega t - kx)}, \tag{9.1}$$

where

$$k = \frac{2\pi}{\lambda} \sin \theta. \tag{9.2}$$

Hence, the total contribution from the whole screen is given by

$$\int_{-\infty}^{\infty} U_o \, f(x) \, e^{j(\omega t - kx)} \, dx = U_o \, e^{j\omega t} \int_{-\infty}^{\infty} f(x) \, e^{-jkx} \, dx. \tag{9.3}$$

Then the diffraction pattern of the screen, which is defined as the ratio of the resultant wave in the direction θ to the incident wave, may be written as

$$\int_{-\infty}^{\infty} f(x) \, e^{-jkx} \, dx = F(k), \tag{9.4}$$

*It is not intended that the individual sections of this chapter be complete and self-sufficient presentations of their respective topics.

where

$$k = \frac{2\pi}{\lambda} \sin \theta.$$

We see that the transmission characteristic $f(x)$ and the diffraction pattern $F(k)$ form a Fourier transform pair. Thus,

$$f(x) = \frac{1}{2\pi} \int_{-\infty}^{\infty} F(k)\, e^{jkx}\, dk. \tag{9.5}$$

PROBLEM 9.2   Consider diffraction by a slit.   Let the slit extend from $x = -\frac{1}{2}a$ to $x = \frac{1}{2}a$, as shown in Fig. 9.2(a). Assume that the amplitude of the light transmitted by the slit is A times the magnitude of the incident wave, and that the screen is completely opaque elsewhere.   Find the intensity distribution of the diffracted light in the direction θ.

Solution: From the assumptions of the problem, the transmission characteristic $f(x)$ is as shown in Fig. 9.2(b), and is given by

$$f(x) = A p_a(x), \tag{9.6}$$

where $p_a(x)$ is defined as

$$p_a(x) = \begin{cases} 1, & |x| < \frac{1}{2}a \\ 0, & |x| > \frac{1}{2}a. \end{cases}$$

Then from the result (4.45) of Prob. 4.10,

$$F(k) = \int_{-\infty}^{\infty} f(x)\, e^{-jkx}\, dx = Aa\, \frac{\sin\left(\dfrac{ka}{2}\right)}{\left(\dfrac{ka}{2}\right)}$$

$$= Aa\, \frac{\sin\left(\dfrac{\pi a \sin\theta}{\lambda}\right)}{\left(\dfrac{\pi a \sin\theta}{\lambda}\right)}. \tag{9.7}$$

Since the intensity distribution of the diffracted light I is proportional to the square of the amplitude of the diffraction pattern,

$$I = (Aa)^2\, \frac{\sin^2\left(\dfrac{\pi a \sin\theta}{\lambda}\right)}{\left(\dfrac{\pi a \sin\theta}{\lambda}\right)^2}, \tag{9.8}$$

where a is the width of the slit and λ, the wavelength of the light.

PROBLEM 9.3   Find the intensity distribution produced by a diffraction grating consisting of N slits of width a and spacing d [Fig. 9.3(a)].

Solution: In the case of a single slit, as shown in Fig. 9.2(b), the transmission characteristic $f(x)$ corresponds to a pulse of width a.   In the case of the grating which consists of N slits of width a and spacing d, the transmission characteristic $f(x)$ corresponds to a finite train of pulses as shown in Fig. 9.3(b).

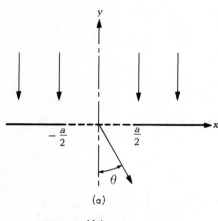

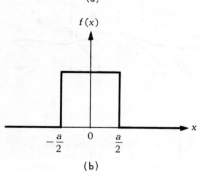

Fig. 9.2 (a) The slit of Prob. 9.2. (b) The transmission characteristic of a single slit.

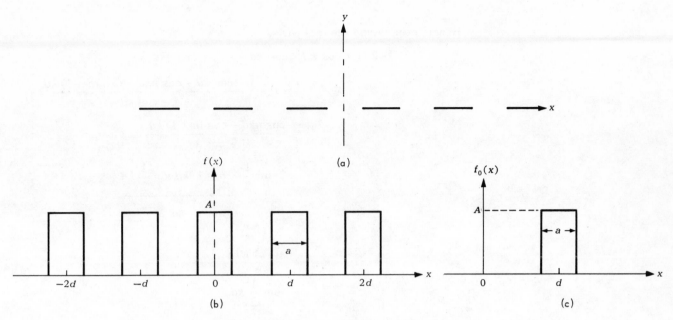

Fig. 9.3 (a) Diffraction grating of Prob. 9.3. (b) The transmission characteristic
of N slits. (c) A single pulse occurring at x = d.

In order to find the Fourier transform of $f(x)$, we proceed as follows:

From (9.7), we have the Fourier transform $F_o(k)$ of a pulse of magnitude A
and width a at the origin; i.e.,

$$F_o(k) = Aa \frac{\sin\left(\dfrac{ka}{2}\right)}{\left(\dfrac{ka}{2}\right)}, \quad k = \frac{2\pi}{\lambda} \sin \theta. \tag{9.9}$$

Then the Fourier transform of a pulse occurring at $x = d$, as shown in Fig. 9.3(c),
is found by means of the shifting theorem (4.73) as

$$e^{-jkd} F_o(k). \tag{9.10}$$

Now consider a train of N pulses occurring at

$$x = -nd, \; -(n-1)d, \; \cdots, \; -d, \; 0, \; d, \; \cdots, \; (n-1)d, \; nd,$$

where $N = 2n + 1$. By superposition,

$$\begin{aligned}
F(k) &= F_o(k) \left(1 + e^{jkd} + e^{-jkd} + \cdots + e^{jnkd} + e^{-jnkd}\right) \\
&= F_o(k) \left[1 + 2\left(\cos kd + \cos 2kd + \cdots + \cos nkd\right)\right] \\
&= F_o(k) \left[-1 + 2\left(1 + \cos kd + \cos 2kd + \cdots + \cos nkd\right)\right].
\end{aligned} \tag{9.11}$$

The series in square brackets may be summed by taking the real part of the
corresponding exponential series, and manipulating in the following fashion:

$$\begin{aligned}
-1 &+ 2\left(1 + \cos kd + \cos 2kd + \cdots + \cos nkd\right) \\
&= -1 + 2 \, Re\left(1 + e^{jkd} + e^{j2kd} + \cdots + e^{jnkd}\right) \\
&= -1 + 2 \, Re\left[\frac{1 - e^{j(n+1)kd}}{1 - e^{jkd}}\right] \\
&= -1 + 2 \, Re\left[\frac{\left(1 - e^{j(n+1)kd}\right)\left(1 - e^{-jkd}\right)}{\left(1 - e^{jkd}\right)\left(1 - e^{-jkd}\right)}\right] \\
&= -1 + 2 \, Re\left[\frac{1 - e^{-jkd} + e^{jnkd} - e^{j(n+1)kd}}{2\left(1 - \cos kd\right)}\right].
\end{aligned}$$

Hence, considering the real parts,

$$-1 + 2 (1 + \cos kd + \cos kd + \cdots + \cos nkd)$$

$$= -1 + \frac{1 - \cos kd + \cos nkd - \cos (n + 1) kd}{1 - \cos kd}$$

$$= \frac{\cos nkd - \cos (n + 1) kd}{1 - \cos kd}$$

$$= \frac{2 \sin \frac{1}{2} (2n + 1) kd \, \sin \frac{1}{2} kd}{2 \sin^2 \frac{1}{2} kd}$$

$$= \frac{\sin \frac{1}{2} Nkd}{\sin \frac{1}{2} kd}. \qquad (9.12)$$

Hence,

$$F(k) = F_o(k) \frac{\sin \left(\frac{1}{2} Nkd\right)}{\sin \left(\frac{1}{2} kd\right)} = Aa \frac{\sin \left(\frac{1}{2} ka\right)}{\left(\frac{1}{2} ka\right)} \frac{\sin \left(\frac{1}{2} Nkd\right)}{\sin \left(\frac{1}{2} kd\right)}. \qquad (9.13)$$

The intensity distribution I produced by a diffraction grating consisting of N slits of width a and spacing d is given by

$$I = |F(k)|^2 = (Aa)^2 \frac{\sin^2 \left(\frac{1}{2} ka\right)}{\left(\frac{1}{2} ka\right)^2} \frac{\sin^2 \left(\frac{1}{2} Nkd\right)}{\sin^2 \left(\frac{1}{2} kd\right)}, \qquad (9.14)$$

where $k = \dfrac{2\pi}{\lambda} \sin \theta$.

PROBLEM 9.4 Show that the variation of light intensity is not affected by displacement of the grating.

Solution: Let the grating be displaced in the x direction and the amount of the displacement be x_o; then, $f(x - x_o)$ represents the change of the transmission characteristic. Then according to the shifting theorem (4.73), the diffraction pattern becomes

$$F(k) \, e^{-jkx_o}. \qquad (9.15)$$

The intensity distribution is given by

$$|F(k) \, e^{-jkx_o}|^2 = |F(k)|^2 \qquad (9.16)$$

since $|e^{-jkx_o}| = 1$.

Equation (9.16) shows that the intensity distribution is not affected by displacement of the grating.

Next let us consider image formation and the two-dimensional Fourier transform.
When a function of two independent variables, such as the light intensity at a point, is reproduced elsewhere as another function of two variables, we speak of image formation.

An image can be fully described by the distribution of the intensity of illumination $I(x, y)$. Let $E(x, y)$ be the image of a point source and $O(x, y)$ represent an object distribution. In fact, since the object is incoherent, the intensity distribution at the image can be obtained by taking the sum of the individual intensities produced by each image of the various points of the object.

Thus the image distribution $I(x, y)$ is obtained from the object distribution $O(x, y)$ by convolution with the point-image distribution $E(x, y)$; i.e.,

$$I(x, y) = \int_{-\infty}^{\infty} \int_{-\infty}^{\infty} O(x', y') E(x - x', y - y') \, dx' dy' \tag{9.17}$$

$$= O(x, y) * E(x, y). \tag{9.18}$$

Equation (9.17) defines the convolution integral of two two-dimensional functions $O(x, y)$ and $E(x, y)$.

9.1a Two-Dimensional Fourier Transform

In order to apply the transform technique to the analysis of image formation, we shall need the theory of two-dimensional Fourier transforms.

The two-dimensional Fourier transform $F(u, v)$ of a two-dimensional function $f(x, y)$ can be defined as a double integral

$$F(u, v) = \int_{-\infty}^{\infty} \int_{-\infty}^{\infty} f(x, y) \, e^{-j(ux + vy)} \, dx \, dy. \tag{9.19}$$

Then $f(x, y)$ can be found from the inversion formula

$$f(x, y) = \frac{1}{(2\pi)^2} \int_{-\infty}^{\infty} \int_{-\infty}^{\infty} F(u, v) \, e^{j(ux + vy)} \, du \, dv. \tag{9.20}$$

PROBLEM 9.5 Using the one-dimensional Fourier transform technique, derive the inversion formula (9.20).

Solution: We denote by $G(u, y)$ the Fourier transform of the function $f(x, y)$, where the transform is taken with respect to x; i.e.,

$$G(u, y) = \int_{-\infty}^{\infty} f(x, y) \, e^{-jux} \, dx. \tag{9.21}$$

Then from the one-dimensional inversion formula (4.16),

$$f(x, y) = \frac{1}{2\pi} \int_{-\infty}^{\infty} G(u, y) \, e^{jux} \, du. \tag{9.22}$$

We now take the Fourier transform $F(u, v)$ of $G(u, y)$ with respect to y, considering x as a parameter; i.e.,

$$F(u, v) = \int_{-\infty}^{\infty} G(u, y) \, e^{-jvy} \, dy. \tag{9.23}$$

The inversion formula (4.16) gives

$$G(u, y) = \frac{1}{2\pi} \int_{-\infty}^{\infty} F(u, v) \, e^{jvy} \, dv. \tag{9.24}$$

Substituting (9.24) into (9.22),

$$f(x, y) = \frac{1}{(2\pi)^2} \int_{-\infty}^{\infty} \int_{-\infty}^{\infty} F(u, v) \, e^{j(ux + vy)} \, du \, dv.$$

Combining (9.23) and (9.21),

$$F(u, v) = \int_{-\infty}^{\infty} \int_{-\infty}^{\infty} f(x, y)\, e^{-j(ux + vy)}\, dx\, dy.$$

PROBLEM 9.6 Show that the Fourier transform of the image of an incoherent object is equal to the product of the Fourier transform of the object and the Fourier transform of the image of a point source.

Solution: Let the Fourier transform of $0(x, y)$, $I(x, y)$, and $E(x, y)$ be $\Omega(u, v)$, $\Psi(u, v)$, and $\Gamma(u, v)$, respectively; i.e.,

$$\Omega(u, v) = \int_{-\infty}^{\infty} \int_{-\infty}^{\infty} 0(x, y)\, e^{-j(ux + vy)}\, dx\, dy, \tag{9.25}$$

$$\Psi(u, v) = \int_{-\infty}^{\infty} \int_{-\infty}^{\infty} I(x, y)\, e^{-j(ux + vy)}\, dx\, dy, \tag{9.26}$$

$$\Gamma(u, v) = \int_{-\infty}^{\infty} \int_{-\infty}^{\infty} E(x, y)\, e^{-j(ux + vy)}\, dx\, dy. \tag{9.27}$$

Then, by the Fourier inversion formula (9.20),

$$0(x, y) = \frac{1}{(2\pi)^2} \int_{-\infty}^{\infty} \int_{-\infty}^{\infty} \Omega(u, v)\, e^{j(ux + vy)}\, du\, dv, \tag{9.28}$$

$$I(x, y) = \frac{1}{(2\pi)^2} \int_{-\infty}^{\infty} \int_{-\infty}^{\infty} \Psi(u, v)\, e^{j(ux + vy)}\, du\, dv, \tag{9.29}$$

$$E(x, y) = \frac{1}{(2\pi)^2} \int_{-\infty}^{\infty} \int_{-\infty}^{\infty} \Gamma(u, v)\, e^{j(ux + vy)}\, du\, dv. \tag{9.30}$$

From (9.30),

$$E(x - x', y - y') = \frac{1}{(2\pi)^2} \int_{-\infty}^{\infty} \int_{-\infty}^{\infty} \Gamma(u, v)\, e^{j\left[u(x - x') + v(y - y')\right]}\, du\, dv. \tag{9.31}$$

Now, referring to (9.17),

$$I(x, y) = \int_{-\infty}^{\infty} \int_{-\infty}^{\infty} 0(x', y') \cdot E(x - x', y - y')\, dx'\, dy' \tag{9.32}$$

Substituting (9.31) into (9.32) and interchanging the order of the integration in (9.32) results in

$$I(x, y) = \frac{1}{(2\pi)^2} \int_{-\infty}^{\infty} \int_{-\infty}^{\infty} \left\{ \Gamma(u, v)\, e^{j(ux + vy)} \right.$$

$$\left. \times \left[\int_{-\infty}^{\infty} \int_{-\infty}^{\infty} 0(x', y')\, e^{-j(ux' + vy')}\, dx'\, dy' \right] \right\}\, du\, dv. \tag{9.33}$$

By using (9.25), (9.33) becomes

$$I(x, y) = \frac{1}{(2\pi)^2} \int_{-\infty}^{\infty} \int_{-\infty}^{\infty} \Omega(u, v)\, \Gamma(u, v)\, e^{j(ux + vy)}\, du\, dv. \tag{9.34}$$

Comparing (9.34) with (9.29), we conclude that

$$\Psi(u, v) = \Omega(u, v)\, \Gamma(u, v). \tag{9.35}$$

Equation (9.35) is the two-dimensional convolution theorem. Equation (9.35) implies that the image formation is closely parallel to the case of filtering which we discussed in Sec. 6.10; i.e., the transition from the object to the image is equivalent to the action of a linear filter. In Sec. 6.10 we started with a function of time which we transformed to get its spectrum. The spectrum was modified by the filter, and the output time function was the inverse transform of the resulting spectral function. In image formation, the optical system behaves as a filter and the spatial spectrum of the intensity is transformed in this way.

9.1b Three-Dimensional Fourier Transform

In the diffraction of X-rays by crystals, we have to consider the Fourier transform in three dimensions. The three-dimensional Fourier transform pair is defined as

$$F(u,v,w) = \int_{-\infty}^{\infty} \int_{-\infty}^{\infty} \int_{-\infty}^{\infty} f(x,y,z)\, e^{-j(ux+vy+wz)}\, dx\, dy\, dz, \tag{9.36}$$

$$f(x,y,z) = \frac{1}{(2\pi)^3} \int_{-\infty}^{\infty} \int_{-\infty}^{\infty} \int_{-\infty}^{\infty} F(u,v,w)\, e^{j(ux+vy+wz)}\, du\, dv\, dw. \tag{9.37}$$

Further discussion of this topic is beyond the scope of this book.

9.2 The Fourier Transform in Probability Theory

The Fourier transform is extensively used in probability theory and random processes. In this section, we shall briefly discuss some basic functions and the Fourier transforms used in probability theory. Some familiarity with probability theory is assumed.

9.2a Probability Distribution Function and Probability Density Function

A random variable X taking real values between $-\infty$ and ∞ may be characterized by a *probability distribution function* $P(x)$. The probability distribution function $P(x)$ is defined as

$$P(x) = Pr(X < x), \tag{9.38}$$

where $Pr(X < x)$ is the probability that random variable X assumes a value less than some given number x.

If $P(x)$ is differentiable, we define the *probability density function* or frequency function $p(x)$ by

$$p(x) = \frac{dP(x)}{dx}. \tag{9.39}$$

The distribution function $P(x)$ has the following properties:

$$P(-\infty) = 0, \qquad P(\infty) = 1, \tag{9.40 a,b}$$

$$P(x_1) \le P(x_2) \quad \text{if } x_1 < x_2. \tag{9.41}$$

From the fact that $Pr(X = -\infty) = 0$, it is obvious that

$$P(-\infty) = 0.$$

Since $X < +\infty$, and certainty corresponds to probability one,

$$P(\infty) = Pr(X < +\infty) = 1.$$

Thus (9.40) indicates that $P(x)$ is positive and has values between 0 and 1.

To prove (9.41), we observe that if x_1 and x_2 are real numbers such that $x_1 < x_2$,

$$Pr(X < x_2) = Pr(X < x_1) + Pr(x_1 < X < x_2) \qquad (9.42)$$

so that

$$Pr(x_1 < X < x_2) = P(x_2) - P(x_1). \qquad (9.43)$$

From this relation and the fact that the probability of any event is always non-negative,

$$P(x_1) \leq P(x_2), \quad \text{if } x_1 < x_2.$$

Equation (9.41) indicates that $P(x)$ is a monotone nondecreasing function.

PROBLEM 9.7   Show that

$$p(x) > 0, \qquad (9.44)$$

$$P(x) = \int_{-\infty}^{x} p(x)\, dx, \qquad (9.45)$$

$$\int_{-\infty}^{\infty} p(x)\, dx = 1, \qquad (9.46)$$

$$Pr(x_1 < X < x_2) = \int_{x_1}^{x_2} p(x)\, dx. \qquad (9.47)$$

Solution: From the definition (9.39) and the fact that $P(x)$ is monotone non-decreasing for all x,

$$p(x) > 0.$$

Integrating (9.39) from $-\infty$ to x,

$$\int_{-\infty}^{x} p(x)\, dx = \int_{-\infty}^{x} \frac{dP(x)}{dx}\, dx = P(x) - P(-\infty).$$

From (9.40a), $P(-\infty) = 0$; thus,

$$\int_{-\infty}^{x} p(x)\, dx = P(x).$$

Then from (9.40b),

$$\int_{-\infty}^{\infty} p(x)\, dx = P(\infty) - P(-\infty) = 1.$$

From (9.45),

$$P(x_2) - P(x_1) = \int_{-\infty}^{x_2} p(x)\, dx - \int_{-\infty}^{x_1} p(x)\, dx = \int_{x_1}^{x_2} p(x)\, dx. \qquad (9.48)$$

From (9.48) and (9.43),

$$Pr(x_1 < X < x_2) = \int_{x_1}^{x_2} p(x)\, dx.$$

PROBLEM 9.8   Suppose that it is certain that the random variable X takes the value x_o. Then,

$$P(x) = 0 \quad \text{for } X < x_o, \quad P(x) = 1 \quad \text{for } X > x_o.$$

Find the probability density function $p(x)$.

Solution: From the assumption, $P(x)$ can be expressed as

$$P(x) = u(x - x_o), \qquad (9.49)$$

a unit step function. In this case, the probability density function $p(x)$ does not exist in the ordinary sense.   However, in the sense of a generalized function (see Sec. 2.4), we can obtain

$$p(x) = \frac{dP(x)}{dx} = \frac{du(x - x_o)}{dx} = \delta(x - x_o) \qquad (9.50)$$

with the use of (2.90).

9.2b Expectation and Moments

Let X be a random variable with probability density function $p(x)$. The mathematical expectation or *mean value* of X, $E[X]$, is defined by

$$E[X] = \int_{-\infty}^{\infty} xp(x)\, dx. \qquad (9.51)$$

For any real-valued function $g(x)$, $g(X)$ is a random variable and the mathematical expectation of $g(X)$ is defined by

$$E[g(X)] = \int_{-\infty}^{\infty} g(x)p(x)\, dx. \qquad (9.52)$$

An expectation generated by a certain function $g(x)$ is sometimes referred to as a statistical parameter.   In the following we shall define the most common of these parameters:

$$Mean\ value\ of\ X = E[X] = \overline{X} = \int_{-\infty}^{\infty} xp(x)\, dx; \qquad (9.53)$$

$$Mean\text{-}squared\ value\ of\ X = E[X^2] = \overline{X^2} = \int_{-\infty}^{\infty} x^2 p(x)\, dx; \qquad (9.54)$$

$$n\text{-}th\ moment\ of\ X = E[X^n] = m_n = \int_{-\infty}^{\infty} x^n p(x)\, dx; \qquad (9.55)$$

$$Variance\ of\ X = \text{mean-squared value of } X \text{ about the mean}$$
$$= E[(X - \overline{X})^2]; \qquad (9.56)$$
$$Standard\ deviation\ \sigma = \sqrt{E(X - \overline{X})^2}. \qquad (9.57)$$

PROBLEM 9.9   Show that

$$Variance\ of\ X = (\overline{X^2}) - (\overline{X})^2. \qquad (9.58)$$

Solution: From (9.56) and (9.52),

$$Variance\ of\ X = E[(X - \overline{X})^2]$$

$$= \int_{-\infty}^{\infty} (x - \overline{X})^2 p(x)\, dx$$

$$= \int_{-\infty}^{\infty} (x^2 - 2x\overline{X} + \overline{X}^2) p(x)\, dx$$

$$= \int_{-\infty}^{\infty} x^2 p(x)\, dx - 2\overline{X} \int_{-\infty}^{\infty} xp(x)\, dx + (\overline{X})^2 \int_{-\infty}^{\infty} p(x)\, dx.$$

Hence,

$$\text{var}(X) = (\overline{X^2}) - 2\,\overline{X}\overline{X} + (\overline{X})^2 = (\overline{X^2}) - (\overline{X})^2. \tag{9.59}$$

Equations (9.53), (9.54), and (9.46) were used to derive (9.59).

PROBLEM 9.10 Show that if the probability density function $p(x)$ is an even function, i.e., $p(-x) = p(x)$, then the mean and all of the odd numbered moments are zero.

Solution: From (9.55),

$$m_n = n\text{-th moment of } X = E[X^n] = \int_{-\infty}^{\infty} x^n p(x)\,dx.$$

If n is odd, then the integrand $x^n p(x)$ is an odd function of x. Hence from (2.14),

$$m_n = \int_{-\infty}^{\infty} x^n p(x)\,dx = 0 \quad \text{for } n = 1, 3, 5, \cdots. \tag{9.60}$$

9.2c Characteristic Function

The characteristic function $\phi(\omega)$ of a random variable X with probability density function $p(x)$ is defined by

$$\phi(\omega) = E[e^{j\omega X}], \tag{9.61}$$

where ω is an arbitrary real-valued parameter.

PROBLEM 9.11 Show that the characteristic function $\phi(\omega)$ of a random variable X is the Fourier transform of its probability density function $p(x)$ with a reversal in sign.

Solution: From (9.52), we can rewrite (9.61) as

$$\phi(\omega) = E[e^{j\omega X}] = \int_{-\infty}^{\infty} e^{j\omega x} p(x)\,dx, \tag{9.62}$$

which is the Fourier transform of $p(x)$ with a reversal in sign. Sometimes this is called the *plus-j Fourier transform*.

PROBLEM 9.12 Show that the probability density function $p(x)$ can be expressed in terms of $\phi(\omega)$ by

$$p(x) = \frac{1}{2\pi} \int_{-\infty}^{\infty} \phi(\omega)\, e^{-j\omega x}\,d\omega, \tag{9.63}$$

which is known as the *inversion formula*.

Solution: Since from (9.62), $\phi(\omega)$ is found to be the Fourier transform of $p(x)$ with a reversal in sign, $p(x)$ can be found from the inverse Fourier transform of $\phi(\omega)$, again with a sign reversal; i.e.,

$$p(x) = \mathscr{F}^{-1}[\phi(\omega)] = \frac{1}{2\pi} \int_{-\infty}^{\infty} \phi(\omega)\, e^{-j\omega x}\,d\omega.$$

Alternate Solution: Substituting (9.62) into the right side of (9.63),

$$\frac{1}{2\pi} \int_{-\infty}^{\infty} \phi(\omega)\, e^{-j\omega x}\,d\omega = \frac{1}{2\pi} \int_{-\infty}^{\infty} e^{-j\omega x} \left[\int_{-\infty}^{\infty} e^{j\omega\lambda}\, p(\lambda)\,d\lambda \right] d\omega. \tag{9.64}$$

Changing the order of integration,

$$\frac{1}{2\pi} \int_{-\infty}^{\infty} \phi(\omega) e^{-j\omega x} d\omega = \int_{-\infty}^{\infty} p(\lambda) \left[\frac{1}{2\pi} \int_{-\infty}^{\infty} e^{j\omega(\lambda - x)} d\omega \right] d\lambda. \qquad (9.65)$$

Using the identity (5.6) of the δ-function,

$$\frac{1}{2\pi} \int_{-\infty}^{\infty} e^{j\omega(\lambda - x)} d\omega = \delta(\lambda - x). \qquad (9.66)$$

Hence, in view of (2.68),

$$\frac{1}{2\pi} \int_{-\infty}^{\infty} \phi(\omega) e^{-j\omega x} d\omega = \int_{-\infty}^{\infty} p(\lambda)\delta(\lambda - x) d\lambda = p(x).$$

One of the important uses of characteristic functions follows from the existence of the Fourier transform pair (9.62) and (9.63). In many problems, when it is required to find the probability density function of a certain random variable, it is easier to compute the characteristic function first and then from this, the density function. Another important application of the characteristic function is illustrated in the following example.

PROBLEM 9.13 Show that the derivatives of the characteristic function of a random variable X are related to its moments

$$m_n = E[X^n] = \int_{-\infty}^{\infty} x^n p(x) \, dx$$

by

$$\left. \frac{d^n \phi(\omega)}{d\omega^n} \right|_{\omega=0} = j^n m_n. \qquad (9.67)$$

Solution: Since

$$e^{j\omega x} = 1 + \frac{j\omega x}{1} + \cdots + \frac{(j\omega x)^n}{n!} + \cdots, \qquad (9.68)$$

substituting (9.68) into (9.62),

$$\phi(\omega) = E[e^{j\omega X}] = \int_{-\infty}^{\infty} p(x) e^{j\omega x} dx \cdot$$

$$= \int_{-\infty}^{\infty} p(x) \left[1 + \frac{j\omega x}{1} + \cdots + \frac{(j\omega x)^n}{n!} + \cdots \right] dx.$$

Assuming that term-by-term integration is valid,

$$\phi(\omega) = \int_{-\infty}^{\infty} p(x) \, dx + j\omega \int_{-\infty}^{\infty} xp(x) \, dx + \cdots + \frac{(j\omega)^n}{n!} \int_{-\infty}^{\infty} x^n p(x) \, dx + \cdots$$

$$= 1 + j\omega m_1 + \cdots + \frac{(j\omega)^n}{n!} m_n + \cdots. \qquad (9.69)$$

Hence,

$$\left. \frac{d^n \phi(\omega)}{d\omega^n} \right|_{\omega=0} = j^n m_n.$$

So far we have dealt with only one random variable. Next we shall extend these concepts for two random variables.

The *joint distribution function* of the random variables X and Y is defined by

$$P(x, y) = Pr\{X < x, Y < y\}. \qquad (9.70)$$

Assuming that $P(x, y)$ has partial derivatives of the second order, the quantity

$$p(x, y) = \frac{\partial^2 P(x, y)}{\partial x \, \partial y} \qquad (9.71)$$

is known as the *joint density function* of the random variables X and Y.

Two random variables X and Y are called *independent* if

$$P(x, y) = P(x) P(y). \qquad (9.72)$$

PROBLEM 9.14 Show that if two random variables X and Y are independent, then

$$p(x, y) = p(x) p(y). \qquad (9.73)$$

Solution: Since the random variables X and Y are independent, from (9.72),

$$P(x, y) = P(x) P(y).$$

Then from (9.71),

$$p(x, y) = \frac{\partial^2 P(x, y)}{\partial x \, \partial y} = \frac{\partial^2 P(x) P(y)}{\partial x \, \partial y} = \frac{\partial P(x)}{\partial x} \frac{\partial P(y)}{\partial y} = p(x) p(y).$$

The expected value of the random variable $g(X, Y)$ is defined by

$$E[g(X, Y)] = \int_{-\infty}^{\infty} \int_{-\infty}^{\infty} g(x, y) p(x, y) \, dx \, dy. \qquad (9.74)$$

Two random variables X and Y are called *uncorrelated* if

$$E[XY] = E[X] E[Y]. \qquad (9.75)$$

They are called *orthogonal* if

$$E[XY] = 0. \qquad (9.76)$$

The *joint characteristic function* of two random variables X and Y is defined by

$$\phi(\omega_1, \omega_2) = E[e^{j(\omega_1 X + \omega_2 Y)}]. \qquad (9.77)$$

PROBLEM 9.15 Show that if the random variables X and Y are independent, then they are also uncorrelated.

Solution: From (9.73) and (9.74),

$$E[XY] = \int_{-\infty}^{\infty} \int_{-\infty}^{\infty} xy \, p(x, y) \, dx \, dy$$

$$= \int_{-\infty}^{\infty} \int_{-\infty}^{\infty} xy \, p(x) \, p(y) \, dx \, dy$$

$$= \int_{-\infty}^{\infty} x p(x) \, dx \int_{-\infty}^{\infty} y p(y) \, dy$$

$$= E[X] E[Y]. \qquad (9.78)$$

Thus from (9.75), two random variables X and Y are uncorrelated.

We note that if X and Y are independent, then $f(X)$ and $g(Y)$ are also independent. Applying (9.78) to $f(X)$ and $g(Y)$,

$$E[f(X)g(Y)] = E[f(X)]E[g(Y)]. \qquad (9.79)$$

PROBLEM 9.16   Show that the joint characteristic function of two random variables X and Y is the double Fourier transform of $p(x, y)$ defined by (9.19) with a reversal in sign.

Solution: From (9.74), we can rewrite (9.77) as

$$\phi(\omega_1, \omega_2) = E[e^{j(\omega_1 X + \omega_2 Y)}]$$

$$= \int_{-\infty}^{\infty} \int_{-\infty}^{\infty} p(x, y) e^{j(\omega_1 x + \omega_2 y)} dx\, dy, \qquad (9.80)$$

which is the two-dimensional Fourier transform of $p(x, y)$ defined by (9.19) with a reversal in sign.

PROBLEM 9.17   Show that the joint probability density function $p(x, y)$ can be expressed in terms of $\phi(\omega_1, \omega_2)$ by

$$p(x, y) = \frac{1}{(2\pi)^2} \int_{-\infty}^{\infty} \int_{-\infty}^{\infty} \phi(\omega_1, \omega_2) e^{-j(\omega_1 x + \omega_2 y)} d\omega_1\, d\omega_2. \qquad (9.81)$$

Solution: Since from (9.80), $\phi(\omega_1, \omega_2)$ is found to be the two-dimensional Fourier transform of $p(x, y)$, by applying the inverse double Fourier transform formula (9.20), with a sign reversal, we obtain (9.81).

PROBLEM 9.18   Show that if the random variables X and Y are independent, then

$$\phi(\omega_1, \omega_2) = \phi(\omega_1)\phi(\omega_2). \qquad (9.82)$$

Solution: If X and Y are independent, then from (9.79),

$$E[e^{j(\omega_1 X + \omega_2 Y)}] = E[e^{j\omega_1 X} e^{j\omega_2 Y}] = E[e^{j\omega_1 X}]E[e^{j\omega_2 Y}]. \qquad (9.83)$$

Hence,

$$\phi(\omega_1, \omega_2) = \phi(\omega_1)\phi(\omega_2).$$

PROBLEM 9.19   Show that if $\phi(\omega_1, \omega_2) = \phi(\omega_1)\phi(\omega_2)$, then the random variables X and Y are independent.

Solution: From (9.81),

$$p(x, y) = \frac{1}{(2\pi)^2} \int_{-\infty}^{\infty} \int_{-\infty}^{\infty} \phi(\omega_1, \omega_2) e^{-j(\omega_1 x + \omega_2 y)} d\omega_1\, d\omega_2$$

$$= \frac{1}{(2\pi)^2} \int_{-\infty}^{\infty} \int_{-\infty}^{\infty} \phi(\omega_1)\phi(\omega_2) e^{-j(\omega_1 x + \omega_2 y)} d\omega_1\, d\omega_2$$

$$= \frac{1}{2\pi} \int_{-\infty}^{\infty} \phi(\omega_1) e^{-j\omega_1 x} d\omega_1 \frac{1}{2\pi} \int_{-\infty}^{\infty} \phi(\omega_2) e^{-j\omega_2 y} d\omega_2$$

$$= p(x)p(y),$$

in view of (9.63). Hence from (9.73) we conclude that X and Y are independent.

PROBLEM 9.20 Show that the probability density function of the sum of two independent random variables equals the convolution of their respective density functions.

Solution: Suppose that

$$Z = X + Y, \tag{9.84}$$

where X and Y are independent random variables.

Let

$$\phi_x(\omega) = E\left[e^{j\omega X}\right],$$

$$\phi_y(\omega) = E\left[e^{j\omega Y}\right],$$

$$\phi_z(\omega) = E\left[e^{j\omega Z}\right].$$

Then,

$$\phi_z(\omega) = E\left[e^{j\omega Z}\right] = E\left[e^{j(\omega X + \omega Y)}\right].$$

Since X and Y are independent, from (9.83),

$$\phi_z(\omega) = E\left[e^{j\omega X}\right] E\left[e^{j\omega Y}\right] = \phi_x(\omega)\,\phi_y(\omega). \tag{9.85}$$

Applying the convolution theorem (4.122),

$$\begin{aligned}
p_z(z) &= \mathcal{F}^{-1}\left[\phi_z(\omega)\right] \\
&= \mathcal{F}^{-1}\left[\phi_x(\omega)\,\phi_y(\omega)\right] \\
&= p_x(x) * p_y(y) \\
&= \int_{-\infty}^{\infty} p_x(x)\,p_y(z-x)\,dx.
\end{aligned} \tag{9.86}$$

9.3 Uncertainty Principle in Fourier Analysis

The uncertainty principle in spectral analysis can be stated as follows: The product of the spectral bandwidth and the time duration of a signal cannot be less than a certain minimum value. This is similar to the well known statement of Heisenberg's uncertainty principle in quantum mechanics.

In this section we shall discuss the relationship between the time spread of a function $f(t)$ and the shape of its Fourier transform $F(\omega)$.

We consider a real signal $f(t)$ and its Fourier transform

$$F(\omega) = \int_{-\infty}^{\infty} f(t)\,e^{-j\omega t}\,dt.$$

Let us define the following:

$$\|f\|^2 = \int_{-\infty}^{\infty} f^2(t)\,dt < \infty, \tag{9.87}$$

$$\bar{t} = \frac{1}{\|f\|^2} \int_{-\infty}^{\infty} t\,f^2(t)\,dt, \tag{9.88}$$

$$(\Delta t)^2 = \frac{1}{\|f\|^2} \int_{-\infty}^{\infty} (t - \bar{t})^2 f^2(t)\,dt < \infty, \tag{9.89}$$

where $\|f\|^2$ is the *energy content* E of the signal $f(t)$ defined in (4.139), $\bar{t}$ is the *center of gravity* of the area under the curve $f^2(t)$, and (Δt) is a measure of how much the signal is spread about $\bar{t}$, called the *dispersion* in time of the signal.

Similarly we define

$$\| F \|^2 = \int_{-\infty}^{\infty} | F(\omega) |^2 \, d\omega, \qquad (9.90)$$

$$\overline{\omega} = \frac{1}{\| F \|^2} \int_{-\infty}^{\infty} \omega | F(\omega) |^2 \, d\omega, \qquad (9.91)$$

$$(\Delta\omega)^2 = \frac{1}{\| F \|^2} \int_{-\infty}^{\infty} (\omega - \overline{\omega})^2 | F(\omega) |^2 \, d\omega. \qquad (9.92)$$

PROBLEM 9.21 Show that $\overline{\omega}$ of (9.91) is equal to zero.

Solution: Since $| F(\omega) |^2$ is even with respect to ω, the integrand of (9.91) is an odd function of ω. Hence from (2.14),

$$\int_{-\infty}^{\infty} \omega | F(\omega) |^2 \, d\omega = 0,$$

i.e., $\overline{\omega} = 0$. With $\overline{\omega} = 0$, (9.92) can be rewritten as

$$(\Delta\omega)^2 = \frac{1}{\| F \|^2} \int_{-\infty}^{\infty} \omega^2 | F(\omega) |^2 \, d\omega. \qquad (9.93)$$

The *spectral bandwidth* of the signal $\Delta\omega$ is a measure of the bandwidth of the signal.

PROBLEM 9.22 Find the time dispersion Δt of the exponentially decaying pulse signal shown in Fig. 9.4.

Solution: From (9.88), the center of gravity of this waveform $\overline{t}$ is found as

$$\overline{t} = \frac{\displaystyle\int_0^{\infty} t A^2 e^{-2t/T} \, dt}{\displaystyle\int_0^{\infty} A^2 e^{-2t/T} \, dt} = \frac{\dfrac{A^2 T^2}{4}}{\dfrac{A^2 T}{2}} = \frac{T}{2}. \qquad (9.94)$$

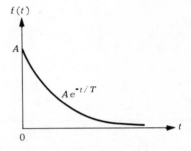

Fig. 9.4 The exponentially decaying pulse signal.

Then from (9.89), because $\| f \|^2 = A^2 T/2$,

$$(\Delta t)^2 = \frac{1}{\dfrac{A^2 T}{2}} \int_0^{\infty} \left(t - \frac{T}{2} \right)^2 A^2 e^{-2t/T} \, dt = \frac{2}{T} \int_0^{\infty} \left(t - \frac{T}{2} \right)^2 e^{-2t/T} \, dt$$

$$= \frac{2}{T} \int_0^{\infty} \left(t^2 - Tt + \frac{1}{4} T^2 \right) e^{-2t/T} \, dt,$$

$$= \frac{2}{T} \left(\frac{T^3}{4} - \frac{T^3}{4} + \frac{T^3}{8} \right)$$

$$= \frac{T^2}{4}. \qquad (9.95)$$

Hence,

$$\Delta t = \frac{1}{2} T. \qquad (9.96)$$

It is noted that the time dispersion Δt of an exponentially decaying signal is proportional to the time constant T.

PROBLEM 9.23   Show that the spectral bandwidth $\Delta\omega$ of a signal $f(t)$ defined by (9.93) will be finite only if the following integral is finite; that is,

$$\int_{-\infty}^{\infty} [f'(t)]^2 \, dt = \text{finite}, \tag{9.97}$$

where $f'(t) = df(t)/dt$.

Solution: Since

$$\omega^2 |F(\omega)|^2 = \omega^2 F(\omega) F^*(\omega) = j\omega F(\omega)[-j\omega F^*(\omega)]$$
$$= j\omega F(\omega)[j\omega F(\omega)]^*$$
$$= |j\omega F(\omega)|^2,$$

we have

$$\int_{-\infty}^{\infty} \omega^2 |F(\omega)|^2 \, d\omega = \int_{-\infty}^{\infty} |j\omega F(\omega)|^2 \, d\omega. \tag{9.98}$$

We now recall that if

$$\mathcal{F}[f(t)] = F(\omega),$$

and if $f(t) \longrightarrow 0$ as $t \longrightarrow \pm\infty$, then from (4.91),

$$\mathcal{F}[f'(t)] = j\omega F(\omega).$$

Therefore from Parseval's theorem (4.136),

$$\int_{-\infty}^{\infty} \omega^2 |F(\omega)|^2 \, d\omega = \int_{-\infty}^{\infty} |j\omega F(\omega)|^2 \, d\omega = 2\pi \int_{-\infty}^{\infty} [f'(t)]^2 \, dt. \tag{9.99}$$

Hence if $\displaystyle\int_{-\infty}^{\infty} [f'(t)]^2 \, dt = \text{finite}$,   then

$$\int_{-\infty}^{\infty} \omega^2 |F(\omega)|^2 \, d\omega = \text{finite}, \tag{9.100}$$

and consequently from (9.93), $\Delta\omega$ will be finite.

Equation (9.100) also means that

$$\lim_{\omega \to \infty} \omega^2 |F(\omega)|^2 = 0. \tag{9.101}$$

It is noted from the result of Prob. 9.23 that the definition of spectral bandwidth, (9.93), can lead to an infinite bandwidth unless the signal $f(t)$ satisfies the condition (9.97) or (9.101). The following example illustrates this instance.

PROBLEM 9.24 Find the spectral bandwidth of the rectangular pulse of Fig. 9.5(a).

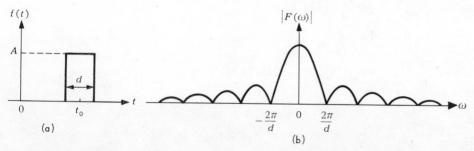

Fig. 9.5 (a) The rectangular pulse of Prob. 9.24. (b) The spectral bandwidth of the rectangular pulse of Fig. 9.5(a).

Solution: From (4.45) and (4.73), the Fourier transform of $f(t)$ is given by

$$F(\omega) = e^{-j\omega t_o} \, Ad \, \frac{\sin\left(\dfrac{\omega d}{2}\right)}{\left(\dfrac{\omega d}{2}\right)}. \tag{9.102}$$

Since $\left| e^{-j\omega t_o} \right| = 1$,

$$\left| F(\omega) \right| = Ad \left| \frac{\sin\left(\dfrac{\omega d}{2}\right)}{\left(\dfrac{\omega d}{2}\right)} \right|. \tag{9.103}$$

From Parseval's theorem (4.136),

$$\| F \|^2 = \int_{-\infty}^{\infty} \left| F(\omega) \right|^2 d\omega = 2\pi \int_{-\infty}^{\infty} f^2(t)\, dt = 2\pi\, A^2 d. \tag{9.104}$$

From (9.93),

$$(\Delta\omega)^2 = \frac{1}{\| F \|^2} \int_{-\infty}^{\infty} \omega^2 \left| F(\omega) \right|^2 d\omega$$

$$= \frac{1}{2\pi A^2 d} \int_{-\infty}^{\infty} A^2 d^2 \omega^2 \, \frac{\sin^2\left(\dfrac{\omega d}{2}\right)}{\left(\dfrac{\omega d}{2}\right)^2} \, d\omega$$

$$= \frac{2}{\pi d} \int_{-\infty}^{\infty} \sin^2\left(\frac{\omega d}{2}\right) d\omega$$

$$= \frac{1}{\pi d} \int_{-\infty}^{\infty} \left[1 - \cos(\omega d) \right] d\omega \tag{9.105}$$

which is infinite since $\displaystyle\lim_{\omega \to 0} \omega^2 \left| F(\omega) \right| \neq 0.$

In practice, the spectral bandwidth of a square pulse is conveniently defined as $2\pi/d$; i.e., the first zero of $\left| F(\omega) \right|$ [See Fig. 9.5(b)]. Within this width, most of the energy of the pulse is included.

The *uncertainty principle* in spectral analysis states that if the signal $f(t)$ is such that the integrals (9.87) to (9.93) are finite, and also $\displaystyle\lim_{t\to\infty} \sqrt{t}\, f(t) = 0$, then

$$\Delta t \, \Delta\omega \geq \frac{1}{2} \,. \tag{9.106}$$

Schwartz's inequality states that for two functions $f(t)$ and $g(t)$,

$$\int_{-\infty}^{\infty} f^2(t)\, dt \int_{-\infty}^{\infty} g^2(t)\, dt \geq \left| \int_{-\infty}^{\infty} f(t)\, g(t)\, dt \right|^2 . \tag{9.107}$$

PROBLEM 9.25 (a) Prove Schwartz's inequality. (b) Prove the uncertainty principle in spectral analysis.

Solution: (a) Let x be any real variable and

$$m(x) = \int_{-\infty}^{\infty} \left[f(t) + x\, g(t) \right]^2 dt = \int_{-\infty}^{\infty} f^2(t)\, dt + 2x \int_{-\infty}^{\infty} f(t)\, g(t)\, dt + x^2 \int_{-\infty}^{\infty} g^2(t)\, dt.$$

Let

$$\int_{-\infty}^{\infty} g^2(t)\, dt = a, \quad 2\int_{-\infty}^{\infty} f(t)\, g(t)\, dt = b, \quad \int_{-\infty}^{\infty} f^2(t)\, dt = c. \tag{9.108}$$

Since $m(x)$ is the integral of a squared value, it is always positive, real; hence,

$$m(x) = ax^2 + bx + c > 0 \quad \text{for real } x. \tag{9.109}$$

From (9.109) it follows that its discriminant $b^2 - 4ac$ must be nonpositive; i.e.,

$$b^2 - 4ac \leq 0 \quad \text{or} \quad ac \geq \frac{1}{4}\, b^2.$$

Substituting for a, b, and c from (9.108), the Schwartz's inequality (9.107) is proved.

(b) From Parseval's theorem (4.136),

$$\int_{-\infty}^{\infty} |F(\omega)|^2\, d\omega = 2\pi \int_{-\infty}^{\infty} f^2(t)\, dt, \tag{9.110}$$

that is,

$$\| F \|^2 = 2\pi \| f \|^2. \tag{9.111}$$

From (9.99),

$$\int_{-\infty}^{\infty} \omega^2 |F(\omega)|^2\, d\omega = 2\pi \int_{-\infty}^{\infty} [f'(t)]^2\, dt. \tag{9.99}$$

Now, multiplying (9.89) and (9.93), and using (9.110) and (9.99),

$$(\Delta t\, \Delta\omega)^2 = \frac{1}{\| f \|^2 \| F \|^2} \int_{-\infty}^{\infty} (t - \bar{t})^2 f^2(t)\, dt \int_{-\infty}^{\infty} \omega^2 |F(\omega)|^2\, d\omega$$

$$= \frac{1}{[\| f \|^2]^2} \int_{-\infty}^{\infty} (t - \bar{t})^2 f^2(t)\, dt \int_{-\infty}^{\infty} [f'(t)]^2\, dt. \tag{9.112}$$

By choosing a suitable time reference, we can set $\bar{t} = 0$ without loss of generality; hence, with this choice,

$$(\Delta t\, \Delta\omega)^2 = \frac{1}{[\| f \|^2]^2} \int_{-\infty}^{\infty} t^2 f^2(t)\, dt \int_{-\infty}^{\infty} [f'(t)]^2\, dt. \tag{9.113}$$

Using Schwartz's inequality theorem (9.107),

$$\int_{-\infty}^{\infty} t^2 f^2(t)\, dt \int_{-\infty}^{\infty} [f'(t)]^2\, dt \geq \left| \int_{-\infty}^{\infty} t f(t) f'(t)\, dt \right|^2. \tag{9.114}$$

Now, integrating by parts,

$$\int_{-\infty}^{\infty} t f(t) f'(t)\, dt = \int_{t=-\infty}^{t=\infty} t f(t)\, df(t)$$

$$= \frac{1}{2} t f^2(t) \Big|_{-\infty}^{\infty} - \frac{1}{2} \int_{-\infty}^{\infty} f^2(t)\, dt.$$

Hence, if $\lim_{t \to \infty} t f^2(t) = 0$, then

$$\int_{-\infty}^{\infty} t f(t) f'(t)\, dt = -\frac{1}{2} \int_{-\infty}^{\infty} f^2(t)\, dt$$

$$= -\frac{1}{2} \| f \|^2. \tag{9.115}$$

Substituting this result in (9.114) and using the resulting inequality in (9.113),

$$(\Delta t \, \Delta \omega)^2 \geq \frac{\frac{1}{4} \, [\| f \|^2]^2}{[\| f \|^2]^2} = \frac{1}{4}. \tag{9.116}$$

Hence,

$$\Delta t \, \Delta \omega \geq \frac{1}{2}. $$

PROBLEM 9.26   Considering the function $f(t)$ shown in Fig. 9.6(a), illustrate the uncertainty principle of Prob. 9.25.

Solution: The function and its derivative are

$$f(t) = at \, e^{-at} \, u(t), \quad a > 0, \tag{9.117}$$

$$f'(t) = a(1 - at) \, e^{-at} \, u(t). \tag{9.118}$$

From (9.88), the center of gravity $\overline{t}$ of this waveform is found as

$$\overline{t} = \frac{\displaystyle\int_0^\infty a^2 t^3 \, e^{-2at} \, dt}{\displaystyle\int_0^\infty a^2 t^2 \, e^{-2at} \, dt} = \frac{\displaystyle\int_0^\infty t^3 \, e^{-2at} \, dt}{\displaystyle\int_0^\infty t^2 \, e^{-2at} \, dt}$$

$$= \frac{\dfrac{3}{2a} \, \dfrac{1}{4a^3}}{\dfrac{1}{(4a^3)}} = \frac{3}{2a}. \tag{9.119}$$

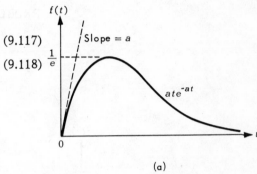

(a)

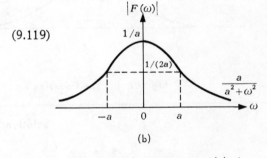

(b)

Fig. 9.6 (a) The function $f(t)$ of Prob. 9.26. (b) The spectrum of the function $f(t)$ of Fig. 9.6(a).

Then from (9.89),

$$(\Delta t)^2 = \frac{1}{\dfrac{1}{4a}} \int_0^\infty \left(t - \frac{3}{2a} \right)^2 a^2 t^2 \, e^{-2at} \, dt$$

$$= \frac{1}{\dfrac{1}{4a}} \, \frac{3}{16a^3} \tag{9.120}$$

$$= \frac{3}{4a^2}. $$

Hence,

$$\Delta t = \frac{\sqrt{3}}{2a}. \tag{9.121}$$

The spectral bandwidth $\Delta\omega$ of $f(t)$ can be found as follows: From (9.93),

$$(\Delta\omega)^2 = \frac{1}{\| F \|^2} \int_{-\infty}^\infty \omega^2 \, | F(\omega) |^2 \, d\omega.$$

From (9.108) and (9.99), we can rewrite (9.93) as

$$(\Delta\omega)^2 = \frac{1}{2\pi \, \| f \|^2} \, 2\pi \int_{-\infty}^\infty [f'(t)]^2 \, dt$$

$$= \frac{1}{\| f \|^2} \int_{-\infty}^\infty [f'(t)]^2 \, dt. \tag{9.122}$$

Hence, from (9.118),

$$(\Delta\omega)^2 = \frac{1}{\dfrac{1}{4a}} \int_0^\infty a^2(1 - at)^2\, e^{-2at}\, dt = \frac{1}{\dfrac{1}{4a}}\,\frac{a}{4} = a^2, \qquad (9.123)$$

$$\Delta\omega = a. \qquad (9.124)$$

Hence,

$$\Delta t\,\Delta\omega = \frac{\sqrt{3}}{2a}\,a = \frac{\sqrt{3}}{2} > \frac{1}{2}. \qquad (9.125)$$

PROBLEM 9.27   Considering the Gaussian function [Fig. 9.7(a)]

$$f(t) = e^{-at^2}, \quad a > 0, \qquad (9.126)$$

illustrate the uncertainty principle of Prob. 9.25.

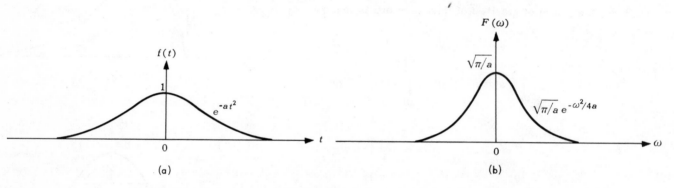

Fig. 9.7 (a) The Gaussian function. (b) The spectrum of the Gaussian function of Fig. 9.7(a).

Solution: Let $F(\omega) = \mathcal{F}[f(t)]$.   Then,

$$F(\omega) = \int_{-\infty}^\infty e^{-at^2}\, e^{-j\omega t}\, dt = \int_{-\infty}^\infty e^{-a(t^2 + j\omega t/a)}\, dt.$$

This kind of integral is evaluated by "completing the square." To do this, multiply the integrand by $e^{-\omega^2/4a} \cdot e^{+\omega^2/4a}$. Then,

$$F(\omega) = \int_{-\infty}^\infty e^{-\omega^2/(4a)}\, e^{-a\left[t + j\omega/(2a)\right]^2}\, dt$$

$$= e^{-\omega^2/(4a)} \int_{-\infty}^\infty e^{-\left\{\sqrt{a}\left[t + j\omega/(2a)\right]\right\}^2}\, dt. \qquad (9.127)$$

Introducing a new variable of integration y by setting

$$\sqrt{a}\left[t + \frac{j\omega}{(2a)}\right] = y,$$

then $\sqrt{a}\, dt = dy$, and we have

$$\int_{-\infty}^\infty e^{-\left\{\sqrt{a}\left[t + j\omega/(2a)\right]\right\}^2}\, dt = \frac{1}{\sqrt{a}} \int_{-\infty}^\infty e^{-y^2}\, dy = \sqrt{\frac{\pi}{a}}, \qquad (9.128)$$

in view of (8.175); i.e.,

$$\int_{-\infty}^\infty e^{-y^2}\, dy = \sqrt{\pi}.$$

Hence,

$$F(\omega) = \mathcal{F}[e^{-at^2}] = \sqrt{\frac{\pi}{a}}\, e^{-\omega^2/(4a)}. \tag{9.129}$$

From (9.126) and (9.129) it is seen that the Fourier transform of the Gaussian function is also Gaussian.

With $a = 1/2$, (9.129) gives

$$\mathcal{F}[e^{-t^2/2}] = \sqrt{2\pi}\, e^{-\omega^2/2}. \tag{9.130}$$

Thus, except for the factor $\sqrt{2\pi}$, the function $e^{-t^2/2}$ is its own Fourier transform.

Since the function e^{-at^2} is even, from (9.88), the center of gravity t of this waveform is zero.

Then from (9.89),

$$(\Delta t)^2 = \frac{\displaystyle\int_{-\infty}^{\infty} t^2\, e^{-2at^2}\, dt}{\displaystyle\int_{-\infty}^{\infty} e^{-2at^2}\, dt}. \tag{9.131}$$

Now, from (9.128),

$$\int_{-\infty}^{\infty} e^{-by^2}\, dy = \sqrt{\frac{\pi}{b}}. \tag{9.132}$$

Differentiating both sides of (9.132) with respect to b,

$$\int_{-\infty}^{\infty} y^2\, e^{-by^2}\, dy = \frac{1}{2b}\, \sqrt{\frac{\pi}{b}}. \tag{9.133}$$

Using (9.132) and (9.133), we can evaluate (9.131) as

$$(\Delta t)^2 = \frac{\dfrac{1}{2(2a)}\,\sqrt{\dfrac{\pi}{2a}}}{\sqrt{\dfrac{\pi}{2a}}} = \frac{1}{2(2a)}. \tag{9.134}$$

Similarly, from (9.93) and (9.129),

$$(\Delta\omega)^2 = \frac{\dfrac{\pi}{a}\displaystyle\int_{-\infty}^{\infty} \omega^2\, e^{-\omega^2/(2a)}\, d\omega}{\dfrac{\pi}{a}\displaystyle\int_{-\infty}^{\infty} e^{-\omega^2/(2a)}\, d\omega}$$

$$= \frac{\displaystyle\int_{-\infty}^{\infty} \omega^2\, e^{-\omega^2/(2a)}\, d\omega}{\displaystyle\int_{-\infty}^{\infty} e^{-\omega^2/(2a)}\, d\omega}$$

$$= \frac{\dfrac{1}{2}(2a)\sqrt{2a\pi}}{\sqrt{2a\pi}}$$

$$= \frac{1}{2}(2a) \tag{9.135}$$

with the use of (9.132) and (9.133).

Hence,

$$(\Delta t)^2 (\Delta \omega)^2 = \frac{1}{2} \frac{1}{(2a)} \frac{1}{2} (2a) = \frac{1}{4}, \qquad (9.136)$$

$$\Delta t \, \Delta \omega = \frac{1}{2}. \qquad (9.137)$$

Equation (9.137) shows that the equality sign in (9.106) holds for the Gaussian function.

In Prob. 9.23, we discussed the condition needed so that $f(t)$ has a finite spectral bandwidth defined by (9.93). With an appropriate definition of spectral bandwidth other than (9.93), we still can establish the general relationship between the signal duration and its spectral bandwidth. The following example illustrates this case.

PROBLEM 9.28   Consider the rectangular pulse given in Prob. 9.24. Show that the product of spectral bandwidth and pulse duration is a constant with "appropriate" selection of some measure of the bandwidth.

Solution: From Fig. 9.5 it is seen intuitively that if we select

$$\Delta t = d,$$

and the spectral bandwidth $\Delta \omega$ as the frequency range to the first zero of $|F(\omega)|$ (within this range most of the energy of the pulse is included),

$$\Delta \omega = \frac{2\pi}{d}. \qquad (9.138)$$

Then we observe that

$$\Delta t \, \Delta \omega = d \, \frac{2\pi}{d} = 2\pi, \qquad (9.139)$$

or that the product of the bandwidth and the pulse duration is a constant.

9.4 Poisson's Summation Formula

The Fourier transform theorems also help us to evaluate sums. In this section we shall derive the Poisson's summation formula and discuss some of its applications.

PROBLEM 9.29   If $f(t)$ is an arbitrary function and $F(\omega)$ its Fourier transform, then prove the following identity:

$$\sum_{n=-\infty}^{\infty} f(t + nT) = \frac{1}{T} \sum_{n=-\infty}^{\infty} e^{jn\omega_0 t} F(n\omega_0), \qquad (9.140)$$

where $\omega_0 = 2\pi/T.$

Solution: Let

$$\delta_T(t) = \sum_{n=-\infty}^{\infty} \delta(t - nT) \qquad (9.141)$$

which is defined in (2.104).

Then from (4.120),

$$f(t) * \delta_T(t) = f(t) * \sum_{n=-\infty}^{\infty} \delta(t - nT)$$

$$= \sum_{n=-\infty}^{\infty} f(t) * \delta(t - nT)$$

$$= \sum_{n=-\infty}^{\infty} f(t - nT)$$

$$= \sum_{n=-\infty}^{\infty} f(t + nT) \tag{9.142}$$

since all positive and negative values of n are included in the summation. Hence,

$$\sum_{n=-\infty}^{\infty} f(t + nT) = f(t) * \delta_T(t). \tag{9.143}$$

Now, from (5.66),

$$\mathcal{F}[\delta_T(t)] = \frac{2\pi}{T} \sum_{n=-\infty}^{\infty} \delta(\omega - n\omega_0), \quad \omega_0 = \frac{2\pi}{T}.$$

Then applying the time convolution theorem (4.122) to (9.143),

$$\mathcal{F}\left[\sum_{n=-\infty}^{\infty} f(t + nT) \right] = F(\omega) \mathcal{F}[\delta_T(t)]$$

$$= F(\omega) \frac{2\pi}{T} \sum_{n=-\infty}^{\infty} \delta(\omega - n\omega_0)$$

$$= \frac{2\pi}{T} \sum_{n=-\infty}^{\infty} F(\omega) \delta(\omega - n\omega_0)$$

$$= \frac{2\pi}{T} \sum_{n=-\infty}^{\infty} F(n\omega_0) \delta(\omega - n\omega_0) \tag{9.144}$$

with the use of the δ-function property (2.74).

From (5.21),

$$\mathcal{F}^{-1}[\delta(\omega - n\omega_0)] = \frac{1}{2\pi} e^{jn\omega_0 t}.$$

Therefore from (9.144),

$$\sum_{n=-\infty}^{\infty} f(t + nT) = \frac{2\pi}{T} \sum_{n=-\infty}^{\infty} F(n\omega_0) \mathcal{F}^{-1}[\delta(\omega - n\omega_0)] = \frac{1}{T} \sum_{n=-\infty}^{\infty} F(n\omega_0) e^{jn\omega_0 t}.$$

Poisson's summation formula states that if $f(t)$ is an arbitrary function and $F(\omega)$ its Fourier transform, then

$$\sum_{n=-\infty}^{\infty} f(nT) = \frac{1}{T} \sum_{n=-\infty}^{\infty} F(n\omega_0), \tag{9.145}$$

where $\omega_0 = 2\pi/T$.

PROBLEM 9.30 Prove Poisson's summation formula.

Solution: Letting $t = 0$ in (9.140),

$$\sum_{n=-\infty}^{\infty} f(nT) = \frac{1}{T} \sum_{n=-\infty}^{\infty} F(n \omega_0).$$

PROBLEM 9.31 Prove that

$$\sum_{n=-\infty}^{\infty} e^{-a|n|} = \sum_{n=-\infty}^{\infty} \frac{2a}{a^2 + (2n\pi)^2}, \quad a > 0. \tag{9.146}$$

Solution: Let

$$f(t) = e^{-a|t|}.$$

Then,

$$F(\omega) = \mathcal{F}[e^{-a|t|}] = \int_{-\infty}^{\infty} e^{-a|t|} e^{-j\omega t} \, dt$$

$$= \int_{-\infty}^{0} e^{at} e^{-j\omega t} \, dt + \int_{0}^{\infty} e^{-at} e^{-j\omega t} \, dt$$

$$= \frac{1}{a - j\omega} + \frac{1}{a + j\omega}$$

$$= \frac{2a}{a^2 + \omega^2}. \tag{9.147}$$

If we set $T = 1$ (hence $\omega_0 = 2\pi$) in the Poisson's summation formula (9.145),

$$\sum_{n=-\infty}^{\infty} f(n) = \sum_{n=-\infty}^{\infty} F(2\pi n). \tag{9.148}$$

Hence, from (9.147),

$$\sum_{n=-\infty}^{\infty} e^{-a|n|} = \sum_{n=-\infty}^{\infty} \frac{2a}{a^2 + (2\pi n)^2}.$$

PROBLEM 9.32 Derive the following identity of the theta function:

$$\frac{a}{\pi} \sum_{n=-\infty}^{\infty} e^{-a(t+n)^2} = 1 + 2 \sum_{n=1}^{\infty} e^{-\pi^2 n^2/a} \cos 2\pi nt. \tag{9.149}$$

Solution: Let

$$f(t) = e^{-at^2}.$$

Then, from (9.129),

$$F(\omega) = \mathcal{F}[e^{-at^2}] = \sqrt{\frac{\pi}{a}} \, e^{-\omega^2/(4a)}. \tag{9.129}$$

If we set $T = 1$ (hence $\omega_0 = 2\pi$) in (9.140),

$$\sum_{n=-\infty}^{\infty} f(t+n) = \sum_{n=-\infty}^{\infty} F(2\pi n) \, e^{j2\pi nt}.$$

Hence, from (9.129),

$$\sum_{n=-\infty}^{\infty} e^{-a(t+n)^2} = \sqrt{\frac{\pi}{a}} \sum_{n=-\infty}^{\infty} e^{-\pi^2 n^2/a} e^{j2\pi nt}, \qquad (9.150)$$

or

$$\sqrt{\frac{a}{\pi}} \sum_{n=-\infty}^{\infty} e^{-a(t+n)^2} = \sum_{n=-\infty}^{\infty} e^{-\pi^2 n^2/a} e^{j2\pi nt}$$

$$= 1 + \sum_{n=-\infty}^{-1} e^{-\pi^2 n^2/a} e^{j2\pi nt} + \sum_{n=1}^{\infty} e^{-\pi^2 n^2/a} e^{j2\pi nt}$$

$$= 1 + \sum_{n=1}^{\infty} e^{-\pi^2 n^2/a} (e^{j2\pi nt} + e^{-j2\pi nt})$$

$$= 1 + 2 \sum_{n=1}^{\infty} e^{-\pi^2 n^2/a} \cos 2\pi nt.$$

9.5 Causality and the Hilbert Transform

In this section, we shall discuss the relationship between the real part and imaginary part of the Fourier transform of a causal function and its application to establishment of the Hilbert transform.

PROBLEM 9.33 Let $F(\omega) = R(\omega) + jX(\omega)$ be the Fourier transform of a causal function $f(t)$. Then show that $f(t)$ can be expressed in terms of $R(\omega)$ or $X(\omega)$ alone.

Solution: Since $f(t)$ is causal, by definition,

$$f(t) = 0 \quad \text{for} \quad t < 0. \qquad (9.151)$$

Accordingly,

$$f(-t) = 0 \quad \text{for} \quad t > 0. \qquad (9.152)$$

Therefore from (2.5) and (2.6),

$$f(t) = 2 f_e(t) = 2 f_o(t) \quad \text{for} \quad t > 0, \qquad (9.153)$$

where

$$f(t) = f_e(t) + f_o(t),$$

and $f_e(t)$ and $f_o(t)$ are the even and odd components of $f(t)$, respectively. Then from (4.38) and (4.40),

$$f(t) = \frac{2}{\pi} \int_0^{\infty} R(\omega) \cos \omega t \, d\omega \qquad (9.154)$$

$$= -\frac{2}{\pi} \int_0^{\infty} X(\omega) \sin \omega t \, d\omega \qquad (9.155)$$

for $t > 0$.

PROBLEM 9.34 Let $F(\omega) = R(\omega) + jX(\omega)$ be the Fourier transform of a causal function $f(t)$. Then show that the functions $R(\omega)$ and $X(\omega)$ are not independent of one another but that one of them can be uniquely determined in terms of the other.

Solution: If $f(t)$ is real and causal, then from the results of Prob. 4.6,

$$R(\omega) = \int_{-\infty}^{\infty} f(t) \cos \omega t\, dt = \int_{0}^{\infty} f(t) \cos \omega t\, dt, \qquad (9.156)$$

$$X(\omega) = -\int_{-\infty}^{\infty} f(t) \sin \omega t\, dt = -\int_{0}^{\infty} f(t) \sin \omega t\, dt. \qquad (9.157)$$

Substituting the expression (9.155) into (9.156),

$$R(\omega) = -\frac{2}{\pi} \int_{0}^{\infty} \int_{0}^{\infty} X(y) \sin yt \cos \omega t\, dy\, dt. \qquad (9.158)$$

Similarly, substituting (9.154) into (9.157),

$$X(\omega) = -\frac{2}{\pi} \int_{0}^{\infty} \int_{0}^{\infty} R(y) \cos yt \sin \omega t\, dy\, dt. \qquad (9.159)$$

PROBLEM 9.35   Let $F(\omega) = R(\omega) + jX(\omega)$ be the Fourier transform of a causal function $f(t)$. Then prove the following identities:

$$\int_{-\infty}^{\infty} R^2(\omega)\, d\omega = \int_{-\infty}^{\infty} X^2(\omega)\, d\omega, \qquad (9.160)$$

$$\int_{0}^{\infty} f^2(t)\, dt = \frac{2}{\pi} \int_{0}^{\infty} R^2(\omega)\, d\omega. \qquad (9.161)$$

Solution: With the decomposition of $f(t)$ into its even and odd components, i.e.,

$$f(t) = f_e(t) + f_o(t),$$

we have from (4.42) and (4.43),

$$\mathcal{F}[f_e(t)] = R(\omega),$$
$$\mathcal{F}[f_o(t)] = jX(\omega).$$

Therefore, from Parseval's theorem (4.136),

$$\int_{-\infty}^{\infty} [f_e(t)]^2\, dt = \frac{1}{2\pi} \int_{-\infty}^{\infty} R^2(\omega)\, d\omega, \qquad (9.162)$$

$$\int_{-\infty}^{\infty} [f_o(t)]^2\, dt = \frac{1}{2\pi} \int_{-\infty}^{\infty} X^2(\omega)\, d\omega. \qquad (9.163)$$

From the causality of $f(t)$, and (9.153), it follows that

$$f(t) = 2f_e(t) = 2f_o(t) \quad \text{for} \quad t > 0.$$

Hence,

$$|f_e(t)| = |f_o(t)|. \qquad (9.164)$$

Therefore, from (9.162) and (9.163),

$$\int_{-\infty}^{\infty} R^2(\omega)\, d\omega = \int_{-\infty}^{\infty} X^2(\omega)\, d\omega.$$

Since

$$|F(\omega)|^2 = R^2(\omega) + X^2(\omega),$$

and from Parseval's theorem (4.136),

$$\int_{-\infty}^{\infty} f^2(t)\, dt = \frac{1}{2\pi} \int_{-\infty}^{\infty} |F(\omega)|^2\, d\omega$$

$$= \frac{1}{2\pi} \int_{-\infty}^{\infty} [R^2(\omega) + X^2(\omega)]\, d\omega$$

$$= \frac{1}{\pi} \int_{-\infty}^{\infty} R^2(\omega)\, d\omega$$

$$= \frac{2}{\pi} \int_{0}^{\infty} R^2(\omega)\, d\omega \qquad (9.165)$$

in view of (9.160) and $R^2(-\omega) = R^2(\omega)$.

For a causal function $f(t)$, since $f(t) = 0$ for $t < 0$,

$$\int_{-\infty}^{\infty} f^2(t)\, dt = \int_{0}^{\infty} f^2(t)\, dt.$$

Hence,

$$\int_{0}^{\infty} f^2(t)\, dt = \frac{2}{\pi} \int_{0}^{\infty} R^2(\omega)\, d\omega.$$

PROBLEM 9.36   Show the equality of the two integrals below:

$$\int_{-\infty}^{\infty} \frac{a^2\, d\omega}{(a^2 + \omega^2)^2} = \int_{-\infty}^{\infty} \frac{\omega^2\, d\omega}{(a^2 + \omega^2)^2}. \qquad (9.166)$$

Solution: Let $f(t) = e^{-at}\, u(t)$.   Then from (4.47),

$$F(\omega) = \mathcal{F}[f(t)] = \frac{1}{a + j\omega} = \frac{a}{a^2 + \omega^2} - j\, \frac{\omega}{a^2 + \omega^2}.$$

Therefore, according to (9.160),

$$\int_{-\infty}^{\infty} \frac{a^2\, d\omega}{(a^2 + \omega^2)^2} = \int_{-\infty}^{\infty} \frac{\omega^2\, d\omega}{(a^2 + \omega^2)^2}.$$

PROBLEM 9.37   If the causal function $f(t)$ contains no impulses at the origin, then show that with $F(\omega) = \mathcal{F}[f(t)] = R(\omega) + jX(\omega)$, $R(\omega)$ and $X(\omega)$ satisfy the following equations:

$$R(\omega) = \frac{1}{\pi} \int_{-\infty}^{\infty} \frac{X(y)}{\omega - y}\, dy, \qquad (9.167)$$

$$X(\omega) = -\frac{1}{\pi} \int_{-\infty}^{\infty} \frac{R(y)}{\omega - y}\, dy. \qquad (9.168)$$

Solution: Let

$$f(t) = f_e(t) + f_o(t),$$

where $f_e(t)$ and $f_o(t)$ are the even and odd components of $f(t)$, respectively.   Since $f(t)$ is causal,

$$f(t) = 0 \quad \text{for} \quad t < 0.$$

Certainly, for any causal function, it can be assumed that

$$f_e(t) = -f_o(t) \quad \text{for} \quad t < 0.$$

Also from (9.153),

$$f_e(t) = f_o(t) \quad \text{for} \quad t > 0.$$

Therefore we may write that

$$f_e(t) = f_o(t) \, \text{sgn} \, t, \tag{9.169}$$

$$f_o(t) = f_e(t) \, \text{sgn} \, t, \tag{9.170}$$

where sgn t is defined as [see (5.45)]

$$\text{sgn} \, t = \begin{cases} 1 & \text{for} \quad t > 0 \\ -1 & \text{for} \quad t < 0. \end{cases}$$

Now, from (4.42), (4.43), and (5.49),

$$\mathcal{F}[f_e(t)] = R(\omega),$$

$$\mathcal{F}[f_o(t)] = jX(\omega),$$

$$\mathcal{F}[\text{sgn} \, t] = \frac{2}{(j\omega)}.$$

Hence, from the frequency convolution theorem (4.125),

$$R(\omega) = \mathcal{F}[f_e(t)] = \mathcal{F}[f_o(t) \, \text{sgn} \, t]$$

$$= \frac{1}{2\pi} \, jX(\omega) * \frac{2}{j\omega}$$

$$= \frac{1}{\pi} \, X(\omega) * \frac{1}{\omega}$$

$$= \frac{1}{\pi} \int_{-\infty}^{\infty} \frac{X(y)}{\omega - y} \, dy.$$

Similarly,

$$jX(\omega) = \mathcal{F}[f_o(t)] = \mathcal{F}[f_e(t) \, \text{sgn} \, t]$$

$$= \frac{1}{2\pi} \, R(\omega) * \frac{2}{j\omega}$$

$$= -j \frac{1}{\pi} \, R(\omega) * \frac{1}{\omega}.$$

Hence,

$$X(\omega) = -\frac{1}{\pi} \, R(\omega) * \frac{1}{\omega} = -\frac{1}{\pi} \int_{-\infty}^{\infty} \frac{R(y)}{\omega - y} \, dy.$$

The pair of equations, (9.167) and (9.168), are known as the *Hilbert transform.*

PROBLEM 9.38   The real part of the system function $H(\omega)$ of a causal system is known to be $\pi\delta(\omega)$. Find the system function $H(\omega)$.

Solution: Let

$$H(\omega) = R(\omega) + jX(\omega).$$

Since $R(\omega) = \pi\delta(\omega)$, from (9.168),

$$X(\omega) = -\frac{1}{\pi} \int_{-\infty}^{\infty} \frac{\pi\delta(y)}{\omega - y} \, dy = -\int_{-\infty}^{\infty} \delta(y) \frac{1}{\omega - y} \, dy = -\frac{1}{\omega} \tag{9.171}$$

with the use of (2.67).

Hence,

$$H(\omega) = \pi \delta(\omega) - j \frac{1}{\omega} = \pi \delta(\omega) + \frac{1}{j\omega}. \tag{9.172}$$

9.6 Evaluation of Some Integrals

Using Parseval's theorem (4.136) and Fourier transform pairs, the evaluation of some integrals can be facilitated. This is illustrated in the following examples.

PROBLEM 9.39 Evaluate

$$\int_{-\infty}^{\infty} \frac{dx}{a^2 + x^2}, \quad \int_{-\infty}^{\infty} \frac{dx}{1 + x^2}.$$

Solution: Let

$$f(t) = e^{-at} u(t).$$

Then from the result of Prob. 4.11,

$$F(\omega) = \mathcal{F}[f(t)] = \frac{1}{a + j\omega},$$

$$|F(\omega)|^2 = \frac{1}{a^2 + \omega^2}. \tag{9.173}$$

Now, according to Parseval's theorem (4.136),

$$\int_{-\infty}^{\infty} f^2(t) \, dt = \frac{1}{2\pi} \int_{-\infty}^{\infty} |F(\omega)|^2 \, d\omega,$$

$$\int_{-\infty}^{\infty} |F(\omega)|^2 \, d\omega = 2\pi \int_{-\infty}^{\infty} f^2(t) \, dt. \tag{9.174}$$

Hence, from (9.173),

$$\int_{-\infty}^{\infty} \frac{d\omega}{a^2 + \omega^2} = 2\pi \int_{-\infty}^{\infty} f^2(t) \, dt = 2\pi \int_{0}^{\infty} e^{-2at} \, dt$$

$$= 2\pi \left. \frac{e^{-2at}}{-2a} \right|_{0}^{\infty} = \frac{\pi}{a}.$$

Thus,

$$\int_{-\infty}^{\infty} \frac{dx}{a^2 + x^2} = \int_{-\infty}^{\infty} \frac{d\omega}{a^2 + \omega^2} = \frac{\pi}{a}. \tag{9.175}$$

Setting $a = 1$,

$$\int_{-\infty}^{\infty} \frac{dx}{1 + x^2} = \pi. \tag{9.176}$$

PROBLEM 9.40 Evaluate

$$\int_{-\infty}^{\infty} \frac{a^2 \, dx}{(a^2 + x^2)^2}, \quad \int_{-\infty}^{\infty} \frac{dx}{(1 + x^2)^2}.$$

Solution: Let

$$f(t) = \frac{1}{2} e^{-a|t|}.$$

Then from (9.147),

$$F(\omega) = \mathcal{F}[f(t)] = \frac{a}{a^2 + \omega^2}.$$

Now, using Parseval's theorem (4.136),

$$\int_{-\infty}^{\infty} |F(\omega)|^2 \, d\omega = 2\pi \int_{-\infty}^{\infty} f^2(t) \, dt.$$

Hence,

$$\int_{-\infty}^{\infty} \frac{a^2}{(a^2 + \omega^2)^2} \, d\omega = 2\pi \int_{-\infty}^{\infty} \left[\frac{1}{2} e^{-a|t|} \right]^2 dt$$

$$= \frac{\pi}{2} \int_{-\infty}^{\infty} e^{-2a|t|} \, dt$$

$$= \frac{\pi}{2} \left[\int_{-\infty}^{0} e^{2at} \, dt + \int_{0}^{\infty} e^{-2at} \, dt \right]$$

$$= \frac{\pi}{2} \left[\frac{e^{2at}}{2a} \bigg|_{-\infty}^{0} + \frac{e^{-2at}}{-2a} \bigg|_{0}^{\infty} \right]$$

$$= \frac{\pi}{2a}. \tag{9.177}$$

Thus,

$$\int_{-\infty}^{\infty} \frac{a^2}{(a^2 + x^2)^2} \, dx = \int_{-\infty}^{\infty} \frac{a^2}{(a^2 + \omega^2)^2} \, d\omega = \frac{\pi}{2a}. \tag{9.178}$$

Setting $a = 1$,

$$\int_{-\infty}^{\infty} \frac{dx}{(1 + x^2)^2} = \frac{\pi}{2}. \tag{9.179}$$

9.7 Supplementary Problems

PROBLEM 9.41 If $\mathcal{F}[f(x, y)] = F(u, v)$, show that

(a) $\mathcal{F}[f(ax, by)] = \dfrac{1}{|ab|} F\left(\dfrac{u}{a}, \dfrac{v}{b} \right),$

(b) $\mathcal{F}[f(x - a, y - b)] = F(u, v) e^{-j(au + bv)}.$

PROBLEM 9.42 Prove Parseval's theorem for two dimensions; i.e.,

$$\iint_{-\infty}^{\infty} |f(x, y)|^2 \, dx\,dy = \frac{1}{(2\pi)^2} \iint_{-\infty}^{\infty} |F(u, v)|^2 \, du\,dv.$$

PROBLEM 9.43 Prove the Fourier transform theorem

$$\mathcal{F}[\nabla^2 f(x, y)] = -(u^2 + v^2) \mathcal{F}[f(x, y)],$$

where ∇^2 is the Laplacian operator $\nabla^2 = \partial^2/\partial x^2 + \partial^2/\partial y^2$.

PROBLEM 9.44 Let the testing function $\phi(x, y)$ be a continuous function which vanishes identically outside some finite region, and let the two-dimensional δ-function be defined as a symbolic function by the relation

$$\iint_{-\infty}^{\infty} \delta(x, y)\, \phi(x, y)\, dxdy = \phi(0, 0).$$

Prove the following properties of the two-dimensional δ-function:

(a) $\displaystyle\iint_{-\infty}^{\infty} \delta(x - \xi, y - \eta)\, \phi(x, y)\, dxdy = \phi(\xi, \eta);$

(b) $\delta(ax, by) = \dfrac{1}{|ab|}\, \delta(x, y);$

(c) $\mathcal{F}[\delta(x, y)] = 1.$

PROBLEM 9.45 In Chap. 6, a system is defined as a mapping of an input function into an output function. [Cf., (6.5).] The input and output are functions of a one-dimensional independent variable (time). For the case of imaging systems, the input and output can be functions of a two-dimensional independent variable (space). Thus, a linear imaging system can be represented by

$$L\{f_i(x, y)\} = f_o(x, y),$$

$$L\{a_1 f_{i_1}(x, y) + a_2 f_{i_2}(x, y)\} = a_1 L\{f_{i_1}(x, y)\} + a_2 L\{f_{i_2}(x, y)\}.$$

The system is said to be *space-invariant* if

$$L\{f_i(x + x_o, y + y_o)\} = f_o(x + x_o, y + y_o).$$

Let $h(x, y)$ be the unit impulse response of the system; i.e.,

$$L\{\delta(x, y)\} = h(x, y).$$

Derive the two-dimensional convolution relationship

$$f_o(x, y) = f_i(x, y) * h(x, y) = \iint_{-\infty}^{\infty} f_i(\xi, \eta)\, h(x - \xi, y - \eta)\, d\xi\, d\eta.$$

PROBLEM 9.46 If $\mathcal{F}[h(x, y)] = H(u, v)$, $\mathcal{F}[f_i(x, y)] = F_i(u, v)$, and $\mathcal{F}[f_o(x, y)] = F_o(x, y)$, show that

$$F_o(u, v) = F_i(u, v)\, H(u, v),$$

where $H(u, v)$ is a two-dimensional system function. [Cf., (9.35).]

PROBLEM 9.47 Find the characteristic function of the gaussian random variable X whose probability density function is $p(x) = \dfrac{1}{\sigma\sqrt{2\pi}}\, e^{-(x-m)^2/2\sigma^2}$

Answer: $\phi(\omega) = e^{jm\omega}\, e^{-\omega^2\sigma^2/2}.$

PROBLEM 9.48 If X is the gaussian random variable of Prob. 9.47, show that $E[X] = m$, and $\text{Var}(X) = \sigma^2$.

PROBLEM 9.49 If $\phi_x(\omega)$ is the characteristic function of a random variable X, find the characteristic function $\phi_y(\omega)$ of the random variable $Y = aX + b$, where a and b are any real numbers, in terms of $\phi_x(\omega)$.

Answer: $\phi_y(\omega) = e^{jb\omega}\phi_x(a\omega).$

PROBLEM 9.50 The random variable X is normally distributed with probability density $p_x(x) = \dfrac{1}{\sigma\sqrt{2\pi}} e^{-x^2/2\sigma^2}$. Find the probability density function of the random variable $Y = aX^2$.

[Hint: If $Y = g(X)$, then $\phi_y(\omega) = \displaystyle\int_{-\infty}^{\infty} e^{j\omega g(x)} p_x(x)\,dx$. With a change of variable $y = g(x)$,

$$\phi_y(\omega) = \int_{-\infty}^{\infty} e^{j\omega y} h(y)\,dy = \int_{-\infty}^{\infty} e^{j\omega y} p_y(y)\,dy \quad \text{and} \quad h(y) = p_y(y).]$$

Answer: $p_y(y) = \dfrac{e^{-y/2a\sigma^2}}{\sigma\sqrt{2\pi a y}}\, u(y)$, where $u(y) = \begin{cases} 1 & \text{for } y > 0 \\ 0 & \text{for } y < 0 \end{cases}$.

PROBLEM 9.51 The probability density of a random variable X is $p(x) = \dfrac{\alpha/\pi}{\alpha^2 + x^2}$. Show that its characteristic function is $\phi(\omega) = e^{-\alpha|\omega|}$.

PROBLEM 9.52 Show that if the probability density of a random variable X is $\frac{1}{2}\alpha e^{-\alpha|x|}$, then its characteristic function $\phi(\omega)$ is $\alpha^2/(\alpha^2 + \omega^2)$.

PROBLEM 9.53 Verify the uncertainty principle in spectral analysis for the signal $f(t) = e^{-|a|t}$.

PROBLEM 9.54 Prove that $\displaystyle\sum_{n=-\infty}^{\infty} \frac{1}{1 + a^2 n^2} = \frac{\pi}{a}\coth\left(\frac{\pi}{a}\right)$.

[Hint: Apply Poisson's summation formula with $f(t) = 1/(1 + t^2)$.]

PROBLEM 9.55 Show that $\hat{m}(t)$ and $m(t)$ of Prob. 6.51 are related by

$$\hat{m}(t) = \frac{1}{\pi}\int_{-\infty}^{\infty} \frac{m(\tau)}{t - \tau}\,d\tau \qquad \text{and} \qquad m(t) = -\frac{1}{\pi}\int_{-\infty}^{\infty} \frac{\hat{m}(\tau)}{t - \tau}\,d\tau.$$

Thus, $\hat{m}(t)$ is also called the *Hilbert transform of* $m(t)$.

PROBLEM 9.56 If a real function $m(t)$ has a Hilbert transform $\hat{m}(t)$, show that the Hilbert transform of $\hat{m}(t)$ is $-m(t)$; that is, $\hat{\hat{m}}(t) = -m(t)$.

PROBLEM 9.57 Show that

$$\int_{-\infty}^{\infty} [m(t)]^2\,dt = \int_{-\infty}^{\infty} [\hat{m}(t)]^2\,dt \quad \text{and} \quad \int_{-\infty}^{\infty} m(t)\,\hat{m}(t)\,dt = 0.$$

[Hint: Use Parseval's theorem.]

CONVERGENCE OF THE FOURIER SERIES AND GIBB'S PHENOMENON |

A.1 Convergence of the Fourier Series

In Sec. 1.6 we briefly mentioned the Dirichlet conditions under which a Fourier series representation for a given periodic function $f(t)$ is possible. We shall now show that the infinite series

$$\frac{1}{2} a_o + \sum_{n=1}^{\infty} (a_n \cos n\omega_0 t + b_n \sin n\omega_0 t), \qquad (A.1)$$

where $\omega_0 = 2\pi/T$, and a_n and b_n are the Fourier coefficients of $f(t)$, converges to the value $f(t)$.

PROBLEM A.1 If $S_k(t)$ denotes the sum of the first $(2k + 1)$ terms of the Fourier series of $f(t)$, i.e.,

$$S_k(t) = \frac{1}{2} a_o + \sum_{n=1}^{k} (a_n \cos n\omega_0 t + b_n \sin n\omega_0 t), \qquad (A.2)$$

where $\omega_0 = 2\pi/T$, and a_n and b_n are given by

$$a_n = \frac{2}{T} \int_{-T/2}^{T/2} f(t) \cos (n\omega_0 t) \, dt, \qquad (A.3)$$

$$b_n = \frac{2}{T} \int_{-T/2}^{T/2} f(t) \sin (n\omega_0 t) \, dt, \qquad (A.4)$$

then show that

$$S_k(t) = \frac{2}{T} \int_{-T/2}^{T/2} f(x) D_k [\omega_0 (x - t)] \, dx, \qquad (A.5)$$

where $D_k(\xi)$ is the so-called "Dirichlet kernel"; i.e.,

$$D_k(\xi) = \frac{\sin \left[\left(k + \frac{1}{2} \right) \xi \right]}{2 \sin \frac{1}{2} \xi}. \qquad (A.6)$$

Solution: In (A.3) and (A.4), t is a dummy variable. Hence,

$$a_n \cos n\omega_0 t + b_n \sin n\omega_0 t$$

$$= \left[\frac{2}{T} \int_{-T/2}^{T/2} f(x) \cos (n\omega_0 x)\, dx \right] \cos n\omega_0 t$$

$$+ \left[\frac{2}{T} \int_{-T/2}^{T/2} f(x) \sin (n\omega_0 x)\, dx \right] \sin n\omega_0 t.$$

$$= \frac{2}{T} \int_{-T/2}^{T/2} f(x) \left[\cos (n\omega_0 x) \cos (n\omega_0 t) + \sin (n\omega_0 x) \sin (n\omega_0 t) \right] dx$$

$$= \frac{2}{T} \int_{-T/2}^{T/2} f(x) \cos [n\omega_0 (x - t)]\, dx. \tag{A.7}$$

Thus,

$$S_k(t) = \frac{1}{2} a_o + \sum_{n=1}^{k} (a_n \cos n\omega_0 t + b_n \sin n\omega_0 t)$$

$$= \frac{1}{T} \int_{-T/2}^{T/2} f(x)\, dx + \sum_{n=1}^{k} \frac{2}{T} \int_{-T/2}^{T/2} f(x) \cos [n\omega_0 (x - t)]\, dx$$

$$= \frac{2}{T} \int_{-T/2}^{T/2} f(x) \left\{ \frac{1}{2} + \cos [\omega_0 (x - t)] + \cos [2\omega_0 (x - t)] \right.$$

$$\left. + \cdots + \cos [k\omega_0 (x - t)] \right\} dx. \tag{A.8}$$

Let $\omega_0 (x - t) = \xi$ and consider the sum

$$D_k(\xi) = \frac{1}{2} + \cos \xi + \cos 2\xi + \cdots + \cos k\xi.$$

Using the trigonometric identity $2 \cos A \sin B = \sin (A + B) - \sin (A - B)$,

$$2 \sin \frac{\xi}{2} D_k(\xi) = \sin \frac{\xi}{2} + 2 \sin \frac{\xi}{2} \cos \xi + 2 \sin \frac{\xi}{2} \cos 2\xi$$

$$+ \cdots + 2 \sin \frac{\xi}{2} \cos k\xi$$

$$= \sin \frac{\xi}{2} - \sin \frac{\xi}{2} + \sin \frac{3}{2} \xi - \sin \frac{3}{2} \xi + \sin \frac{5}{2} \xi$$

$$- \cdots - \sin \left[\left(k - \frac{1}{2} \right) \xi \right] + \sin \left[\left(k + \frac{1}{2} \right) \xi \right]$$

$$= \sin \left[\left(k + \frac{1}{2} \right) \xi \right].$$

Thus,

$$D_k(\xi) = \frac{1}{2} + \sum_{n=1}^{k} \cos n\xi = \frac{\sin \left[\left(k + \frac{1}{2} \right) \xi \right]}{2 \sin \frac{1}{2} \xi}. \tag{A.9}$$

Hence,

$$S_k(t) = \frac{2}{T} \int_{-T/2}^{T/2} f(x) \; \frac{\sin\left[\left(k + \frac{1}{2}\right)\omega_0(x - t)\right]}{2 \sin\left[\frac{1}{2}\,\omega_0(x - t)\right]} \; dx$$

$$= \frac{2}{T} \int_{-T/2}^{T/2} f(x) \, D_k[\omega_0(x - t)] \; dx, \tag{A.10}$$

where $\quad D_k(\xi) = \dfrac{\sin\left[\left(k + \frac{1}{2}\right)\xi\right]}{2 \sin \frac{1}{2}\,\xi}.$

PROBLEM A.2   Show that (A.10) can be rewritten as

$$S_k(t) = \frac{2}{T} \int_{-T/2}^{T/2} f(t + \lambda) \; \frac{\sin\left[\left(k + \frac{1}{2}\right)\omega_0\lambda\right]}{2 \sin\left(\frac{1}{2}\,\omega_0\lambda\right)} \; d\lambda. \tag{A.11}$$

Solution: Change variables by setting $x - t = \lambda$ in (A.10). The result is

$$S_k(t) = \frac{2}{T} \int_{-\frac{T}{2}-t}^{\frac{T}{2}-t} f(t + \lambda) \; \frac{\sin\left[\left(k + \frac{1}{2}\right)\omega_0\lambda\right]}{2 \sin\left(\frac{1}{2}\,\omega_0\lambda\right)} \; d\lambda. \tag{A.12}$$

Now, from (A.9),

$$\frac{\sin\left[\left(k + \frac{1}{2}\right)\omega_0\lambda\right]}{2 \sin\left(\frac{1}{2}\,\omega_0\lambda\right)} = \frac{1}{2} + \sum_{n=1}^{k} \cos n\omega_0\lambda. \tag{A.13}$$

Hence,

$$\frac{\sin\left[\left(k + \frac{1}{2}\right)\omega_0\lambda\right]}{2 \sin\left(\frac{1}{2}\,\omega_0\lambda\right)}$$

is periodic in the variable λ, with period T. Since the function $f(t + \lambda)$ is also periodic in the variable λ with period T, the integrand of (A.12) is periodic in the variable λ with period T. Then from (1.6), we can rewrite (A.12) as

$$S_k(t) = \frac{2}{T} \int_{-T/2}^{T/2} f(t + \lambda) \; \frac{\sin\left[\left(k + \frac{1}{2}\right)\omega_0\lambda\right]}{2 \sin\left(\frac{1}{2}\,\omega_0\lambda\right)} \; d\lambda$$

which is the desired solution.

PROBLEM A.3   Let $f(t)$ be periodic with period T and also be absolutely integrable over a period. Then show that at every continuity point where the derivative exists, the Fourier series of $f(t)$ converges to the value $f(t)$; i.e.,

$$\lim_{k \to \infty} S_k(t) = f(t). \tag{A.14}$$

Solution: Let t be a continuity point of $f(t)$. According to (A.11),

$$\lim_{k \to \infty} S_k(t) = \lim_{k \to \infty} \frac{2}{T} \int_{-T/2}^{T/2} f(t + \lambda) \frac{\sin\left[\left(k + \frac{1}{2}\right) \omega_0 \lambda\right]}{2 \sin\left(\frac{1}{2} \omega_0 \lambda\right)} \, d\lambda. \tag{A.15}$$

From (A.13),

$$
\int_{-T/2}^{T/2} \frac{\sin\left[\left(k + \frac{1}{2}\right) \omega_0 \lambda\right]}{2 \sin\left(\frac{1}{2} \omega_0 \lambda\right)} \, d\lambda = \int_{-T/2}^{T/2} \left[\frac{1}{2} + \sum_{n=1}^{k} \cos n \omega_0 \lambda\right] d\lambda
$$

$$
= \frac{1}{2} \int_{-T/2}^{T/2} d\lambda + \sum_{n=1}^{k} \int_{-T/2}^{T/2} \cos (n \omega_0 \lambda) \, d\lambda
$$

$$
= \frac{T}{2} \tag{A.16}
$$

in view of (1.19a). Hence,

$$\frac{2}{T} \int_{-T/2}^{T/2} \frac{\sin\left[\left(k + \frac{1}{2}\right) \omega_0 \lambda\right]}{2 \sin\left(\frac{1}{2} \omega_0 \lambda\right)} \, d\lambda = 1 \tag{A.17}$$

for any k.

From (A.17),

$$f(t) = \frac{2}{T} \int_{-T/2}^{T/2} f(t) \frac{\sin\left[\left(k + \frac{1}{2}\right) \omega_0 \lambda\right]}{2 \sin\left(\frac{1}{2} \omega_0 \lambda\right)} \, d\lambda. \tag{A.18}$$

From (A.18) and (A.15),

$$\lim_{k \to \infty} S_k(t) - f(t) = \lim_{k \to \infty} \frac{2}{T} \int_{-T/2}^{T/2} [f(t + \lambda) - f(t)] \frac{\sin\left[\left(k + \frac{1}{2}\right) \omega_0 \lambda\right]}{2 \sin\left(\frac{1}{2} \omega_0 \lambda\right)} \, d\lambda. \tag{A.19}$$

Now consider the function

$$g(\lambda) = \frac{f(t + \lambda) - f(t)}{2 \sin\left(\frac{1}{2} \omega_0 \lambda\right)} = \frac{f(t + \lambda) - f(t)}{\lambda} \frac{\lambda}{2 \sin\left(\frac{1}{2} \omega_0 \lambda\right)}. \tag{A.20}$$

Since $f(t)$ has a derivative at the point t,

$$\frac{f(t + \lambda) - f(t)}{\lambda}$$

remains bounded as $\lambda \longrightarrow 0$.

On the other hand, the function

$$\frac{\lambda}{2 \sin\left(\frac{1}{2} \omega_0 \lambda\right)}$$

is continuous for $\lambda \neq 0$ and approaches $1/\omega_0$ as $\lambda \longrightarrow 0$, since

$$\lim_{\theta \to 0} \frac{\sin \theta}{\theta} = 1.$$

From these results and since $f(t)$ is absolutely integrable, the function $g(t)$ defined in (A.20) is absolutely integrable. Then from the result (1.79) of Prob. 1.19,

$$\lim_{k \to \infty} S_k(t) - f(t) = \lim_{k \to \infty} \frac{2}{T} \int_{-T/2}^{T/2} g(\lambda) \sin\left[\left(k + \frac{1}{2}\right) \omega_0 \lambda\right] d\lambda = 0. \quad (A.21)$$

Hence, $\lim_{k \to \infty} S_k(t) = f(t)$.

PROBLEM A.4 Let $f(t)$ be piecewise continuous and periodic with period T and also be absolutely integrable over a period. Then show that at every point of discontinuity where $f(t)$ has a right-hand and a left-hand derivative, the Fourier series of $f(t)$ converges to the value

$$\frac{1}{2}\left[f(t+) + f(t-)\right],$$

where $f(t+)$ is the value of $f(t)$ just on the right side of the discontinuity, and $f(t-)$ is the value of $f(t)$ just on the left of the discontinuity; i.e.,

$$\lim_{k \to \infty} S_k(t) = \frac{1}{2}\left[f(t+) + f(t-)\right]. \quad (A.22)$$

Solution: From (A.15),

$$\lim_{k \to \infty} S_k(t) = \lim_{k \to \infty} \frac{2}{T} \int_{-T/2}^{T/2} f(t + \lambda) \frac{\sin\left[\left(k + \frac{1}{2}\right) \omega_0 \lambda\right]}{2 \sin\left(\frac{1}{2} \omega_0 \lambda\right)} d\lambda$$

$$= \lim_{k \to \infty} \frac{2}{T} \int_{-T/2}^{0} f(t + \lambda) \frac{\sin\left[\left(k + \frac{1}{2}\right) \omega_0 \lambda\right]}{2 \sin\left(\frac{1}{2} \omega_0 \lambda\right)} d\lambda$$

$$+ \lim_{k \to \infty} \frac{2}{T} \int_{0}^{T/2} f(t + \lambda) \frac{\sin\left[\left(k + \frac{1}{2}\right) \omega_0 \lambda\right]}{2 \sin\left(\frac{1}{2} \omega_0 \lambda\right)} d\lambda. \quad (A.23)$$

Since the integrand in (A.17) is even, according to (2.13),

$$\frac{2}{T} \int_{0}^{T/2} \frac{\sin\left[\left(k + \frac{1}{2}\right) \omega_0 \lambda\right]}{2 \sin\left(\frac{1}{2} \omega_0 \lambda\right)} d\lambda = \frac{2}{T} \int_{-T/2}^{0} \frac{\sin\left[\left(k + \frac{1}{2}\right) \omega_0 \lambda\right]}{2 \sin\left(\frac{1}{2} \omega_0 \lambda\right)} d\lambda = \frac{1}{2}. \quad (A.24)$$

Hence from (A.24),

$$\frac{1}{2} f(t+) = \frac{2}{T} \int_{0}^{T/2} f(t+) \frac{\sin\left[\left(k + \frac{1}{2}\right) \omega_0 \lambda\right]}{2 \sin\left(\frac{1}{2} \omega_0 \lambda\right)} d\lambda. \quad (A.25)$$

Thus,

$$\lim_{k \to \infty} \frac{2}{T} \int_0^{T/2} f(t + \lambda) \frac{\sin\left[\left(k + \frac{1}{2}\right)\omega_0 \lambda\right]}{2 \sin\left(\frac{1}{2}\omega_0 \lambda\right)} \, d\lambda - \frac{1}{2} f(t+)$$

$$= \lim_{k \to \infty} \frac{2}{T} \int_0^{T/2} [f(t + \lambda) - f(t+)] \frac{\sin\left[\left(k + \frac{1}{2}\right)\omega_0 \lambda\right]}{2 \sin\left(\frac{1}{2}\omega_0 \lambda\right)} \, d\lambda. \quad (A.26)$$

Now consider the function

$$g(\lambda) = \frac{f(t + \lambda) - f(t+)}{2 \sin\left(\frac{1}{2}\omega_0 \lambda\right)} = \frac{f(t + \lambda) - f(t+)}{\lambda} \frac{\lambda}{2 \sin\left(\frac{1}{2}\omega_0 \lambda\right)}. \quad (A.27)$$

Since $f(t)$ has a right-hand derivative at t,

$$\frac{f(t + \lambda) - f(t+)}{\lambda}, \quad \lambda > 0,$$

remains bounded as $\lambda \longrightarrow 0$, and the function

$$\frac{\lambda}{2 \sin\left(\frac{1}{2}\omega_0 \lambda\right)}$$

is also bounded. As in the case where $f(t)$ is continuous, we conclude that the function $g(\lambda)$ is absolutely integrable on $[0, T/2]$. Thus from (1.79),

$$\lim_{k \to \infty} \frac{2}{T} \int_0^{T/2} f(t + \lambda) \frac{\sin\left[\left(k + \frac{1}{2}\right)\omega_0 \lambda\right]}{2 \sin\left(\frac{1}{2}\omega_0 \lambda\right)} \, d\lambda - \frac{1}{2} f(t+)$$

$$= \lim_{k \to \infty} \frac{2}{T} \int_0^{T/2} g(\lambda) \sin\left[\left(k + \frac{1}{2}\right)\omega_0 \lambda\right] d\lambda$$

$$= 0. \quad (A.28)$$

Hence,

$$\lim_{k \to \infty} \frac{2}{T} \int_0^{T/2} f(t + \lambda) \frac{\sin\left[\left(k + \frac{1}{2}\right)\omega_0 \lambda\right]}{2 \sin\left(\frac{1}{2}\omega_0 \lambda\right)} \, d\lambda = \frac{1}{2} f(t+). \quad (A.29)$$

Similarly,

$$\lim_{k \to \infty} \frac{2}{T} \int_{-T/2}^{0} f(t + \lambda) \frac{\sin\left[\left(k + \frac{1}{2}\right)\omega_0 \lambda\right]}{2 \sin\left(\frac{1}{2}\omega_0 \lambda\right)} \, d\lambda = \frac{1}{2} f(t-). \quad (A.30)$$

Hence from (A.29), (A.30), and (A.23),

$$\lim_{k \to \infty} S_k(t) = \frac{1}{2} [f(t+) + f(t-)].$$

A.2 Gibb's Phenomenon

When a given function is approximated by a partial sum of a Fourier series, there will be a considerable error in the vicinity of a discontinuity, no matter how many terms one may be willing to use. This effect is known as *Gibbs's phenomenon*.

We shall illustrate this phenomenon by considering the square wave we studied earlier (Prob. 1.10).

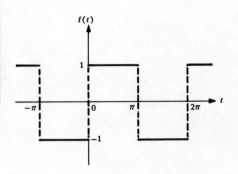

PROBLEM A.5 Consider the square wave of unit amplitude and period 2π (Fig. A.1), i.e.,

$$f(t) = \begin{cases} -1 & -\pi < t < 0 \\ 1 & 0 < t < \pi \end{cases}$$

Fig. A.1 The square wave of Prob. A.5.

Discuss the sum of a finite number of terms of the Fourier series.

Solution: From the result of Prob. 1.10, we obtain the Fourier series (with $\omega_0 = 2\pi/T = 1$) as

$$f(t) = \frac{4}{\pi} \left(\sin t + \frac{1}{3} \sin 3t + \frac{1}{5} \sin 5t + \cdots \right). \tag{A.31}$$

This series exhibits the nonuniformity of the convergence of a Fourier series near a discontinuity. Successive approximations are illustrated in Fig. A.2.

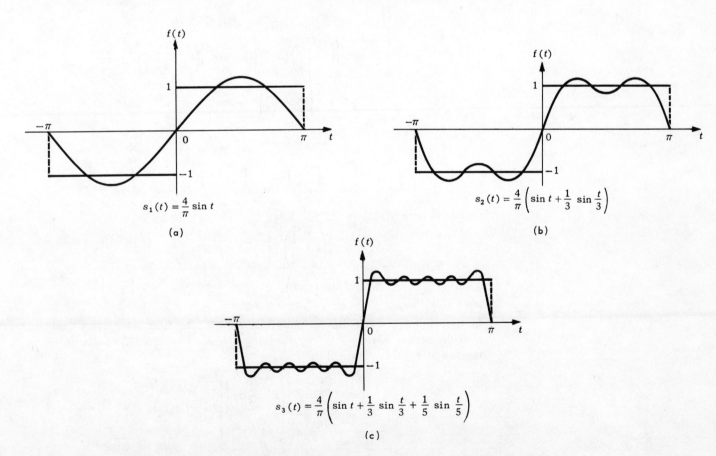

$$s_1(t) = \frac{4}{\pi} \sin t$$

(a)

$$s_2(t) = \frac{4}{\pi} \left(\sin t + \frac{1}{3} \sin \frac{t}{3} \right)$$

(b)

$$s_3(t) = \frac{4}{\pi} \left(\sin t + \frac{1}{3} \sin \frac{t}{3} + \frac{1}{5} \sin \frac{t}{5} \right)$$

(c)

Fig. A.2 The first three finite sums of the Fourier series of the square wave of Fig. A.1.

Next, consider the sum of a finite number of terms of the series $S_k(t)$. From (A.10), this is given by ($T = 2\pi$, $\omega_0 = 2\pi/T = 1$)

$$S_k(t) = \frac{2}{T} \int_{-T/2}^{T/2} f(x) \frac{\sin\left[\left(k + \frac{1}{2}\right)\omega_0(x-t)\right]}{2\sin\left[\frac{1}{2}\omega_0(x-t)\right]} \, dx$$

$$= \frac{1}{2\pi} \int_{-\pi}^{\pi} f(x) \frac{\sin\left[\left(k + \frac{1}{2}\right)(x-t)\right]}{\sin\left[\frac{1}{2}(x-t)\right]} \, dx$$

$$= \frac{1}{2\pi} \int_{0}^{\pi} \frac{\sin\left[\left(k + \frac{1}{2}\right)(x-t)\right]}{\sin\left[\frac{1}{2}(x-t)\right]} \, dx - \frac{1}{2\pi} \int_{-\pi}^{0} \frac{\sin\left[\left(k + \frac{1}{2}\right)(x'-t)\right]}{\sin\left[\frac{1}{2}(x'-t)\right]} \, dx'. \tag{A.32}$$

Substituting $x - t = y$ and $t - x' = y'$,

$$S_k(t) = \frac{1}{2\pi} \int_{-t}^{\pi-t} \frac{\sin\left[\left(k + \frac{1}{2}\right)y\right]}{\sin\left(\frac{1}{2}y\right)} \, dy + \frac{1}{2\pi} \int_{\pi+t}^{t} \frac{\sin\left[\left(k + \frac{1}{2}\right)y'\right]}{\sin\left(\frac{1}{2}y'\right)} \, dy'. \tag{A.33}$$

This is because

$$dy' = -dx',$$

$$\sin\left[\left(k + \frac{1}{2}\right)(-y')\right] = -\sin\left[\left(k + \frac{1}{2}\right)y'\right],$$

$$\sin\left[\frac{1}{2}(-y')\right] = -\sin\left[\frac{1}{2}y'\right].$$

Since

$$\int_{-t}^{\pi-t} + \int_{\pi+t}^{t} = \int_{-t}^{t} + \int_{t}^{\pi-t} + \int_{\pi+t}^{\pi-t} + \int_{\pi-t}^{t} = \int_{-t}^{t} + \int_{\pi+t}^{\pi-t},$$

we can rewrite (A.33) as

$$S_k(t) = \frac{1}{2\pi} \int_{-t}^{t} \frac{\sin\left[\left(k + \frac{1}{2}\right)y\right]}{\sin\left(\frac{1}{2}y\right)} \, dy + \frac{1}{2\pi} \int_{\pi+t}^{\pi-t} \frac{\sin\left[\left(k + \frac{1}{2}\right)y\right]}{\sin\left(\frac{1}{2}y\right)} \, dy. \tag{A.34}$$

In the vicinity of the discontinuity, i.e., $t = 0$, the first integral is evaluated over the region where $y = 0$. By applying *L'Hospital's rule*, the value of the integrand at $y = 0$ is obtained as

$$\left. \frac{\left(k + \frac{1}{2}\right)\cos\left[\left(k + \frac{1}{2}\right)y\right]}{\frac{1}{2}\cos\left(\frac{1}{2}y\right)} \right|_{y=0} = 2k + 1.$$

The second integral is evaluated over the region where $y = \pi$. The integrand of the second integral at $y = \pi$ is $(-1)^k$. We can neglect the contribution from the second integral in comparison with that from the first. Hence,

$$S_k(t) = \frac{1}{2\pi} \int_{-t}^{t} \frac{\sin\left[\left(k + \frac{1}{2}\right)y\right]}{\sin\left(\frac{1}{2}y\right)} \, dy = \frac{1}{\pi} \int_{0}^{t} \frac{\sin\left[\left(k + \frac{1}{2}\right)y\right]}{\sin\left(\frac{1}{2}y\right)} \, dy \quad \text{(A.35)}$$

since the integrand is even in y.

Since we are interested in the vicinity of the discontinuity, i.e., $t = 0$, and

$$\lim_{\theta \to 0} \frac{\sin\theta}{\theta} = 1,$$

we can replace $\sin 1/2 \, y$ by $1/2 \, y$, and obtain

$$S_k(t) = \frac{1}{\pi} \int_{0}^{t} \frac{\sin\left[\left(k + \frac{1}{2}\right)y\right]}{\frac{1}{2}y} \, dy = \frac{2}{\pi} \int_{0}^{t} \frac{\sin\left[\left(k + \frac{1}{2}\right)y\right]}{y} \, dy. \quad \text{(A.36)}$$

Substituting $(k + 1/2)y = \zeta$,

$$S_k(t) = \frac{2}{\pi} \int_{0}^{(k+1/2)t} \frac{\sin\zeta}{\zeta} \, d\zeta = \frac{2}{\pi} \, Si\left[\left(k + \frac{1}{2}\right)t\right], \quad \text{(A.37)}$$

where $Si(y)$ is the sine integral function discussed in Prob. 6.34. Since $Si(0) = 0$ and $Si(\infty) = \pi/2$ (see Prob. 6.34),

$$S_k(0) = 0,$$

$$\lim_{k \to \infty} S_k(t) = 1.$$

From the graph of $Si(y)$ (Fig. 6.18) and Fig. A.2 it is observed that at $t = 0$ the value of $S_k(t)$ is zero. It then rises rapidly as t increases and overshoots the value 1 and oscillates about the line $f(t) = 1$ with decreasing amplitude. As the number of terms increases, the resulting curve oscillates with increasing frequency and decreasing amplitude. On either side of the discontinuities, every curve overshoots. Although the magnitude of the peak does diminish as k increases, there is a lower bound of 9% overshoot even as $k \longrightarrow \infty$.

B | THE RELATIONSHIP BETWEEN THE FOURIER AND LAPLACE TRANSFORMS

APPENDIX

B.1 Definitions and Basic Properties of the Laplace Transform

Given a function $f(t)$, the *Laplace transform* is defined as

$$\mathcal{L}[f(t)] = F(s) = \int_0^\infty f(t) e^{-st} dt, \tag{B.1}$$

where s is a complex variable, $s = \sigma + j\omega$. The operator notation $\mathcal{L}[f(t)]$ stands for "the Laplace transform of $f(t)$."

In order that $F(s)$ of (B.1) exists, it is sufficient that

$$\int_0^\infty |f(t)| e^{-\sigma_1 t} dt < \infty \tag{B.2}$$

for a real, positive σ_1.

The condition of (B.2) is satisfied by most $f(t)$ encountered in engineering. The *inverse Laplace transform* is given by the complex inversion integral

$$f(t) = \mathcal{L}^{-1}[F(s)] = \frac{1}{2\pi j} \int_{\sigma_1 - j\infty}^{\sigma_1 + j\infty} F(s) e^{st} ds, \tag{B.3}$$

where $\sigma_1 > \sigma_c$, σ_c being the abscissa of convergence.

It should be pointed out that in many instances the inverse Laplace transform can be obtained without formal integration. This is based on the uniqueness property of the Laplace transform, i.e., corresponding to a function $f(t)$, $F(s)$ is unique, and vice versa. This is true only for $t > 0$. Further discussion of the existence, convergence, and uniqueness properties of the Laplace transform and the formal evaluation of (B.3) are beyond the scope of our treatment.

PROBLEM B.1 Find the Laplace transform of the unit step function

$$f(t) = u(t) = \begin{cases} 1, & t > 0 \\ 0, & t < 0. \end{cases} \tag{B.4}$$

Solution: Using (B.1),

$$F(s) = \mathcal{L}[u(t)] = \int_0^\infty e^{-st} dt = -\frac{1}{s} e^{-st} \Big|_0^\infty = \frac{1}{s}. \tag{B.5}$$

PROBLEM B.2 Find the Laplace transform of

$$f(t) = \begin{cases} e^{\alpha t}, & t > 0 \\ 0, & t < 0, \end{cases} \tag{B.6}$$

where α is a constant.

256

Solution: Using (B.1),

$$F(s) = \mathcal{L}[e^{\alpha t}] = \int_0^\infty e^{\alpha t} e^{-st} dt = \int_0^\infty e^{-(s-\alpha)t} dt = \frac{1}{s-\alpha}, \quad Re[s] > \alpha. \quad (B.7)$$

PROBLEM B.3 If $f_1(t)$ and $f_2(t)$ are two functions of time and a_1 and a_2 are constants, then show that

$$\mathcal{L}[a_1 f_1(t) + a_2 f_2(t)] = a_1 \mathcal{L}[f_1(t)] + a_2 \mathcal{L}[f_2(t)] = a_1 F_1(s) + a_2 F_2(s). \quad (B.8)$$

Solution: Using (B.1),

$$\mathcal{L}[a_1 f_1(t) + a_2 f_2(t)] = \int_0^\infty [a_1 f_1(t) + a_2 f_2(t)] e^{-st} dt$$

$$= a_1 \int_0^\infty f_1(t) e^{-st} dt + a_2 \int_0^\infty f_2(t) e^{-st} dt$$

$$= a_1 \mathcal{L}[f_1(t)] + a_2 \mathcal{L}[f_2(t)]$$

$$= a_1 F_1(s) + a_2 F_2(s).$$

PROBLEM B.4 Find the Laplace transform of

$$f(t) = \begin{cases} \cos \omega t, & t > 0 \\ 0, & t < 0. \end{cases} \quad (B.9)$$

Solution: From the identity $e^{\pm j\omega t} = \cos \omega t \pm j \sin \omega t$,

$$\cos \omega t = \frac{1}{2} (e^{j\omega t} + e^{-j\omega t}).$$

Using the result (B.7) of Prob. B.2,

$$\mathcal{L}[e^{j\omega t}] = \frac{1}{s - j\omega}, \quad \mathcal{L}[e^{-j\omega t}] = \frac{1}{s + j\omega}, \quad Re[s] > 0. \quad (B.10)$$

Then using (B.8),

$$\mathcal{L}[\cos \omega t] = \frac{1}{2} \left[\frac{1}{s - j\omega} + \frac{1}{s + j\omega} \right] = \frac{s}{s^2 + \omega^2}, \quad Re[s] > 0. \quad (B.11)$$

Next we shall consider the relationship between the Laplace transform of a function and the Laplace transforms of its derivatives and integrals.

PROBLEM B.5 If $\mathcal{L}[f(t)] = F(s)$, find the Laplace transform of

$$\frac{df(t)}{dt}.$$

Solution: By definition,

$$\mathcal{L}\left[\frac{df(t)}{dt}\right] = \int_0^\infty \frac{df}{dt} e^{-st} dt,$$

and integrating by parts,

$$\mathcal{L}\left[\frac{df}{dt}\right] = [f(t) e^{-st}]_0^\infty + s \int_0^\infty f(t) e^{-st} dt.$$

Since for $Re[s] > 0$, $\lim\limits_{t \to \infty} [f(t)\, e^{-st}] = 0$,

$$\mathscr{L}\left[\frac{df}{dt}\right] = sF(s) - f(0). \tag{B.12}$$

It is noted that (B.12) is vague when $f(t)$ is not continuous at $t = 0$, when $f(0)$ is not defined, or when $f(0-)$ differs from $f(0+)$. If we choose $0-$ as the lower limit in the defining integral for the Laplace transform, i.e.,

$$F(s) = \mathscr{L}[f(t)] = \int_{0-}^{\infty} f(t)\, e^{-st}\, dt, \tag{B.13}$$

then

$$\mathscr{L}\left[\frac{df}{dt}\right] = sF(s) - f(0-). \tag{B.14}$$

This is a very convenient form to use since in most problems initial conditions at $t = 0-$ are known, while the $t = 0+$ conditions must be derived.

If, however, we choose $0+$ as the lower limit in the defining integral for the Laplace transform, i.e.,

$$F(s) = \mathscr{L}[f(t)] = \int_{0+}^{\infty} f(t)\, e^{-st}\, dt, \tag{B.15}$$

then

$$\mathscr{L}\left[\frac{df}{dt}\right] = sF(s) - f(0+). \tag{B.16}$$

PROBLEM B.6 Find the Laplace transform of the unit impulse function $\delta(t)$.

Solution: In Prob. 2.27, we have shown that

$$\delta(t) = \frac{du(t)}{dt}. \tag{B.17}$$

Using this together with (B.12) and (B.5),

$$\mathscr{L}[\delta(t)] = \mathscr{L}\left[\frac{du(t)}{dt}\right]$$

$$= s\,\mathscr{L}[u(t)] - u(0)$$

$$= s\,\frac{1}{s} - u(0)$$

$$= 1 - u(0). \tag{B.18}$$

Note that in the definition of $u(t)$ in (B.4), $u(0)$ is not defined. If we use (B.16), then

$$\mathscr{L}[\delta(t)] = 1 - u(0+) = 1 - 1 = 0, \tag{B.19}$$

while if we use (B.14), then

$$\mathscr{L}[\delta(t)] = 1 - u(0-) = 1 - 0 = 1. \tag{B.20}$$

As in the case of the Fourier transform, we find it convenient to have

$$\mathscr{L}[\delta(t)] = 1. \tag{B.21}$$

Thus we again see an advantage of choosing $0-$ as the lower limit in the defining integral for the Laplace transform.

PROBLEM B.7   If $\mathcal{L}[f(t)] = F(s)$, find the Laplace transform of

$$\int_{-\infty}^{t} f(\tau)\, d\tau.$$

Solution: Let

$$g(t) = \int_{-\infty}^{t} f(\tau)\, d\tau. \tag{B.22}$$

Then

$$\frac{dg(t)}{dt} = f(t),$$

so that using (B.14),

$$sG(s) - g(0-) = F(s), \tag{B.23}$$

where $G(s) = \mathcal{L}[g(t)]$. From (B.23),

$$G(s) = \frac{1}{s} F(s) + \frac{1}{s} g(0-). \tag{B.24}$$

Since $g(0-) = \int_{-\infty}^{0-} f(\tau)\, d\tau$,

$$\mathcal{L}\left[\int_{-\infty}^{t} f(\tau)\, d\tau\right] = \frac{1}{s} F(s) + \frac{1}{s} \int_{-\infty}^{0-} f(\tau)\, d\tau. \tag{B.25}$$

In linear-system analysis, we generally deal with causal source functions, i.e., sources that are assumed zero prior to $t = 0$. If $f(t)$ is causal, i.e., $f(t) = 0$ for $t < 0$, we can write

$$\mathcal{L}\left[\int_{-\infty}^{t} f(t)\, dt\right] = \frac{1}{s} F(s). \tag{B.26}$$

B.2 The Relationship between the Fourier and Laplace Transforms

A comparison of the definition forms for Laplace and Fourier transforms shows considerable similarity:

$$\mathcal{L}[f(t)] = \int_{0}^{\infty} f(t)\, e^{-st}\, dt, \quad s = \sigma + j\omega, \tag{B.27}$$

$$\mathcal{F}[f(t)] = \int_{-\infty}^{\infty} f(t)\, e^{-j\omega t}\, dt. \tag{B.28}$$

For some $f(t)$ the formulas can be made the same. This is illustrated in the following examples.

PROBLEM B.8   If $f(t)$ is causal, i.e.,

$$f(t) = 0 \quad \text{for} \quad t < 0, \tag{B.29}$$

$$\int_{0}^{\infty} |f(t)|\, dt < \infty, \tag{B.30}$$

then show that

$$\mathcal{F}[f(t)] = \mathcal{L}[f(t)]_{s=j\omega}. \qquad (B.31)$$

Solution: From (B.28),

$$\mathcal{F}[f(t)] = \int_{-\infty}^{\infty} f(t) \, e^{-j\omega t} \, dt$$

$$= \int_{-\infty}^{0} f(t) \, e^{-j\omega t} \, dt + \int_{0}^{\infty} f(t) \, e^{-j\omega t} \, dt$$

$$= \int_{0}^{\infty} f(t) \, e^{-j\omega t} \, dt \qquad (B.32)$$

since $f(t) = 0$ for $t < 0$.

With the condition (B.30), there exists $\mathcal{F}[f(t)]$.   Comparing (B.32) with (B.27),

$$\mathcal{F}[f(t)] = \mathcal{L}[f(t)]_{s=j\omega}.$$

PROBLEM B.9   Use (B.31) to find the Fourier transform of

$$f(t) = \begin{cases} e^{-\alpha t}, & t > 0 \\ 0, & t < 0, \end{cases}$$

where $\alpha > 0$.

Solution: Since $f(t) = 0$ for $t < 0$ and for $\alpha > 0$,

$$\int_{0}^{\infty} |f(t)| \, dt = \int_{0}^{\infty} e^{-\alpha t} \, dt = -\frac{1}{\alpha} \, e^{-\alpha t} \Big|_{0}^{\infty} = \frac{1}{\alpha} < \infty,$$

and (B.31) can be applied.   From the result (B.7) of Prob. B.2,

$$\mathcal{L}[f(t)] = \frac{1}{s + \alpha}.$$

Hence by (B.31),

$$\mathcal{F}[f(t)] = \frac{1}{s + \alpha} \Big|_{s=j\omega} = \frac{1}{j\omega + \alpha} \qquad (B.33)$$

which is exactly the result obtained in (4.47).

PROBLEM B.10   Show that the Fourier transform of the unit step function $u(t)$ can not be found from (B.31).

Solution: Since

$$\int_{0}^{\infty} |u(t)| \, dt = \int_{0}^{\infty} 1 \, dt = \infty,$$

condition (B.30) is not satisfied.   Hence (B.31) can not be applied.   As a matter of fact, from the results of Prob. B.1 and Prob. 5.9,

$$\mathcal{L}[u(t)] = \frac{1}{s} \qquad \text{and} \qquad \mathcal{F}[u(t)] = \pi \delta(\omega) + \frac{1}{j\omega}.$$

PROBLEM B.11   If

$$\int_{-\infty}^{\infty} |f(t)| \, dt < \infty,$$

then show that

$$\mathcal{F}[f(t)] = \mathcal{L}[f(t)]_{s=j\omega} + \mathcal{L}[f(t)]_{s=-j\omega} \quad \text{if } f(t) \text{ is even,}\qquad (B.34)$$

$$\mathcal{F}[f(t)] = \mathcal{L}[f(t)]_{s=j\omega} - \mathcal{L}[f(t)]_{s=-j\omega} \quad \text{if } f(t) \text{ is odd.}\qquad (B.35)$$

Solution: By (B.28),

$$\mathcal{F}[f(t)] = \int_{-\infty}^{\infty} f(t)\, e^{-j\omega t}\, dt$$

$$= \int_{0}^{\infty} f(t)\, e^{-j\omega t}\, dt + \int_{-\infty}^{0} f(t)\, e^{-j\omega t}\, dt. \qquad (B.36)$$

If $\int_{-\infty}^{\infty} |f(t)|\, dt < \infty$, then there exists $\int_{0}^{\infty} f(t)\, e^{\pm j\omega t}\, dt$ which is equal to $\mathcal{L}[f(t)]_{s=\mp j\omega}$.

If $f(t)$ is even, i.e., $f(-t) = f(t)$, then by changing integration variables,

$$\int_{-\infty}^{0} f(t)\, e^{-j\omega t}\, dt = \int_{0}^{\infty} f(-\tau)\, e^{j\omega \tau}\, d\tau$$

$$= \int_{0}^{\infty} f(\tau)\, e^{-(-j\omega)\tau}\, d\tau$$

$$= \mathcal{L}[f(t)]_{s=-j\omega}. \qquad (B.37)$$

If $f(t)$ is odd, i.e., $f(-t) = -f(t)$, then

$$\int_{-\infty}^{0} f(t)\, e^{-j\omega t}\, dt = \int_{0}^{\infty} f(-\tau)\, e^{j\omega t}\, d\tau$$

$$= -\int_{0}^{\infty} f(\tau)\, e^{-(-j\omega)\tau}\, d\tau$$

$$= -\mathcal{L}[f(t)]_{s=-j\omega}. \qquad (B.38)$$

Substituting (B.37) and (B.38) in (B.36),

$$\mathcal{F}[f(t)] = \mathcal{L}[f(t)]_{s=j\omega} + \mathcal{L}[f(t)]_{s=-j\omega} \quad \text{if } f(-t) = f(t),$$

$$\mathcal{F}[f(t)] = \mathcal{L}[f(t)]_{s=j\omega} - \mathcal{L}[f(t)]_{s=-j\omega} \quad \text{if } f(-t) = -f(t).$$

PROBLEM B.12 Show that an $f(t)$ which has a value for negative t can not be uniquely represented as an inverse Laplace transform.

Solution: Since the Laplace transform is defined only for $t > 0$ (this is often called the *one-sided Laplace Transform*), there will be many functions having the same waveform for $t > 0$ and differing in the region $t < 0$ but corresponding to the same Laplace transform. Therefore an inverse Laplace transform can not uniquely represent $f(t)$ which has a value for negative t.

PROBLEM B.13 Discuss the difference between the Fourier transform and the so-called *two-sided Laplace transform* defined by

$$\mathcal{L}_{II}[f(t)] = \int_{-\infty}^{\infty} f(t)\, e^{-st}\, dt, \quad s = \sigma + j\omega. \qquad (B.39)$$

Solution: The two-sided Laplace transform (B.39) can be written as

$$\mathcal{L}_{II}[f(t)] = \int_{-\infty}^{0} f(t)\,e^{-st}\,dt + \int_{0}^{\infty} f(t)\,e^{-st}\,dt. \qquad (B.40)$$

In order to have the two-sided Laplace transform, we must find a convergence factor $Re[s] = \sigma = \sigma_1$ for the first integral and $Re[s] = \sigma = \sigma_2$ for the second. The two-sided Laplace transform then exists for $\sigma_1 < Re[s] < \sigma_2$.

On the other hand, if the Fourier transform exists, then it is valid for the entire real variable ω.

Hence, from these observations we conclude that the Laplace and Fourier transforms are distinct and that neither is a generalization of the other.

THREE FORMS OF FOURIER SERIES

Form 1: Trigonometric

$$f(t) = \frac{a_0}{2} + \sum_{n=1}^{\infty} (a_n \cos n\omega_0 t + b_n \sin n\omega_0 t).$$

Form 2: Trigonometric

$$f(t) = C_0 + \sum_{n=1}^{\infty} C_n \cos(n\omega_0 t - \theta_n).$$

Form 3: Complex exponential

$$f(t) = \sum_{n=-\infty}^{\infty} c_n e^{jn\omega_0 t}.$$

For all of the above

$$f(t + T) = f(t), \qquad \omega_0 = \frac{2\pi}{T}.$$

Conversion formulas:

For $n \neq 0$,

$$c_n = \frac{1}{2}(a_n - jb_n), \qquad c_{-n} = \frac{1}{2}(a_n + jb_n) = c_n^*,$$

$$c_n = |c_n| e^{j\phi_n}, \qquad |c_n| = \frac{1}{2}\sqrt{a_n^2 + b_n^2}, \qquad \phi_n = \tan^{-1}\left(-\frac{b_n}{a_n}\right),$$

$$a_n = 2\,Re\,[c_n], \qquad b_n = -2\,Im\,[c_n],$$

$$C_n = 2\,|c_n| = \sqrt{a_n^2 + b_n^2}, \qquad \theta_n = \tan^{-1}\left(\frac{b_n}{a_n}\right) = -\phi_n.$$

For $n = 0$,

$$c_0 = \frac{1}{2}a_0 = C_0.$$

APPENDIX

SUMMARY OF
SYMMETRY CONDITIONS

Summary of Symmetry Conditions for Periodic Waveforms and Fourier Coefficients

Type of Symmetry	Conditions	Form of the Fourier Series	Formulas for the Fourier Coefficients
Even	$f(t) = f(-t)$	$f(t) = \dfrac{a_0}{2} + \displaystyle\sum_{n=1}^{\infty} a_n \cos n\omega_0 t$	$a_n = \dfrac{4}{T}\displaystyle\int_0^{T/2} f(t)\cos(n\omega_0 t)\,dt$
Odd	$f(t) = -f(-t)$	$f(t) = \displaystyle\sum_{n=1}^{\infty} b_n \sin n\omega_0 t$	$b_n = \dfrac{4}{T}\displaystyle\int_0^{T/2} f(t)\sin(n\omega_0 t)\,dt$
Half-wave	$f(t) = -f\left(t + \dfrac{T}{2}\right)$	$f(t) = \displaystyle\sum_{n=1}^{\infty} [a_{2n-1}\cos(2n-1)\omega_0 t$ $+\, b_{2n-1}\sin(2n-1)\omega_0 t]$	$\left.\begin{matrix}a_{2n-1}\\ b_{2n-1}\end{matrix}\right\} = \dfrac{4}{T}\displaystyle\int_0^{T/2} f(t)\begin{Bmatrix}\cos\\ \sin\end{Bmatrix}[(2n-1)\omega_0 t]\,dt$
Even quarter-wave	$f(t) = f(-t)$ and $f(t) = -f\left(t + \dfrac{T}{2}\right)$	$f(t) = \displaystyle\sum_{n=1}^{\infty} a_{2n-1}\cos(2n-1)\omega_0 t$	$a_{2n-1} = \dfrac{8}{T}\displaystyle\int_0^{T/4} f(t)\cos[(2n-1)\omega_0 t]\,dt$
Odd quarter-wave	$f(t) = -f(-t)$ and $f(t) = -f\left(t + \dfrac{T}{2}\right)$	$f(t) = \displaystyle\sum_{n=1}^{\infty} b_{2n-1}\sin(2n-1)\omega_0 t$	$b_{2n-1} = \dfrac{8}{T}\displaystyle\int_0^{T/4} f(t)\sin[(2n-1)\omega_0 t]\,dt$

PROPERTIES OF THE FOURIER TRANSFORM

APPENDIX

The functions are periodic with period T, $a > 0$; and b, t_o, and $\omega_o = 2\pi/T$ are real constants with $n = 1, 2, \cdots$.

$f(t)$	$F(\omega)$
$a_1 f_1(t) + a_2 f_2(t)$	$a_1 F_1(\omega) + a_2 F_2(\omega)$
$f(at)$	$\dfrac{1}{|a|} F\left(\dfrac{\omega}{a}\right)$
$f(-t)$	$F(-\omega)$
$f(t - t_0)$	$F(\omega) e^{-j\omega t_0}$
$f(t) e^{j\omega_0 t}$	$F(\omega - \omega_0)$
$f(t) \cos \omega_0 t$	$\dfrac{1}{2} F(\omega - \omega_0) + \dfrac{1}{2} F(\omega + \omega_0)$
$f(t) \sin \omega_0 t$	$\dfrac{1}{2j} F(\omega - \omega_0) - \dfrac{1}{2j} F(\omega + \omega_0)$
$f_e(t) = \dfrac{1}{2} [f(t) + f(-t)]$	$R(\omega)$
$f_o(t) = \dfrac{1}{2} [f(t) - f(-t)]$	$jX(\omega)$
$f(t) = f_e(t) + f_o(t)$	$F(\omega) = R(\omega) + jX(\omega)$
$F(t)$	$2\pi f(-\omega)$
$f'(t)$	$j\omega F(\omega)$
$f^{(n)}(t)$	$(j\omega)^n F(\omega)$
$\displaystyle\int_{-\infty}^{t} f(x)\,dx$	$\dfrac{1}{j\omega} F(\omega) + \pi F(0)\delta(\omega)$
$-jt\,f(t)$	$F'(\omega)$
$(-jt)^n f(t)$	$F^{(n)}(\omega)$
$f_1(t) * f_2(t) = \displaystyle\int_{-\infty}^{\infty} f_1(x) f_2(t - x)\,dx$	$F_1(\omega) F_2(\omega)$

$f(t)$	$F(\omega)$
$f_1(t)\,f_2(t)$	$\dfrac{1}{2\pi}\,F_1(\omega)*F_2(\omega)=\dfrac{1}{2\pi}\displaystyle\int_{-\infty}^{\infty}F_1(y)F_2(\omega-y)\,dy$
$e^{-at}u(t)$	$\dfrac{1}{j\omega+a}$
$e^{-a|t|}$	$\dfrac{2a}{a^2+\omega^2}$
e^{-at^2}	$\sqrt{\dfrac{\pi}{a}}\;e^{-\omega^2/(4a)}$
$p_a(t)=\begin{cases}1 & \text{for}\quad |t|<a/2\\ 0 & \text{for}\quad |t|>a/2\end{cases}$	$a\,\dfrac{\sin\left(\dfrac{\omega a}{2}\right)}{\left(\dfrac{\omega a}{2}\right)}$
$\dfrac{\sin at}{\pi t}$	$p_{2a}(\omega)$
$te^{-at}u(t)$	$\dfrac{1}{(j\omega+a)^2}$
$\dfrac{t^{n-1}}{(n-1)!}\,e^{-at}u(t)$	$\dfrac{1}{(j\omega+a)^n}$
$e^{-at}\sin bt\,u(t)$	$\dfrac{b}{(j\omega+a)^2+b^2}$
$e^{-at}\cos bt\,u(t)$	$\dfrac{j\omega+a}{(j\omega+a)^2+b^2}$
$\dfrac{1}{a^2+t^2}$	$\dfrac{\pi}{a}\,e^{-a|\omega|}$
$\dfrac{\cos bt}{a^2+t^2}$	$\dfrac{\pi}{2a}\left[e^{-a|\omega-b|}+e^{-a|\omega+b|}\right]$
$\dfrac{\sin bt}{a^2+b^2}$	$\dfrac{\pi}{2aj}\left[e^{-a|\omega-b|}-e^{-a|\omega+b|}\right]$
$\delta(t)$	1
$\delta(t-t_0)$	$e^{-j\omega t_0}$
$\delta'(t)$	$j\omega$
$\delta^{(n)}(t)$	$(j\omega)^n$
$u(t)$	$\pi\delta(\omega)+\dfrac{1}{j\omega}$
$u(t-t_0)$	$\pi\delta(\omega)+\dfrac{1}{j\omega}\,e^{-j\omega t_0}$
1	$2\pi\delta(\omega)$
t	$2\pi j\,\delta'(\omega)$
t^n	$2\pi j^n\,\delta^{(n)}(\omega)$

$f(t)$	$F(\omega)$
$e^{j\omega_0 t}$	$2\pi\delta(\omega - \omega_0)$
$\cos \omega_0 t$	$\pi[\delta(\omega - \omega_0) + \delta(\omega + \omega_0)]$
$\sin \omega_0 t$	$-j\pi[\delta(\omega - \omega_0) - \delta(\omega + \omega_0)]$
$\sin \omega_0 t\, u(t)$	$\dfrac{\omega_0}{\omega_0^2 - \omega^2} + \dfrac{\pi}{2j}[\delta(\omega - \omega_0) - \delta(\omega + \omega_0)]$
$\cos \omega_0 t\, u(t)$	$\dfrac{j\omega}{\omega_0^2 - \omega^2} + \dfrac{\pi}{2}[\delta(\omega - \omega_0) + \delta(\omega + \omega_0)]$
$t\, u(t)$	$j\pi\,\delta'(\omega) - \dfrac{1}{\omega^2}$
$\dfrac{1}{t}$	$\pi j - 2\pi j\, u(\omega)$
$\dfrac{1}{t^n}$	$\dfrac{(-j\omega)^{n-1}}{(n-1)!}[\pi j - 2\pi j\, u(\omega)]$
$\operatorname{sgn} t$	$\dfrac{2}{j\omega}$
$\delta_T(t) = \displaystyle\sum_{n=-\infty}^{\infty} \delta(t - nT)$	$\omega_0 \delta_{\omega_0}(\omega) = \omega_0 \displaystyle\sum_{n=-\infty}^{\infty} \delta(\omega - n\omega_0)$

Other properties:

$$\int_{-\infty}^{\infty} f_1(t)\, f_2(t)\, dt = \frac{1}{2\pi} \int_{-\infty}^{\infty} F_1(\omega)\, F_2^*(\omega)\, d\omega,$$

$$\int_{-\infty}^{\infty} |f(t)|^2\, dt = \frac{1}{2\pi} \int_{-\infty}^{\infty} |F(\omega)|^2\, d\omega,$$

$$\int_{-\infty}^{\infty} f(x)\, G(x)\, dx = \int_{-\infty}^{\infty} F(x)\, g(x)\, dx.$$

APPENDIX

LIST OF SYMBOLS

$\left.\begin{array}{l} a_n \\ b_n \\ c_n \end{array}\right\}$	Fourier coefficients	$m(t)$	Message signal
		$n(t)$	Noise
$a(t)$	Unit step response	p	Operator d/dt
B	Damping coefficient	$p(x),\ p(x,y)$	Probability density or frequency function
C	Capacitance		
d	Pulse duration	$p_d(t)$	Rectangular pulse with unit amplitude and duration d
$D_k(\xi)$	Dirichlet kernel		
E	Energy content, Mathematical expectation		
		P	Power
E_k	Mean-square error	$P(x),\ P(x,y)$	Probability distribution function
f	Frequency		
$f(t)$	Time function	$P(\omega)$	Power spectral density, Power spectrum
$\|f\|^2$	Energy content of $f(t)$		
$F(\omega),\ F(j\omega)$	Fourier transform of $f(t)$	R	Resistance
$F_c(\omega)$	Fourier cosine transform of $f(t)$	$R(\omega)$	Real part of $F(\omega)$
		$R_{11},\ R_{22},\ \ldots$	Autocorrelation functions
$F_s(\omega)$	Fourier sine transform of $f(t)$	$R_{12},\ R_{21},\ \ldots$	Cross-correlation functions
		$\overline{R}_{11},\ \overline{R}_{22},\ \ldots$	Average autocorrelation functions
$\|F\|^2$	Energy content of $F(\omega)$	$\overline{R}_{12},\ \overline{R}_{21},\ \ldots$	Average cross-correlation functions
G	Conductance	Si	Sine-integral function
$h(t)$	Unit impulse response	$Sa(t)$	Sampling function
$H(p)$	Operation system function	$S_k(t)$	Sum of the first $(2k+1)$ terms of a Fourier series of $f(t)$
$H(\omega),\ H(j\omega)$	Fourier transform of $h(t)$, System function		
$i,\ I$	Current	t	Time
$\mathbf{I}_m$	Amplitude phasor representing current $i(t)$	T	Period of periodic wave form, Temperature, Tension
k	Boltzmann constant, Spring constant	$\overline{t}$	Center of gravity of the area under the curve $f^2(t)$
K	Thermal conductivity	t_r	Rise time
$k^2,\ k_x,\ldots,\ k_{mn}$	Separation constant	T_d	Effective pulse duration
L	Inductance, Linear operator	u	Deflection of string or membrane, Electrostatic potential, Temperature distribution
m	Mass		
m_n	n-th moment of X		

$u(t)$	Unit-step function	λ	Wavelength
v, V	Voltage	ρ	Mass density
$\mathbf{V}_m$	Amplitude phasor representing voltage $v(t)$	σ	Standard deviation
		ϕ	Characteristic function, Phase angle, Testing function
x	Displacement, Variable		
X	Random variable		
$X(\omega)$	Imaginary part of $F(\omega)$	ϕ_m	Modulation index
$Y(p), Y(j\omega)$	Admittance function	ω	Radian frequency
$Z(p), Z(j\omega)$	Impedance function	$\overline{\omega}$	Center of gravity of the area under the curve $|F(\omega)|^2$
α	Attenuation constant		
β	Phase constant		
α_n, β_n	Fourier coefficients	$\mathcal{F}, (\mathcal{F}_c, \mathcal{F}_s)$	Fourier (cosine, sine) transform of
γ	Propagation constant	$\mathcal{F}^{-1}, (\mathcal{F}_c^{-1}, \mathcal{F}_s^{-1})$	Inverse Fourier (cosine, sine) transform of
$\delta(t)$	Delta function or Unit impulse function		
$\delta_T(t), \delta_{\omega_0}(\omega)$	Periodic train of unit impulses	$\mathcal{L}$	Laplace transform of
		$\mathcal{L}^{-1}$	Inverse Laplace transform of
Δt	Dispersion in time	$\mathcal{L}_{II}$	Two-sided Laplace transform of
$\Delta \omega$	Spectral bandwidth		
ε_k	Error between $f(t)$ and $S_k(t)$	Re	The real part of
		Im	The imaginary part of
θ	Phase angle		

INDEX